First International Conference on
Congenital Malformations

First International Conference on Congenital Malformations

Papers and Discussions Presented at the
First International Conference on Congenital Malformations,
London, England, July 18-22, 1960

COMPILED AND EDITED FOR

THE INTERNATIONAL MEDICAL CONGRESS, LTD.

J . B . LIPPINCOTT COMPANY

Philadelphia and Montreal

EDITORIAL NOTE.

The material in this volume comprises a record of the First International Conference on Congenital Malformations. The original presentations have been included in toto. The discussions and the addresses have been edited carefully and specially prepared for publication. All of the material, delivered in several languages and transcribed by recording, has been edited in the interests of accuracy and brevity.

Library of Congress Catalog Card Number 61-18547

Printed in the United States of America

Dedication

Dedicated to Dr. Thomas M. Rivers, Vice President for Medical Affairs of The National Foundation, whose great knowledge and intensive leadership in the planning, the functioning and the effectiveness of the Conference contributed so vastly to its success.

FOREWORD

The Proceedings of the First International Conference on Congenital Malformations are offered to carry forward the tradition of scientific publication followed in the publication of five volumes of Proceedings of the International Conferences on Poliomyelitis. In making these available, the National Foundation recognizes the importance of a permanent record.

The program of the First International Conference on Congenital Malformations was designed to indicate the scope of the problems now apparent, the approaches to these problems from the points of view of genetics, anatomy, pathology, immunology, embryology, and the other sciences intimately involved in finding solutions. The co-operation generously tendered by the British colleagues who participated fully in designing the program, planning the meetings, and the associated events is especially appreciated. Appreciation is also tendered to the Royal Society of Medicine for making space available for the British office of the Conference.

MORRIS FISHBEIN, M.D.
Editor

The International Medical Congress, Ltd.

First International Conference on Congenital Malformations

Organized by

THE INTERNATIONAL MEDICAL CONGRESS, LTD.

at

CHURCH HOUSE, Dean's Yard, Westminster, London, S.W.1, England

SPONSOR

The National Foundation (U.S.A.)

OFFICERS OF THE CONFERENCE

Honorary Presidents

Mr. Basil O'Connor, A.B., LL.B. (U.S.A.)
Sir Geoffrey Marshall, K.C.V.O., C.B.E., M.D., F.R.C.P. (U.K.)

General Chairman

Prof. J. D. Boyd, M.D. (U.K.)

Executive Secretary and Treasurer

Mr. Stanley E. Henwood (U.S.A.)

Secretary

Miss Hilda Kerr (U.K.)

Committee of Honor

Dr. G. F. Abercrombie, President, College of General Practitioners
Dr. Georgiana Bonser, President, Medical Women's Federation
Prof. John Bruce, President, Royal College of Surgeons of Edinburgh
Prof. Sir Andrew Claye, President, Royal College of Obstetricians and Gynæcologists
Dr. Charles F. Harris, Vice-Chancellor, University of London
Sir Harold Himsworth, Secretary, The Medical Research Council
Prof. Sir Cyril Hinshelwood, President, Royal Society
Sir Arthur Porritt, President, British Medical Association
Sir Robert Platt, President, Royal College of Physicians
Prof. Sir James Paterson Ross, President, Royal College of Surgeons of England
Sir Arthur Thomson, British Medical Association

COMMITTEES

SCIENTIFIC PROGRAM COMMITTEE

Dr. James L. Wilson, Chairman (U.S.A.)
Dr. Thomas M. Rivers, Vice-Chairman
  (U.S.A.)
Dr. James D. Ebert
Dr. Louis B. Flexner
Dr. F. Clarke Fraser
Dr. Louis M. Hellman
Dr. Frank L. Horsfall, Jr.
Mr. Hedley J. B. Atkins
Prof. J. D. Boyd

Dr. Walter Landauer
Dr. Richard L. Masland
Dr. James L. Neel
Dr. Edith L. Potter
Dr. Edward L. Tatum
Dr. Josef Warkany
Dr. James G. Wilson
Prof. Conrad H. Waddington
Prof. Robert Debré

EXECUTIVE PROGRAM COMMITTEE

J. D. Boyd, M.D. *(Chairman)*
H. J. B. Atkins, D.M., M.Ch., F.R.C.S.
R. J. V. Battle, M.B.E., F.R.C.S.
J. G. Bonnin, F.R.C.S.
John Bruce, C.B.E., T.D., P.R.C.S.Ed.
W. A. Fell, M.B., B.Ch.
E. R. Graham Kerr, M.B., B.Ch.

H. M. M. Mackay, F.R.C.P.
P. Malpas, M.Ch., F.R.C.S., F.R.C.O.G.
J. S. Mitchell, C.B.E., M.D., F.R.S.
J. A. Fraser Roberts, M.D., F.R.C.P.
E. W. Somerville, F.R.C.S.
L. M. Snaith, F.R.C.S., F.R.C.O.G.
A. W. Wilkinson, Ch.M., F.R.C.S.Ed.

LADIES' PROGRAM COMMITTEE

Mrs. H. J. B. Atkins
Mrs. R. J. V. Battle
Mrs. D. Bergsma
Mrs. J. G. Bonnin
Mrs. J. D. Boyd
Mrs. T. Boyd
Mrs. J. Bruce
Mrs. W. S. Clark
Mrs. W. A. Fell
Mrs. M. Fishbein
Mrs. T. Francis, Jr.
Mrs. M. A. Glasser
Mrs. F. L. Horsfall, Jr.
Mrs. P. Malpas

Lady Marshall
Mrs. R. McIntosh
Mrs. J. S. Mitchell
Mrs. Basil O'Connor
Mrs. T. M. Rivers
Mrs. J. A. Fraser Roberts
Mrs. P. Sandifer
Mrs. E. W. Somerville
Mrs. L. M. Snaith
Mrs. Wm. F. Snyder
Mrs. E. L. Tatum
Mrs. N. H. Topping
Mrs. A. W. Wilkinson
Mrs. J. L. Wilson

ACKNOWLEDGEMENTS

The Organizers are indebted to the following, for the help they have given to the Conference:

THE ROYAL SOCIETY OF MEDICINE
THE WOMEN'S VOLUNTARY SERVICE

The Organizers of the Conference wish to make known their appreciation to E. R. Squibb & Sons Ltd., who supplied the portfolios.

CONTENTS

xi

OPENING SESSION

Monday Morning, July 18, 1960

Introductory Remarks

PROFESSOR J. D. BOYD, M.D.

Professor of Anatomy, University of Cambridge,
Cambridge, United Kingdom

Opening Address

MISS EDITH PITT, O.B.E., M.P.

Parliamentary Secretary to the Minister of Health,
Savile Row, London, W. 1, United Kingdom

Theme Addresses

Congenital Malformations: The Problem and the Task

DR. GEORGE W. CORNER, M.A., M.D., Sc.D., Formerly Memb. R.S.
Historian and Affiliate, The Rockefeller Institute, New York 21, N.Y., U.S.A.

The Significance of a Concerted Approach to the Problems of Congenital Malformations

MR. BASIL O'CONNOR, A.B., LL.B.
President, The National Foundation, 800 Second Avenue, New York 17, N.Y., U.S.A.

Introductory Remarks

PROFESSOR J. D. BOYD, M.D.

I am deeply conscious of the honorable position in which I find myself. Self-depreciation in public is never particularly edifying; nevertheless, in my estimation those responsible for putting me into this position should have gone further and fared perhaps rather better. In the circumstances, however, I also think it is not inappropriate that an anatomist should find himself in this august position.

Anatomy was the first scientific discipline which concerned itself seriously with malformations. It was a great French anatomist, Geoffroy St. Hilaire, who first codified and rationalized knowledge on human abnormalities. You now have, as chairman of this Conference, an anatomist, and I, personally, regard this fact as a tribute to the basic work which has been done by anatomists in the field of teratology.

Second, my duty is to welcome those of you who have come here, most warmly. To arrange a Conference like this has not been an easy matter. All of us who have been concerned in the arrangement are deeply conscious of having committed errors both of omission and of commission. In fact, it has not been at all easy to make contact across national barriers, more particularly as those interested in congenital malformations do not at the moment constitute a coherent group; hence, we have found it difficult from time to time to disseminate our preliminary information and, on occasion, we doubtless have committed blunders in making our contacts. Therefore, there are many in the world who, I know, would have been interested in attending this Conference, who have not received adequate notice or appropriate information. This we regret. Nevertheless, there are several points on which we can congratulate ourselves. First, nearly 500 physicians and scientists have registered for this Conference, and these 500 represent more than 21 countries. That such a Conference, the first of its sort at such a level, should have attracted such wide interest is, I think, the best assurance we can have that the endeavors that have gone into the Conference have been worthwhile.

Again, on the positive side, and as our subsequent proceedings will undoubtedly reveal, we count ourselves indeed fortunate in having obtained the co-operation of the distinguished group who will present their work to us and assess the current position in a number of disparate fields of knowledge which are essential to forwarding our understanding of congenital malformation.

Now, all our endeavors, of course, are directed toward a solution of an urgent human problem. None of us is naïve enough to believe that such a problem can be solved by other than basic and hard work. In order that this work be forwarded, it is absolutely essential that we have the co-operation and the stimulus that can come from the people who govern us. We are fortunate on this occasion in having with us a representative of Her Majesty's Government, Miss Edith Pitt, O.B.E., M.P., who is Parliamentary Secretary to the Ministry of Health. She has very kindly agreed to speak to us and to give us, as it were, the formal acknowledgment by the British Government of an active interest in our proceedings. I have the greatest pleasure, now, in asking Miss Pitt to give the opening address to this Conference.

Opening Address

MISS EDITH PITT, O.B.E., M.P.

I am both happy and diffident to be invited to this first Conference on Congenital Malformations. Happy, because it is a great pleasure to welcome you on behalf of my ministry and a personal pleasure to be associated with this tremendous endeavor; diffident, because when I studied the list of those who were to speak and to take part in this Conference, I realized that it was—to borrow a phrase—star-studded with people of the highest qualifications, and I feel somewhat modest as a lay person coming before you so early in the program. Nevertheless, I represent one of those who, for all of my life, has tried to help other people with human problems, and I would hope that in the course of the work which you do here, you may give me something which will help in the work to which I have given all of my time in all of my adult years.

Digressing for one moment, because I felt slightly nervous coming before you, I did put on my prettiest hat to give me confidence. I hoped also that it might please your ladies, whom I am delighted to see here.

I would like to welcome all who are attending the Conference, but I think you would wish me to make special mention of three men. The first is Mr. Basil O'Connor. Mr. O'Connor has made a significant contribution to the welfare of man in many countries. His pioneering efforts to extend and to increase the benefits of good health have been achieved largely through his activities as president of The National Foundation for Infantile Paralysis, now The National Foundation, in New York. His work to assist refugees and to extend legal protection in time of war to civilians was accomplished as president of the American National Red Cross in Washington and as chairman of the League of Red Cross Societies in Geneva. I think we all feel very honored, Mr. O'Connor, to have you with us today.

Sir Geoffrey Marshall, the distinguished chest physician, is otherwise well-known to my ministry as consultant physician to the Ministry of Pensions and National Insurance and chief medical referee of the Civil Service Commission, as well as for his work on behalf of the Medical Research Council. However, it is in his capacity as president of our Royal Society of Medicine that I particularly wish to mention him, as I understand that the Society has done a very great deal to facilitate the arrangements for this particular Conference. And, Sir Geoffrey, we are happy to have you, too.

Professor Boyd, who opened the proceedings, is, as I think you all know, the eminent Professor of Anatomy at Cambridge University, Fellow of the International Institute of Embryology and Editor of *The Journal of Anatomy,* whose contributions in the field covered by this Conference are outstanding.

May I also welcome so many distinguished members from home, and I think that they in turn will wish to join with me in welcoming the honored and distinguished members from abroad who have joined us in the Conference.

The National Foundation for Infantile Paralysis, Inc. promoted the first international conference concerning poliomyelitis in 1948, and these conferences have continued so that the fifth is being held in

Copenhagen this year immediately following this conference. However, about 2 years ago, The Foundation began to extend its activities to other diseases of locomotion and to congenital malformations now that so much is known about poliomyelitis. That disease, while not conquered, is, we hope, on the way to its final defeat. The striking reduction in poliomyelitis in this and other countries is one of the most recent of many achievements which have been significant in preventing disability and in saving the lives of children. At the beginning of this century in this country, the mortality rate for children under the age of 12 months was 150 for every 1,000 live births, compared with 22 per 1,000 last year. Dirt, disease, ignorance and bad feeding all have played their part in causing these deaths. Gradually, however, infant feeding and care has improved. The appalling deaths from gastroenteritis and "summer disease" was halted. How happy we all feel, especially those of us—and I am one—who have known one such case, one such death in their own family. The cause, the cure and the prevention of infectious diseases, such as diphtheria, were solved. Again, I have personal experience with my own sister, fallen victim to this particular disease and knowing the after-effects which troubled her. Tuberculosis—again, a member of my own family was involved—which so very few years ago seemed still a protracted, though not an insurmountable problem, rapidly is disappearing as a cause of illness and death in childhood. But as each obstacle is overcome and melts away into the past, so the remaining problems, because they now stand isolated, loom before us more forbiddingly. So now today, we are faced with the two main remaining causes of infant death: prematurity and congenital malformations. The great improvement in health and the prospect of survival of all children have affected those with congenital abnormalities as they have those in full health. Many children born with defects succumbed to the infections in infancy.

The modern drugs now prevent fatal outcome far more commonly, and so we have the paradox that better medicine may in this respect give us more defective children living to a later age. That has been a challenge to the surgeon whose triumphs in the treatment of "blue" babies have been widely publicized. Here in London we now have our first chair of pediatric surgery, and here and elsewhere surgical treatment of many of these conditions has made possible a better, even a normal life for these children. We hope to see more special centers for this work in the National Health Service in this country.

Looking through your program at your varied interests has made me realize how many diverse fields of learning are brought together in the study of congenital malformations. Here we have experts in biology, zoology, biochemistry, physics, virology, immunology, epidemiology, social medicine, genetics, embryology, anatomy, pathology, physiology, obstetrics, pediatrics, as well as general medicine and surgery—a truly impressive list. Each has his or her part to play in overcoming the cause of so much loss of life and of so much of the misery which may result from an imperfect body or mind. When one considers the problems which were encountered in overcoming a single disease, such as diphtheria, the complications of attempting to analyze the genetic and the environmental factors involved in the causation of congenital malformations, one realizes what a formidable task lies before you at this Conference. One feels that no one human being could be able to find enough time in his life, even if he filled every moment with work, to become sufficiently knowledgeable in these sciences. Therefore, it seems that the only solution can be reached by the close co-operation of all these experts. Thus, the virologists studying the effects of maternal rubella, the physicists studying the hazards of radiation, the geneticists studying chromosomal abnormalities in mongolism, may, by reaching all the other specialties, each studying his own particular aspect, find some common links in the causation of these malformations; for, once the mechanism which brings about an abnormality is known, perhaps finally its prevention may be in sight. Although the miracles of modern surgery, such as the parting of conjoined twins and the surgical reconstruction of congenital heart defects, have brought life and happiness to many whose lives in earlier generations would have been short and often miserable, the ultimate aim for us all surely must be its prevention. Therefore, it is my earnest hope that as the First International Conference on Poliomyelitis in New York City in 1948 heralded the beginning of the conquest of that disease, so this, the First International Conference on Congenital Malformations, held in Great Britain in 1960, may give a greater stimulus to the development of methods of early detection and treatment of congenital abnormalities, but even more to the investigation of their causes and the possibility of prevention. It is for that reason that I am very happy to be with you. I hope I may say, to bless the work which you will do together.

Congenital Malformations: The Problem and the Task

GEORGE W. CORNER, M.A., M.D., Sc.D.

We have been called together from many lands, to discuss a problem of grave human concern and high scientific importance. That we are meeting not in a laboratory or an academic auditorium, but at Church House, in the very precincts of Westminster Abbey, is altogether appropriate. From that venerable shrine, for a thousand years without ceasing, prayers have been ascending to God to reveal truth, to relieve suffering and to solace the afflicted. In our laboratories and clinics we too seek the truth and strive to aid the maimed and the deformed. Like Jeremiah at Ramah, we have heard the voice of Rachel weeping for her children. From this hall as from the Abbey's altars there rise to high heaven an aspiration and a resolve that our labors shall help to lift the burden of congenital abnormality from the race of man.

In this undertaking we pit our science against an ancient curse. Congenital defects appear in surviving records of the oldest civilizations. Achondroplasia, according to Sir Armand Ruffer, is depicted in Egyptian paintings 5,000 years old. Clubfoot is known from the 11th and the 12th dynasties; and Septah, last king of the 19th dynasty, was thus afflicted. Cleft palate has been observed in an Egyptian mummy; cases of harelip and congenital amputation of the arms are recorded in prehistoric Peruvian pottery. The memory of some of these awesome deformities passed into legend and myth, conjuring up a race of cyclopean monsters who forged Jove's thunderbolts in caverns under Mt. Etna, and that dreadful one of Virgil's mighty line, "Monstrum horrendum, informe, ingens, cui lumen ademptum."

Today we know that congenital defects may occur at all stages of development from the fertilized ovum to the full term of gestation and may run the whole gamut from total breakdown to local deformity with all sorts of intermediate variations and combinations. However, these facts were not obvious before the development of the embryo was well understood. When, in Renaissance times, physicians began to think about the nature and the causes of prenatal abnormality, they considered only the more monstrous instances. The abortion of a small embryo could be passed over as a mishap, such an embryo was seldom critically examined, whereas the birth of Siamese twins or a child with no legs awoke superstitions and created fear, so that even the physicians were inclined to ascribe such unfortunate events to supernatural or psychical causes.*

To illustrate this point I quote a tabulation of the causes of monstrosity drawn up in the 16th century by the famous French surgeon Ambroise Paré. His list begins, you will note, with God and ends with the Devil, with a little science in the middle.

There are reckoned up many causes of monsters; the first whereof is the glory of God, that his immense power may be manifested to

---

* The historical review in the first half of the present address includes, by permission of the publisher, several passages quoted or adapted from the author's book (now out of print), *Ourselves Unborn*, New Haven, Yale University Press, 1944.

those which are ignorant of it. . . . Another cause is, that God may punish men's wickedness, or show signs of punishment at hand. . . . The third cause is, an abundance of seed and overflowing matter. . . . If, on the contrary, the seed be anything deficient in quantity, some or more members will be wanting, or more short and decrepite. . . . The ancients have marked other causes of the generation of monsters . . . the force of imagination hath much power over the infant. . . Monsters are bred and caused by the straightnesse of the womb . . . by the ill placing of the mother in sitting, lying downe or any other site of the body in the time of her being with child. . . . By the injury of hereditary diseases, infants grow monstrous, for crooke-backt produce crooke-backt, lame produce lame, flat-nosed their like. . . . Monsters are also occasioned by the craft and subtlety of the Devill.

Paré's explanation, as you have seen, fall into three classes based, respectively, on religion and superstition, on environmental factors, and on heredity. Since his day, science and, also, theology of the enlightened kind accepted in Church House, have eliminated the hypothesis of direct intervention by God and the Devil; the other two still hold good, although altered in detail. Even today in this Conference we shall be trying to balance the relative importance of environment and heredity. Of course, geneticists have considerably refined Paré's concept of inheritance. Gene action is much more complex than "crooke-backt produce crooke-backt, lame produce lame." On the other hand, the environmental hypothesis, at first crudely mechanical, has also become more and more subtle as embryologists acquired the use of the microscope and learned to recognize early embryos, and still more subtle in our present age of biochemistry. From faulty maternal postures and narrowness of the womb, we have reached the realm of enzymes and molecules.

Under the lead of Fabricius of Aquapendente, William Harvey and Marcello Malpighi, 17th century embryologists sketched the development of the chick from egg to hatching, of some mammals beginning with the blastocyst, and of man from the later somite stages on. With this information in hand, leading anatomists of the latter half of the 18th century—John Hunter, Albrecht von Haller, and Caspar Friedrich Wolff—began to see that congenital defects and deformities do not represent random disorderly growth, but rather modifications of the normal pattern of embryonic development. In 1822, J. F. Meckel in his *Handbook of Pathological Anatomy* pointed out that certain defects, for example cleft palate and ectopia cordis, result from the persistence of conditions that are normal at an earlier stage of embryonic life. Thus attention was focused on normal embryology as the basis for understanding the abnormal. Descriptive teratology became a recognized branch of science, rapidly acquiring an immense literature, including such vast handbooks as Taruffi's *Teratology* in 8 volumes (1881-1895) and the equally detailed Schwalbe's *Missbildungen* of 1906. All the malformations ever reported have been classified and given Greco-Latin names of tongue-twisting complexity. For a hundred years as human embryology progressed the explanation of all these deformities, deficiencies, reduplications and redundancies in terms of the normal pattern from which they deviate has given occupation to many puzzle-loving embryologists. But morphologic description, however clearly it traces the genesis of abnormalities, at best can give only hints of their causes. At the beginning of the present century it became increasingly clear that a complete analysis of fetal anomalies, aimed at understanding their origin, could be attained only by observing them in their beginnings. In other words, the embryologists who were already searching for younger and younger stages of normal development henceforth also must seek the earliest abnormal embryos.

Between 1880 and 1900, a number of young pathologic embryos were described by the great Leipzig anatomist Wilhelm His, by Carlo Giacomini and others in Europe;

but the most significant contribution of this sort was that of Franklin P. Mall of Baltimore. After a year with His in 1884-1885 he began to collect early abnormal human embryos and by 1908 had the material for a great monograph, *The Origin of Human Monsters*. At that time he possessed 434 embryos of which 163 were pathologic. These specimens became the nucleus of the collection of the Carnegie Institution's Department of Embryology.

Mall's abnormal embryos were of course not monsters in the popular sense of the word. Most of them were less than 8 weeks old, and they were simply embryos that had failed to develop in a normal way, manifesting every grade of change from an almost normal state to mere nodules of undifferentiated tissue scarcely recognizable as embryos. In past centuries, their relation to monstrosity in the ordinary sense would have been missed. However, Mall was struck by the fact that many of them exhibited certain defects which also are seen very commonly in deformed fetuses. His 163 early pathologic embryos included, for example, cases of spina bifida, anencephaly, deformity of the extremities and ectopia cordis. Therefore, Mall came to the very significant conclusion that early disturbances of embryonic growth and other late abnormalities of the kinds classifiable as congenital defects, or (when extreme) as monstrosities, represent simply different degrees of damage and must result from similar causes, for which we must search in the early embryonic period. Although this conclusion was not entirely original with Mall, he was the first to support it with extensive evidence. His monograph of 1908 made it clear that the causation of human embryonic defects is a problem open to investigation by experimental biology and medicine. I am happy to pay tribute to my teacher, Franklin P. Mall, on this distinguished occasion. He left behind him at the Carnegie Embryologic Laboratory a continuing interest in this subject, to which each of his successors in turn has

contributed. The first of these, the late George L. Streeter, made important observations to which I shall refer later; I was next, and my successor James D. Ebert has helped to plan the present conference.

When Mall turned to experimental embryologists for clues to the nature of human embryonic abnormality, they had much to tell him. A century earlier the French zoologist Geoffroy St. Hilaire, working with hen's eggs, had produced embryonic defects, including spina bifida and anencephaly, by pricking the embryo with a needle through a hole in the shell, or by varnishing the shell to cut off the oxygen supply. In 1892, the philosopher-zoologist Hans Driesch produced double monsters from sea-urchins' eggs by placing them in warm water. This feat set off a wave of similar experimentation. Jacques Loeb created similar double embryos by lowering the salt content of the water in which sea urchins' eggs were dividing. E. B. Wilson did the same with *Amphioxus* by shaking the 2-cell stages; Hans Spemann, by mechanical partial separation of the blastomeres. I need not catalog here the long list of experiments on fish and amphibian eggs by which many other workers using diverse chemical, radioactive and mechanical stimuli elicited defects and deformities of the extremities, the spine and the head, including cyclopia.

This brilliant epoch of biologic research was at its height just at the time when Mall was collecting and studying the abnormal human embryos of his 1908 monograph. Eminent experimenters whom he knew personally—Jacques Loeb, T. H. Morgan, E. B. Wilson, Charles R. Stockard—were producing a whole series of anatomic defects quite similar to those Mall had found in his human specimens, and they were doing this by subjecting aquatic embryos to injurious environmental factors. However, the human embryo in utero is protected from all such directly harmful influences. What then can be the agent of prenatal injury and destruction in our own species? Mall thought he found this at the site of implantation. Examining his specimens under the microscope he observed degenerative changes in the placenta, and in the lining of the uterus he often found evidence of inflammation. Therefore, he concluded that the cause of retardation, dissociation and malformation of the human embryo, comparable with the deleterious agents of the experimenters, is impaired nutrition caused by faulty implantation resulting from disease of the endometrium, chiefly inflammatory. In those of his specimens which came from tubal pregnancies, the unfavorable site alone sufficed to impair the nutrition of the embryo.

Today, a half-century later, we know that much of the damage Mall saw in the placenta and the endometrium was the result, not the cause, of embryonic death, and that some of the supposed endometrial inflammation was actually a normal response to the hormones of gestation. Although younger members of this audience may find it hard to believe, what we now know as the premenstrual or progestational phase of the cycle was thought to be a pathologic condition, glandular endometritis, until Hitschmann and Adler of Vienna described the human endometrial cycle in 1908, the very same year in which Mall published his monograph.

The physiology of reproduction being in its infancy, and ovarian endocrinology scarcely born, embryologists accepted Mall's conjecture for want of anything better. At this time, however, a number of men were studying the earliest stages of development in laboratory and domestic animals, and their observations began to throw doubt on the concept of endometrial inflammation as a cause of embryonic death and abnormality. In 1920, Arthur Robinson of Edinburgh, who had collected a large series of early embryos of the ferret *Mustela putorius,* reported that he had found defective embryos in uteri which were quite free from infection, and that normal and abnormal embryos were seen sharing the same healthy uterine environment. Furthermore, he pointed out, abnormality may begin before implantation, as Carl Huber of Ann Arbor had already reported for the rat. I, myself, described in 1921 an early blastocyst of the domestic pig, bearing an ectodermal tumor instead of a normal embryonic disk. This is, I suppose, the youngest mammalian individual as yet seen which properly may be termed a monster; it was already deformed some days before implantation.

What Huber, Robinson and other students of early mammalian embryology were saying was that these very young embryos must be going wrong from some inherent defect of their own constitution, and by inference the same must be true of abnormalities which begin later. By that time, however, knowledge of the endometrial cycle was getting about, and critics of our assumption might well have queried whether these embryos were necessarily living in an adequate environment. The endometrium might be free from pathologic changes, and yet because of some endocrine failure might not have attained a physiologic state adapted to shelter and nourish the developing ovum. I was in a position to answer this question, having just completed a day-to-day study of the state of the sow's endometrium in the estrous cycle and the first weeks of pregnancy. To make a long story short, I examined 535 uteri at all stages of pregnancy. Among almost 3,800 embryos and fetuses in these uteri there were many abnormal ones. The commonest type of abnormality was general breakdown and maceration, but there were also cases of amorphous growth, cleft palate, and absence of the tail. The important fact is that no maternal disease existed in any of these cases; the implantation site of a dead or deformed embryo was like that of its normal litter-mates, not only in general condition but in histologic response to the endocrine control of the ovary at successive stages following ovulation. As far as the microscope could tell us, the uterine environment was not to blame for these failures.

Just as Mall had turned to experimental embryology for an explanation of his findings, so, in 1923, I turned to another new science, genetics, for help in thinking about human embryonic morbidity in terms of my observations on the sow. Its leaders had an answer for us in the theory of lethal genes, already well established for *Drosophila* and many other lower animals and plants, and for mammals. At least one instance was discovered in that fruitful year of 1908 by the French biologist L. Cuénot. This was the case of the yellow mouse, afterward worked out in detail by W. B. Castle, C. C. Little and W. B. Kirkham. All yellow mice carry a recessive lethal gene, and when 2 of them are bred together, the embryos homozygous for that gene, statistically, one fourth of each litter, die in utero about the time of implantation. In those days, mammalian genetics had little more to offer on the subject; but since then, as everyone here knows, a large number of embryonic and congenital anomalies in several species of mammals have been found to occur as hereditary characters subject to classic genetic analysis. Experts in this field are with us at this conference. Some of the gene defects they have studied result in death in utero; others give rise to anatomic anomalies of the same kinds as those which occur in man and those which experimental embryologists readily produce in the eggs of fish, amphibians and birds. Again we list cleft palate, clubfoot, microphthalmia, in fact the whole familiar series of bodily malformations, retardations, reduplications and redundancies.

The genetic explanation of congenital malformations developed so rapidly and was so soundly based on experiment that for a time it almost completely displaced the environmental hypothesis, at least in the circle of obstetricians, pathologists and human embryologists with whom I was associated. Ectopic pregnancy, we admitted, was a special case; an embryo implanted in the oviduct is indeed in an unfavorable environment, but as for those sheltered in a healthy uterus, what external harm could reach them?

A few years earlier we should have been perplexed by an astonishing fact, to which I have alluded more than once; the defects and the deformities of human infants which we supposed to result from genetic causes, and those of laboratory animals deliberately bred by the geneticists, are in general of the same sort as those which the experimental embryologists produced from healthy eggs by environmental agencies, such as physical and chemical traumata, unaccustomed temperatures, x-rays and the like. Charles R. Stockard helped to resolve this dilemma by pointing out, in 1921, that one and the same defect can result from damage that strikes an embryonic region which is undergoing rapid developmental changes, no matter whether that damage is caused by an external agent or by gene action. This concept was promptly supported by the organizer theory of embryonic induction developed by Hans Spemann of Freiburg im Breisgau and his followers, which pictures embryonic development as a series of steps of differentiation, each depending on the successive accomplishment of the preceding step.

Moreover, the genetic hypothesis offered a reasonable explanation of certain puzzling aspects of congenital malformation. No other conjecture, for example, can so plausibly account for the presence of the same defect in each of 2 identical twins. Among such occurrences perhaps the most remarkable of all is that seen in the Dionne quintuplets, all of whom exhibited a slight degree of webbing between the 2nd and the 3rd toes of each foot. Difficult as it is to imagine a chromosome defect in the single ovum from which the 5 girls developed waiting until the embryonic toes were separating and then acting at the same point in each of 10 little feet—difficult, I repeat, as this seems, it is the only acceptable explanation.

Some sort of gene action has been called on also to explain the so-called intra-uterine amputations. These had been thought to be caused by amniotic adhesions pinching off an extremity, or by strangulation of a part of the body by a loop of the umbilical cord; but G. L. Streeter in a brilliant article in 1930 showed that these curious lesions actually represent focal deficiencies of the embryonic and fetal tissues. The adhesions and the cord loops are secondary to the fetal changes. As Mall's successor, Streeter had accepted the latter's view as a working hypothesis, but now, directly influenced by my observations on pig embryos, he assumed a genetic cause of focal necrosis and of intra-uterine amputations.

At least one type of congenital malformation in human beings—mongolism—can now be definitely ascribed to a genetic mechanism. Only last year, through the work of Lejeune and others who so promptly followed up his report, we have gained an explanation in chromosomal terms of the mongoloid complex. Even though this discovery raises a whole new set of unanswered questions, it has shown us at least where to begin studying this seemingly hopeless enigma.

In short, the hypothesis of genetic origin of human congenital malformations, and of many instances of disease and death of the embryo and the fetus, is inescapably plausible. I suppose that everyone here has accepted the gene mechanism as operative in many cases of congenital malformation, probably in most of them, for the human infant in utero is obviously vulnerable through its genes and, on the other hand, seems to be well protected from all the drastic environmental disturbances to which experimenters can subject the embryos of lower forms. But two decades ago the pendulum of our thought on this subject began to swing the other way once more. New discoveries came pouring in; some of the people who made them are here today. In the first place, experimenters learned to produce embryonic defects in mammals, just

as their predecessors a generation ago did with the more accessible eggs of aquatic animals, amphibians and birds, by the action of environmental agents; however, not in quite the same ways, for the experimenter cannot easily get at the closely guarded mammalian embryo with his needles and probes, nor alter its temperature, nor change the osmotic concentration of the fluid in which it lives. Uterine homeostasis protects it too well against that sort of attack. However, he can cut down its oxygen supply by partially asphyxiating the mother; he can hit it with penetrating radiation; he can alter its vitamin supply and its mineral content through the mother's diet; he can clog its circulation with fine particles of dyestuffs pushed across the placenta. If he does these things at critical phases of embryonic development, with properly adjusted dosage or force, then we see once more the familiar pattern: of deficiencies and deformities in those embryos that were just sufficiently injured at sensitive stages of the inductor mechanism, with death and dissolution of those which were harder-hit.

Moreover, nature has provided us in recent years with new, or rather newly recognized experiments of her own upon the human subject. I refer to such instances as infection with rubella (German measles) with consequent malformation of the eyes, the ears and sometimes the heart and the brain; Professor Töndury now incriminates poliomyelitis, and an English health officer, M. J. Pleydell, observing the results of last year's epidemic of Asiatic influenza in his community, suggests that it too may be responsible for damage to the embryo. Fetal erythroblastosis affords a striking example of damage to the child in utero by an immunologically unfavorable environment, resulting not exactly in a malformation but in a drastic malfunction of the blood-forming tissues. Dr. Salome Waelsch has paralleled this in experiments in mice in which she produced brain damage in the embryo by immunizing the mother against mouse brain tissue. Contemplation of these two kinds of damage, both resulting from immune reactions, one of them to blood-cell production and the other to brain tissues, reminds us that we can draw no sharp line between malformations of an anatomic structure and maladjustments of a biochemical and/or biophysical constitution. A child may be just as badly off for lack of an essential enzyme system as if it had anencephaly or a congenital amputation.

Returning to our main theme, we are now back with Paré, for we must admit both genetic and environmental causes of prenatal abnormality; but as the program of our present Conference shows, each of these two general classes now covers an alarming multiplicity in detail. Paré's "deficiency of the seed" and "crooke-backt produce crooke-backt" has grown into a complex system of genetic factors. Our knowledge of the extrinsic causes also has multiplied. Paré's list includes only concepts that would have been used by a 16th century gardener or farmer to explain a crooked plant or a lean crop— the seed sown too thickly, or too sparsely; the uterus too narrow, like a flowerpot too small for its plant; malposition, as when the wind blows down the seedlings or a flowerpot is overturned in the greenhouse. To these, any farmer would add Mall's concept of inadequate soil—the seed sown upon stony ground. But while the embryologists and the geneticists have been disclosing the intrinsic mechanisms of the gametes and the embryo, a new branch of biology, the physiology of reproduction, has come forward to analyze the environment in which the human seedling develops. This science reminds us that the embryo is not growing in an open field or a flowerpot but in the interior of another living organism. At one and the same time it depends on the maternal tissues for its very life, and yet competes with them for nutriment. Accepting the shelter of the uterus, it takes also the risks of maternal disease or malnutrition, and of biochemical, immunologic and hormonal maladjustment.

Even before it strikes its roots in the living tissues of the endometrium it has a week's journey to make, as long as a submarine takes to pass beneath the polar ice-cap. Like the U-boat it has to carry most of its supplies with it in its trip down the oviduct and the uterine lumen, and to add to its difficulties is surrounded by a far more variable and chemically active medium than ice-cold sea water.

Let us briefly trace this journey and the subsequent period of gestation, giving consideration to the needs of the embryo and the contingencies it faces, as far as we have learned to understand them. While the fertilized egg is undergoing its earliest divisions, it is bathed in the fluid of the oviduct, about which we have only limited information. Even at this time it is subject to injury; my colleague Csapo finds that a very small dose of estrogen given to a rabbit at this stage of pregnancy destroys the ova. Through some unpublished experiments of my own, I learned that small burns of the ovary or other tissues near the fimbriated extremity cause the segmenting ova to disappear. Several investigators have found that in the guinea pig estrogen locks the ova in the oviduct by interfering with their transportation. If the transport mechanism, about which we know very little, fails to work properly, the venturing ovum will be as badly off as Columbus without his fleet, or Lindbergh without the *Spirit of St. Louis*. However, damage or retardation in the oviduct is likely to result in total destruction rather than in survival with deformity. In the domestic sow, on the average, 10 per cent of the ova shed at a given ovulation are lost before they reach the uterus. The Carnegie collection contains several human embryos of only a few cells each, already showing the stigmata of abnormality.

Once in the uterine cavity the embryo, now a blastocyst, finds itself in a fluid environment about which we know little except that it seems to be a glycogen-containing physiologic salt solution held to appropriate pH and oxygen tension. Within the tiny mass of the ovum, metabolic processes of great complexity are already under way. Although the ovum no doubt starts to replicate its genetic materials at the first division, it does not add to its general bulk during segmentation. Exactly when it does begin to build its own protoplasm is difficult to decide by microscopic observation while it is rapidly changing its shape as well as size; apparently, it starts to gain weight about the 4th day, while still free in the uterine cavity. Among all the steps a human being takes in his career, surely the manufacture of his own first protein molecules is one of the most critical.

Transport of the embryo toward the implantation site doubtless depends, as in the oviduct, upon a correct balance of the ovarian hormones controlling the uterine muscle. By this time, if all is going well, the lining of the uterus, by no means ordinarily a suitable tissue to receive and care for the embryo, has been brought into a favorable progestational state by action of the corpus luteum hormone, progesterone. If this mechanism fails, the nutrition of the embryo is impaired, and implantation will not occur.

The embryo is guided or rather drawn to a suitable implantation site by physico-chemical reactions determined, according to Bent Böving, by oxygen-CO_2 exchanges in and out of blood vessels under the endometrial surface. In those species, including our own, in which the embryo imbeds itself within the endometrium, rather than on the surface, we must suppose that enzymes in the trophoblast digest the maternal tissue, to excavate a bed for the embryo.

Although I am still talking about a creature only 2 millimeters in diameter, I have already hinted at a whole array of complicated biochemical reactions on which its fate depends—glycogenic nutrition, redox mechanisms, pH regulation, hormonal effects on myometrium and endometrium, and proteolytic enzyme systems. About the time of implantation—the 6th or the 7th day in man—still more complex activities are getting under way, the tissues of the embryonic area begin to be visibly differentiated into ectoderm, mesoblast and endoderm. Presumably, the organizer system has gone into action, creating new cell types with increasingly diverse functions. From now on the possibility exists that some slight fault in the environment, or a failure of gene action, sufficient to disturb biochemical reactions in a rapidly differentiating area, but not enough to destroy the viability of the whole embryo, may result in deficiency or maldevelopment eventuating in a deformed infant.

This is the time—the 2nd to the 6th week of gestation—when the majority of congenital malformations arise. The neural folds appear about day 19 and begin to close 2 days later; if they fail to close, spina bifida results. The future lens of the eye is recognizable at 28 days. The limb buds appear in the 5th week; the hand is defined at the 30th day, the fingers and the toes about the 35th. The lateral elements of the future lips and palate are fusing in the 5th and the 6th weeks. In these same weeks, the heart and the great vessels are shifting toward their ultimate pattern. I need not expand this catalog of embryonic differentiations and shifts, with abandonment of old structural patterns and establishment of new ones. As already mentioned, we know by direct observation of our own species that gene defects and certain virus infections can alter the progress of organs and tissues rendered vulnerable by these rapid developmental changes. Experiments on other mammalian species, as already mentioned, tell us also that many physical and chemical agents will damage the embryo at comparable periods; direct trauma, oxygen deficit, altered salt balance, particulate matter in the blood, radiation, enzyme poisons, certain steroid hormones. By analogy with experiments on inframammalian species, alterations of temperature in febrile diseases of the mother are to be suspected. The children of insulin-treated diabetic mothers evince a relatively high proportion of malformations, for which we must blame either the mother's high blood sugar or the action of insulin on the early embryo, or both. We may guess too at other conditions as yet little explored, which possibly affect essential physiologic mechanisms, for instance hormonal failure of the progestational state of the endometrium, and abnormal activity of the uterine muscles, which might congest the placental circulation. One of the purposes of this present Conference is to consider which of these factors, and others that may be conjectured, are actually operative in the production of human malformations and thus to point out ways and means of averting their action.

By the end of the 7th week, the external appearance of the developing organism is unmistakably human, even to the eyes of a layman, and we now call it not an embryo but a fetus. Although it is still only 30 millimeters long, weighs but a few grams, and has 7 months' growing to do before birth, the general pattern of its form is achieved, and it has a full complement of internal organs. The major organizer centers have done their work; from now on a deleterious change in the environment or a delayed gene effect is likely to affect only local organization in already specialized regions. The critical period for the development of congenital malformations is over except for a few structures still subject to fundamental change, for example the ductus arteriosus and the foramen ovale.

The fetus continues to be vulnerable to many dangers, but these will result more often in its death and expulsion than in malformation. It is subject to failure of the hormonal control of the myometrium, exerted first by the corpus luteum and then by the placenta, by which the uterus is restrained from expelling its contents until gestation is complete. It may suffer from failure of the placental circulation which brings it oxygen and nutriment and carries away its carbon dioxide and organic wastes. Its vulnerability to rubella ceases after the 3rd month, but other microbes may still infect it; we have long known that the spirochete of syphilis can pass the placenta; fetal smallpox seems to be authenticated, at least as a rarity; infection with *Toxoplasma gondii* has been described. I repeat, however, that in the fetal period all these potential dangers are more likely to result in death or disease of the conceptus than in malformation.

The great exception to this broad statement is a class of malformations resulting from local disturbance in already formed structures. Such a disturbance may prevent a part of the body from growing further, as for example when an arm remains a stump bearing rudimentary fingers. It may even cause retrogressive damage; there is some evidence for instance that anencephaly may represent a secondary breakdown of fetal brain structures already well organized. Or, working in the opposite sense, it may produce local gigantism, as of a limb or a digit.

Among the most frequent of these relatively late disturbances of growth are fetal amputations, and the less conspicuous yet often distressing constriction rings about the limbs, the fingers or the toes. When such a lesion occurs on the lower extremity, clubfoot may be associated with it. Streeter, as already mentioned, was convinced that these defects are genetically caused, but the opposing assumption that they result from mechanical action still survives, even though crude notions involving amniotic bands and loops of the cord have been discarded. Mr. Denis Browne, an experienced orthopedic surgeon of London, recently suggested that the constriction rings result from getting a fetal limb caught in a hole in the amnion. This idea might be tested by animal experiment and also by watching for constriction rings in identical twins. If both twins had them, the genetic explanation would be more plausible than the mechanical. Clubfoot, Mr. Browne suggests, may be produced by pressure of the uterine wall on the fetal legs. Our fellow conferee, F. C. Fraser, and his collaborators have produced cleft palate in mice by puncturing the amniotic sac just before closure of the secondary palate; one of his group, Bruce Walker, conjectures that in such experiments reduction of amniotic fluid pressure allows the uterus to compress the fetus, altering its posture and forcing the tongue into the palatal cleft, impeding closure. If, indeed, such pressure produced experimentally can somehow cause a malformation, we must expect that similar pressure produced by natural causes can also damage the embryo and the fetus. The 2nd month of human gestation, when according to my colleague Arpad Csapo the placenta presumably takes over progesterone production from the ovary and begins to exert local control of the myometrium, is a critical period in the regulation of intra-uterine pressure, at a time when fundamental centers of embryonic organization are still susceptible to damage. Then, if ever, pressure by the uterine musculature could disturb embryonic development.

At a later stage of gestation, skeletal weakness due to faulty maternal diet, such as Josef Warkany and James G. Wilson have studied, might make the limbs abnormally responsive to external pressure. Although I personally still suppose that cleft palate and clubfoot in human subjects, and indeed practically all types of congenital malformation, result more often from genetic than from environmental causes, in the present state of our knowledge we cannot close our minds to possible environmental factors, even in those malformations which begin early and are clearly reproducible by inheritance in experimental animals.

The National Foundation, undertaking to support research on congenital malformations, has entered a very broad field. As we have seen, its campaign must begin with the study of developmental biology, for we have hardly begun to understand the forces and the reactions that drive and guide the development of a fertilized ovum into a human infant. Embryology of the classic morphologic type, experimental embryology, cytology, histochemistry—all have their contribution to make. The genes, and the whole sequence of events by which they determine the infinite detail of bodily structure, await new discoveries. There are countless unsolved questions in the physiology of reproduction, touching on the maternal environment of the embryo and its control by hormones and other chemical agents of the body. The chemistry of respiration and nutrition must be called upon to explain the marvelous homeostatic balances through which, after all, the child generally enters the world sound and healthy. Microbiology must detect for us all the various pathogenic organisms which can invade and damage the fetus in utero; clinical medicine and obstetrics must teach us what illnesses of the mother may affect her offspring in the susceptible earliest days of its development.

Shall we have to call also upon the psychologists and the psychiatrists? Are there mental causes of intra-uterine disturbance? Once I would not even have raised such a question before fellow scientists; indeed, in my book of 1944, *Ourselves Unborn,* I attacked, with all the irony I could command, the ancient superstition that makes maternal impressions during pregnancy a cause of fetal malformation. The placenta, I said, completely shuts off the infant in utero from its mother's states of mind; her mental images, shocks and agitations are certainly insoluble in blood plasma and therefore cannot pass a semipermeable membrane of living protoplasm. Put in this dogmatic way, my statement was correct; but, after all, the mother's state of mind can affect her body's chemistry and alter her nutritional state; adrenalin and adrenocortical steroids can pass the placenta; the posterior pituitary well may contribute to abnormal behavior of the myometrium. There is some little evidence from experiments on animals that irritation and frustration of the mother during pregnancy somehow makes her offspring less stable, more responsive in their turn to psychic trauma. Whether the human mother's emotional upsets and alarms can disturb the environment of the embryo in utero sufficiently to produce physical anomalies I would in the whole still doubt, yet at present the question cannot be excluded from our wide-ranging inquiries.

I trust that the officers and The National Foundation, listening to this rapid summary of a great problem, are not appalled by the complexity of the task they have assumed. When leading the attack on infantile paralysis, they fostered researches scarcely less complex, sympathizing with the investigators in their difficulties and sharing their joy in success. Into the larger task they now undertake, as in the fight against poliomyelitis, they will put heart as well as money, knowing that for every experiment we perform in the detachment of our laboratories, somewhere in the world a malformed child is born to bitter disappointment and a woman's tears. This is a long, hard battle in which they have enlisted us; it must be fought on many fronts. We dare not pledge an early victory; but if in this hall scientific caution bids us withhold a promise, in yonder Abbey an ancient prophecy proclaims our hope:

A voice was heard in Ramah, lamentation and bitter weeping, Rachel weeping for her children refused to be comforted. . . . Thus saith the Lord, refrain thy voice from weeping and thine eyes from tears; for thy work shall be rewarded, saith the Lord, and thy children shall come again from the land of the enemy.

The Significance of a Concerted Approach to the Problem of Congenital Malformations

BASIL O'CONNOR, A.B., LL.B.

As a layman, I am conscious of the very special privilege of welcoming you to this International Conference on Congenital Malformations. There is one way in which a lay speaker can return the courtesy extended to him at a conference of scientists: he can be brief. I have observed that at international meetings, no matter how many languages are represented, the promise of brevity is one that never seems to lose anything in translation.

To anyone who knows anything about the size and the gravity of the problem you are here to discuss, to anyone who knows anything about the tragic historic background of that problem, this world conference on congenital malformations is a stirring event. Unmistakably it marks a significant stride in the long march of modern medicine.

Only in recent years has any serious effort been made to assess the damage to humanity from congenital malformations. Such findings as we have are sporadic and incomplete. But they are also appalling. We know that in America alone these "errors of nature" bring shock and desolation into at least a quarter of a million homes each year. And we have no reason to think the blow falls any the less heavily on the peoples of other nations.

We know these inborn anomalies date back through the ages, perhaps to the beginnings of human life. We know, too, that a curtain of superstition and guilt long has inhibited society from coming to grips with the problem.

Yet suddenly we are witnessing a "break-through." In the United States, The National Foundation, the country's leading voluntary health agency, announced in 1958 that henceforth congenital malformations will be a major target of its program. And 2 years later, in London, representatives of the scientific leadership of many nations respond to this agency's proposal to meet and to plan and to begin a concerted effort—in effect to enter upon a joint declaration of war on this greatest of all present-day medical threats to the health of children.

Now, let me assure you that the decision of The National Foundation to enter this field was not made by laymen. Nor was this conference inspired by laymen. The movement has arisen out of the recommendation —rather I should say at the urgent insistence —of scientists.

But why urgent at this time? Why an international conference on congenital malformations now? If it is urgent today, it was urgent 10 or 20 or 100 years ago. Is there some special compulsion in the year 1960 that leads science to shift from isolated effort, scattered individual studies, to a concerted worldwide attack on this problem?

I believe there *is* that special urgency. This is a meeting of experts in specialized fields. Your primary interest in coming together is, naturally, the opportunity that is afforded you for exchange of technical knowledge and theory. But to me, the very concept of this meeting, the presence of authorities from many lands, east and west, signify that something else is happening, a new ferment within the scientific community,

18

of profound meaning to the health of all people and to the hope of peace among all nations.

I refer to the vast accountability of science for what is happening in the world and to a growing recognition, by scientists, of that accountability. The scientist of today is conscious of an obligation beyond that of citizens in other callings and beyond that of the scientist of other times. It is something more than a responsibility for technical competence. It is something overreaching the purely professional ethic.

You respond in this way because you have seen your works grow in influence until they encompass man's fate. You have seen technology in its stride, far outpacing other human progress during your lifetime and leaving in its wake an enormous and frightening slough of obsolescence. Floundering there, with their time-honored concepts outmoded and shaken, are the professions of the statesman, the diplomat, the soldier, even the philosopher and the moralist. And when you can make a moralist flounder, you may be sure you have shaken the world!

In the past, the scientist followed a general pattern of creating and then turning his creation over to others to apply and manage. This has been true especially of the worker engaged in pure or basic research. Guarded from the slings of outrageous fortune—in fact, rather too effectively guarded from any kind of fortune at all—he was kept pure whether he liked it or not. And he did like his freedom from the toils and cares of a pragmatic society.

But in the sense that it may mean detachment from one's fellow man, there is such a thing as being too pure. When you are instrumental in creating mechanisms that can destroy all human life at the push of a button, how "pure" are you being if you relinquish the control over them indiscriminately to a world that is full of all kinds of people, including some who are pathologically unable to refrain from pushing buttons? Today your profession is putting that

question to itself and answering it. No, you can no longer follow the relatively simple pattern of your predecessors. Science is not an island; it has become the mainland of the world's hope. You are not free to forget freedom. What you have always thought of as your "life work" cannot absorb you to the point where you are cut off from that larger life which cries out to all men of vision.

I am speaking now not only of scientists in the nuclear field. In many fields, in the uses of peace as well as war, you and your colleagues are assuming a larger initiative, a direct, personal responsibility. Therefore you are undertaking to do many things you have never done before.

One of these great new ventures is in its formative stage here in this meeting. Why a concerted attack on congenital malformations, beginning now? Because now, as never before, basic research is laying the groundwork and providing the tools for this effort. In genetics, in body chemistry, in fundamental biology, now as never before, your profession is equipping itself with a new and highly productive methodology. I am told that the development of these approaches has brought you to many exciting thresholds of new knowledge; and I am told that there is a need for co-ordination of many lines of inquiry—a need of organization *for* research, not *of* it. Not to cross those thresholds, not to plan so that they can be crossed, would be a failure to accept the new accountability of science that I have mentioned. That is why, in 1960, an open conference of this magnitude and scope is being held for the first time among nations on the subject of congenital anomalies.

Your conference is international because congenital anomalies do not respect national boundaries and because the professional talents required in meeting this challenge are spread around the world. It is international because our declaration of war against this menace to child health is total war. In it there is only one alliance—the alliance of all humanity. It is true that some countries are not represented at this gathering. But our enemy is also their enemy. It is our hope and plan to make this the first of many world conferences on congenital malformations. They will be "summit-conferences"— the summit of the world of science—and I believe these summit conferences *will not fail.*

You are not acting too soon. In the warning words of many of the world's great scientists against the possible consequences of radiation, an additional note of urgency is injected into the challange you have taken up. We have been put on notice by at least some of these authorities—and they include experts of the highest repute—that whether any more nuclear explosions take place or not, the radiation from those which have already occurred represents a danger of increasing congenital malformations. Dr. Albert Schweitzer, on information that has been furnished him by these experts, has said:

The most sinister aspect of internal as well as external radiation is that years may pass before the evil consequences appear. Indeed, they make themselves felt, not in the first or second generation but in the following ones. Generation after generation, for centuries to come, will witness the birth of an ever-increasing number of children with mental and physical defects.*

"Generation after generation for centuries to come." It is a long way off. We shall be gone then. But does this mean that *our* problem, the onus that rests on our generation, is any the lighter? Whatever one's views may be on further nuclear bomb testing, the effects of that which is already done are irrevocable. If Dr. Schweitzer and the authorities who have informed him are correct, we cannot erase from the skies the thing we have done.

Certainly there remains before us the grim necessity to do whatever we can on earth —all that lies within our power to help coming generations cope with a possible increase in congenital malformations, by way of prevention if any such ways can be found, or failing this, by way of the care that may make life livable for innocent victims-to-be.

The causes of congenital malformations are varied and complex. We are told that some of them are environmental. Scientists have shown that they can cause such defects to appear, virtually at will, in animals. We are told that some of them are hereditary. And, scientists have demonstrated that they can breed such defects, at will, in animals. The study, like that of any major disease problem, has deepened as it progresses in the field of fundamental biology until its investigations have converged on the secrets of life itself.

Ought we to know such secrets? And if we learn them, ought we to exercise new controls over human destiny that could emerge from this knowledge? There are some who say no. There are some who hold to ancient beliefs and superstitions—for example, that birth defects are foreordained and therefore that man should not try to prevent them. And there are some who believe that birth defects and other weaknesses in humankind are part of the mechanism that nature has evolved through the ages to ensure the survival of the fittest. They wonder why science should try to save the lives of children who are born imperfect and who might, in the natural course, be soon removed.

These people turn to the geneticist, the biologist, and ask, "Where are you taking us?" They point to the threat of annihilation which nuclear physics has hung over the world. They want to know whether man, from his probing of the depths of biology, will emerge with other dangerous tools—dangerous because he is not wise enough to use them well.

The answer, I believe, lies not in fostering ignorance. Rather it is in the limitless

* Schweitzer, Albert: An obligation to tomorrow, Saturday Review, p. 22, May 24, 1958.

accumulation of more and more knowledge of ourselves and of the world we live in. For it is only when we *know enough* that we can decide wisely how far we may go, safely and morally, in determining our own destiny. It is only when we know enough that we can leave to nature those things that nature does best.

It is in knowing this that you can go on with confidence in your search for truth, with the certainty that the truth you find is right and beautiful.

SESSION I

Incidence

Moderator

PROFESSOR A. BRADFORD HILL, C.B.E., D.S.C., F.R.S.
Statistical Research Unit, London School of Hygiene and Tropical Medicine
Keppel Street, London, W.C.1

EPIDEMIOLOGIC AND STATISTICAL PITFALLS IN INVESTIGATION OF ETIOLOGY
CARL L. ERHARDT, M.P.A., S.M.(hyg.)
Director of Statistics, New York City Department of Health, New York, New York, U.S.A.

THE FREQUENCY OF CONGENITAL MALFORMATIONS
PROFESSOR MAURICE LAMY
Clinique de Génétique Médical, Hôpital des Enfants Malades
149 rue des Sèvres, Paris 15, France

SOURCES OF VARIATION IN THE INCIDENCE OF MALFORMATIONS
PROFESSOR THOMAS McKEOWN, M.D., F.R.C.P.
Department of Social Medicine, The Medical School, Edgbaston, Birmingham

Epidemiologic and Statistical Pitfalls in Investigations of Etiology*

CARL L. ERHARDT, M.P.A., S.M.(hyg.)

The pathogenic course in teratology from inciting event to observed defect follows many pathways. The same inciting event may result in quite different defects; yet similar defects may derive from various etiologic factors.[12,17] A given factor does not invariably produce the effect that might have been expected. Some embryos affected by a specific type of insult may die and be aborted, while others proceed to a term delivery despite a serious malformation.[2,5] Simple relationships obviously are not to be anticipated in research relating to the etiology of congenital malformations.

Stevenson and colleagues,[46] summarizing the complexities that beset the researcher, have this to say:

Research into the etiology of congenital malformations is made more difficult by the fact that acquired defects, or phenocopies, may simulate inherited defects with great exactness. Furthermore, they may be repeated in members of the same family because the same unfavorable environment is at work: familial cretinism and toxoplasmosis are possible examples of this. Inherited defects, on the other hand, may not repeat in the members of a family under observation: they may be inherited as recessive characters and the small size of human sample studies may not reveal them; they may require several abnormal genes for their expression and so be exhibited only rarely; or they may have reduced expressivity and thus cause only a minor abnormality not obvious to casual observation. Thus, familial occurrence does not always imply an inherited

defect and lack of it does not exclude an inherited one. Some malformations, furthermore, may be the result of a defective gene which is allowed to express itself only under certain environmental conditions.

Gruenwald[17] adds the problems of environmental or host factors that produce effects remote (in time or site) from that originating the effect. He especially emphasizes the later degeneration of normally formed organs,[18] a further complication that interferes with the establishment of an important element: the stage of development when an "insult" to the organism may have occurred.

Obviously, teratologic complexity is such that etiologic research can readily result in improper conclusions. Nevertheless, this complexity and the interactions of agent, host and environment that occur do not disqualify, but recommend, the traditional statistical-epidemiologic methods. With experimental methods denied in research into human maldevelopment, statistical evaluation of large groups of cases may answer many questions that otherwise could not be answered.[19] Francis[11] emphasizes that the clinical and epidemiologic are interwoven, saying:

Discrimination between agents may shed light on epidemiological variations. Epidemiological variation may suggest different clinical entities or varying combinations of such entities.

Yet the factors involved must be disentangled[27] if valid conclusions are to be drawn.

---

* Paper was read by: Louis M. Hellman, M.D., Department of Obstetrics and Gynecology, Downstate Medical Center, University of New York College of Medicine, Brooklyn, New York, U.S.A.

Two general approaches exist—the descriptive and the analytic. Each has its own merits, disadvantages and problems.

DESCRIPTIVE STUDIES

In a descriptive study an attempt is made to determine, for as many variables as possible, whether a group in the study population exhibiting a specific characteristic (i.e., a congenital anomaly in this context) differs from the remainder with respect to these variables. The objective, of course, is to identify the variables peculiarly associated with the characteristic under investigation and hence gain insight as to the etiology of the condition.

DEFINITION AND DIAGNOSIS

Although the problem of definition and diagnosis is common to both descriptive and analytic studies, its importance merits immediate mention.

Ingalls[24] remarks:

If there is one broad principle which emerges clearly from experimental teratology, it is that all anomalies can no more be treated as a single universe than can all rashes or all tumors.

MacMahon and co-workers[31] agree that individual malformations must be investigated separately unless clear evidence is available that a group of malformations represents a "complex," even though there may be variation in the extent to which the several organs are affected. Therefore, the origin of the complex rather than of its parts must be sought lest an otherwise marked trail be missed. Yet the recognition of such complexes is, itself, a major problem.

However, if specifically defined anomalies are singly investigated, the expected incidence is thereby reduced from that of the aggregate; hence, augmented numbers of observations will be required.[12,27] Moreover, apparent lack of association or weak association with a given possible etiologic factor may result because of dilution of the series with cases of other etiologies.[27] Böök[5] has expressed the feeling that "not even patent ductus arteriosus should be considered an entity of single etiology."

Most serious impairments can be adequately defined morphologically. However, Stevenson and colleagues[46] insist that such classifications are inadequate because similar morphologic effects are produced by a variety of inherited factors and noxious agents. Presuming that additional axes of classification can be devised, the diagnosis in the particular case is not always made readily.

Embryonal pathology requires careful microscopy; fetal and infant postmortem examinations are a necessity to confirm clinical diagnoses of anomalous internal organs. Stevenson and colleagues[46] report, for example, an "epidemic" of pilonidal sinus existing only in the imagination of an intern with a fondness for the diagnosis; misdiagnosis of congenital heart disease and even of clubfoot occurs. Moreover, diagnosis may not be made until long after birth[32] or may go completely unrecognized.

Direct observation by the researcher is not demanded, but certainly it behooves him to ascertain that appropriate diagnostic criteria were established and that they were followed consistently if he is relying on information recorded by others.

SOURCES OF DATA

In descriptive studies, the population of a specific hospital or hospital service may be utilized. However, the meager facilities available to the individual research worker may preclude tabulation and analysis of all the events occurring during a specific period of time; yet a sample of total deliveries as a control may not be adequate in size for multivariate analysis that would perhaps be revealing.[53] Furthermore, hospital populations may be biased, as has been emphasized repeatedly;[3,9,27,30,35,49] hence, data derived from them may lead to erroneous conclusions.

In some measure, this type of bias may

be reduced by aggregating the experiences of a number of hospitals, as is being done in the Co-operative Study directed by Dr. Schuyler Kohl at the Downstate Medical College of the University of the State of New York. A similar attempt (but an analytic rather than descriptive approach) is represented by the Collaborative Project sponsored by the U. S. National Institute of Neurological Diseases and Blindness.[36] However, the reluctance of physicians to have their private patients included in such a series, or the difficulties in controlling the recording of data if private patients are included may introduce a new source of bias if environmental influences are at issue. As Bross[7] says, it is relatively easier to keep bias from entering than to remove it.

   . . . statistical tinkering (he remarks) is generally an unsatisfactory way to deal with bias. Fancy "adjustments" designed to avoid a suspected bias may very well introduce an unsuspected bias.

Plans offering comprehensive medical care, such as the Health Insurance Plan of Greater New York, afford the opportunity for examining experience in a defined population group served by private physicians with uniform methods of recording data about patients; a well-organized research program enhances the opportunity.[42]

The vital records (registration) system has much to recommend it for descriptive studies if the system is well developed. Thus, all events for an entire community may be included in the study, and, in some areas, relatively large numbers of deliveries are involved. Usually, a routine process has been established for tabulation and analysis of data from the records, and this process can be modified to accommodate special studies. However, incomplete registration of births, deaths or fetal deaths can vitiate the most carefully done analysis, particularly if the failure to register a birth should be related to a defect in the infant or to its loss. An especially serious limitation rests in the few factors that can be investigated because

little or no information regarding the medical history of the pregnancy and delivery is required to be reported on birth certificates. Even in the few areas where items of medical history are included on the certificate forms, omissions or misreporting occur; these must be evaluated carefully lest they introduce biases because of any form of selectivity.[29,41] Hellman,[23] discussing the need for accurate basic information, has made the pungent remark:

   Putting holes in a punched card to record data doesn't impart to that card either a soul or integrity, and that is a thing a lot of people forget.

A population consisting of children in school recognizably omits those too seriously handicapped to attend school as well as those who have died as a result of congenital defects before school age. On the other hand, conscientious investigators sometimes forget that a series of neonatal deaths ignores the fetal deaths or that a perinatal series ignores the survivors; therefore, results are biased.[6,53] Worcester and associates[53] have observed that maternal age appears to be an important factor in survival of the infant, but did not appear to be of teratologic significance in their series. They conclude that studies implicating maternal age may have become heavily weighted with dead infants in the desire for confirmed diagnoses. The nonrandom nature and hence the bias of autopsy material has been clearly shown by Mainland.[34]

Similarly, it must be remembered that descriptive studies of total deliveries reported to the registration office generally are limited to fetuses that have reached a specified stage of uterogestation. Hence, damaged embryos aborted during early pregnancy are lost to observation; therefore, what we do observe, is the prevalence of specific defects at birth rather than their incidence.[5]

ANALYTIC STUDIES

Analytic studies are specifically designed to test hypotheses by comparing the experiences of a test group with those of a control group; they are of two basic types. The retrospective (or case history) type has its point of departure among affected patients for whom search is made in their past history (or that of their parents) for factors possibly related etiologically to the defect under observation. Prospective (or cohort) research starts with a defined population about whom many factors may be recorded; the objective then is to determine whether a specific anomaly occurs more frequently among the children of persons possessing a factor than among children of those without this factor. Whether retrospective or prospective analytic research is undertaken, the same cautions about definition and diagnosis of anomalies apply, as has been discussed previously.

RETROSPECTIVE VS. PROSPECTIVE

Unfortunately, because of misinterpretation of findings and failure to understand its limitations, retrospective studies have gained an inferior reputation. Mantel and Haenszel[35] observe:

> Statisticians have been somewhat reluctant to discuss the analysis of data gathered by retrospective techniques, possibly because their training emphasizes the importance of defining a universe and specifying rules for counting events or drawing samples possessing certain properties. To them, proceeding from "effect to cause," with its consequent lack of specificity of a study population at risk, seems an unnatural approach. Certainly, the retrospective study raises some questions concerning the representative nature of the cases and controls in a given situation which cannot be completely satisfied by internal examination of any single set of data.

Yet, one of the few agreed causative factors of specific malformations is rubella. Admittedly, the hazard is not as great as was first believed,[15,32,43] but if Gregg[16] had not used his insight retrospectively, the clear risk might still be unrecognized. Similarly, the relatively prompt indictment of excess oxygen administration as a cause of retrolen-

tal fibroplasia represents what can be done with concentrated effort by means of retrospective epidemiology.[26] Gentry and colleagues[14] have looked into background radiation as etiologic factors by this mechanism, too, with suggestive results.

We must be clear that retrospective findings frequently are interpreted fallaciously. Dorn has pointed out[8,9] the difficulty of distinguishing between causal association and the operation of time, as well as the problem of defining the population from which the cases arose. Fraser[12] stresses both confusion of cause with coincidence and maternal memory bias, while Mantel and Haenszel[35] emphasize that the choice of controls is not always immediately evident. Furthermore, spurious conclusions may result because more detailed information is recorded for complicated or "interesting" cases in records consulted retrospectively.[6,9]

However, White and Bailar,[50] conclude that differentiation between types of studies rests on the kind of sampling involved, other factors being equal, and that the same conclusions will result whether a retrospective or a prospective plan is followed. They say:

> Scientific theory thrives on the investigation of anomalous instances, and the follow-up method is an inefficient way of bringing them to attention; it is best adapted to the detailed and definitive study of factors which have already come under strong suspicion.

Technics for reducing the limitations of the retrospective study have been discussed by MacMahon,[30] Dorn,[8,10] and Mantel and Haenszel,[35] among others.

The prospective approach leads to more reliable estimates of occurrence of events relative to their antecedent causes, but a serious drawback is the need for a large number of cases if expected incidence is low.[30] This method does represent the only possible approach when the required information is not available in records or reliably in the memory of the patient. However, cohort studies requiring long-term follow-up can become discouraging to the observer, and losses of patients during a long course can make findings difficult to interpret. Of even greater consequence is the necessity for strong suspicion in advance of the etiologic precursors in order to record whether or not they exist among the persons in the cohort.[10]

It should be kept in mind that a prospective study can be set up retrospectively, if the necessary records are available; that is, the population of interest can be reconstructed as of some date in the past for the study of some event occurring after that date.[9] For example, from physicians' or clinic prenatal records or from birth certificates, all women with puerperal toxemia could be selected as a cohort to investigate the influence of this condition on the infant. Despite the fact that some or all of the women may already have been delivered, such a cohort would constitute a prospective group. Such a procedure assumes, of course, that all women with puerperal toxemia can be identified from the records and, also, that an adequate control group also can be established. Worcester[52] recommends this method, commenting that "the mother is a better starting point than the baby."

The mere fact that a study is done prospectively does not assure unequivocal conclusions: witness the smoking-cancer controversy. With either retrospective or prospective method, the major hazard is indiscriminate acceptance of the results of observations without considering the design of the study and its possible biases.

THE TIME FACTOR

The importance of the time during the development of the embryo when an insult was received has been discussed by many investigators.[17,20,21,25,31,51,53] A genetically determined anomaly is established at the time of fertilization. An aberration resulting from environmental factors must arise from a stimulus applied at or during some time, usually the period of differentiation. Yet, a genetically inspired degeneration may present the same picture as an environmen-

tally induced defect.[17,20] Moreover, as indicated earlier, both genetic and environmental influences may be operating jointly.

Worcester and colleagues[53] have experimented with classification of congenital anomalies by month of gestation when the defect presumably developed, since seasonal variation in the occurrence of various malformations has been noted.[12] Determination of the month when the defect was likely to have developed was based on Arey's[1] tabulation of development of the organs according to the age of the embryo. This classification method indicated, for example, that defects of the cardiovascular and the musculoskeletal systems were likely to have arisen in the 2nd month of pregnancy, while central nervous system defects were initiated over a period of several of the months.

The objective of this procedure was to relate the data for years when malformation rates were high to epidemic incidence of communicable diseases. Monthly figures had to be used to clarify the relationships, since infection presumably would affect only that segment of a specific year's deliveries that was at the appropriate stage of embryonal development when the mother was infected. The relationship of high malformation rates with an epidemic of rubella seemed to be clear, but similar relationships with other epidemic diseases were not. Of course, variation in both host and environment are influential in determining whether or not a malformation can be induced by a specific infection; hence, the severity of the disease is of consequence as well as the period of gestation when the infection occurred.[6]

An apparently more precise method of investigating the influence on the embryo of seasonal factors or of other events specific in time is the use of a cohort of women conceiving during a specified limited period; each would be subject (within limitations) to similar external environmental circumstances at the same stage of pregnancy throughout its course. Control groups could consist of women conceiving during other intervals of time whose pregnancies could not have been affected by the given event. In other words, an estimated date of conception should be the criterion for setting up the cohorts rather than the date of delivery, since those *delivered* in a certain interval, being of different gestational ages, will have had different external environmental experiences. An association of a congenital defect with an environmental factor affecting the embryo at a specific stage of gestation may fail of detection because of this dilution of the affected cohort.

Despite deficiencies in use of the initial date of the last menstrual period,[13] such cohorts (or at least that portion of them as have survived some specific duration of pregnancy) can be set up retrospectively by resort to the recorded first date of the last menstrual period. Since this information, presumably from the physician's record or the clinic record made at the first prenatal visit, is reported on New York City birth certificates, we are presently exploring this concept. A similar approach might be to classify delivered infants and fetuses by period of gestation for analysis; however, this appears to be a more cumbersome procedure.

An analogous confusion may occur in genetic studies if the method of ascertainment is haphazard. Inclusion of fraternities in which the propositus was preceded by a sibling with the same defect under investigation may produce too high a rate if likelihood of a third malformation in a fraternity is greater than that of a second. Hence, those fraternities should be excluded in which the first malformation occurring is found only because the second has turned up as a propositus.[33] Haenszel[22] recently has discussed in detail the problems of estimation of familial risks of disease.

Heredity or Environment?

Myrianthopoulos[38] points out that heredity does not work in a vacuum. He says:

The environment influences its expression to a greater or lesser degree, so that it is well nigh impossible to differentiate between "purely genetic" and "purely environmental" disease.

Neel and Schull[39] have listed criteria for determining the influence of genetic factors; yet these criteria cannot be relied upon in all circumstances.

The occurrence of phenocopies, difficulties in recognizing the heterozygotic carrier state, identification of effects of abnormality rather than the true anomaly as in Wilson's disease[39]—these are further occurrences that militate against straightforward determinations. Bass[2] offers the comment:

We have become so accustomed to regarding defective offspring as a result of genetic hereditary factors that when the physician encounters a congenital defect he often completely ignores the history of abnormalities in the present or in previous pregnancies.

This is a point with which Böök agrees.[6] This criticism of the physician leads to the question, too, whether concentration on "penetrance" and "expressivity" as concepts, useful as they are, may delay somewhat investigation of the environmental or host factors that may account for these phenomena.

Need for Large Numbers

Snyder[45] points out that only a few of the hundreds of severe abnormalities in man that may be attributed to single-gene substitutions have an incidence above 1 in 10,000. Defects of other genetic or of environmental etiology also have low incidence. Any descriptive study or prospective type of analytic research must have large numbers of cases for reliable conclusions.

The Collaborative Project of the NINDB, already referred to,[36] envisions intensive study of 40,000 pregnancies, a respectable number of observations. Yet, the expected frequency of specific defects is likely to be so low that the 40,000 pregnancies will not be adequate to discriminate with sufficient certainty between incidence rates for groups of women of selected characteristics that may be associated with given defects.

Taylor[47] has prepared tables showing the probability of missing a difference (beta error) at specific significance levels (alpha) in a sample of 40,000 when various proportions of the total sample exhibit a certain characteristic. He then estimates the probability of missing, in a sample of 40,000, an observed difference of the magnitude observed in the Lilienfeld-Parkhurst study of cerebral palsy.[28] They had found that about 1 per cent of the women under study had nonpuerperal complications and that their infants had a cerebral palsy incidence rate of 18.2 per 1,000. The cerebral palsy rate among the infants of the women without such complications was about 5 per 1,000. Taylor showed that even this trebling of the rate has an almost 50 per cent chance of being missed in a 40,000 sample and that reduction of the beta error to 5 per cent probability will occur only with an incidence rate almost 8 times that in the comparison population.

Hence, one of the major problems of descriptive or cohort research into the etiology of congenital malformations is the large numbers of observations required to demonstrate associations convincingly.[27] However, large numbers alone, are not to be taken as proving the case unless adequate care has been taken otherwise in planning an investigation.[30]

CONCLUSION

Muench[37] has said:

To a good many clinicians, a biostatistician is a mechanism devoted mainly to asking embarrassing questions after it is too late to get an answer.

The obvious solution is to let the statistician pose the questions at the beginning of an investigation so that the answers may be anticipated or the statistician must share the onus for lack of the answers. Therefore, because of the insistence of my profession[40] that the statistician must share in the gesta-

tion of research efforts rather than solely in the pathologic postmortem of data, it has been a particular satisfaction that the first paper to follow Dr. Corner's theme address relates to epidemiologic and statistical problems.

The statistician's insistence on being a full partner should not be interpreted, of course, as a claim to omniscience in every field. It has been pointed out repeatedly that the statistician cannot be a substitute for the clinician, but that each is more effective for an understanding of the other's field.[40,48] Berkson[4] is emphatic, with reference to the smoking-lung cancer hypotheses:

Cancer is a biologic, not a statistical problem. Statistics can soundly play an ancillary role in its elucidation. But if biologists permit statisticians to become the arbiters of biologic questions, scientific disaster is inevitable.

Simon[44] has demonstrated that causal interpretations of partial correlations in multivariate situations can be made only upon the introduction of *a priori* assumptions rejecting certain other possible causal relationships whose precise effects cannot, or have not, been measured. The formulation of such assumptions, and particularly decision whether they are valid, remain the peculiar province of the clinician.

The statistical-epidemiologic approach represents a method of attack. The clinician or geneticist must, in the final analysis, pose the questions requiring investigation. The statistician extracts from these questions the implications suggesting testable hypotheses, designs the research, directs its execution and prepares a statistical analysis of the results. The biologic interpretation of the findings again must be the responsibility of the clinician or the geneticist. To make such investigations most profitable, as Böök[5] has emphasized for cardiac malformations, work in pathogenesis, pathophysiology and embryology of congenital defects must be intensified, and co-ordination of all types of research in this field is needed.[6]

The essentially negative tenor of this discussion was demanded by its title but is not intended to denote a hopeless cause. Many of the authors cited have proposed positive steps for avoiding or overcoming the pitfalls mentioned or, by example, have shown the way. Nature has erected a complicated barrier to knowledge of the etiology of congenital malformations. Concerted attack has tumbled many bastions; it will overcome this one, too.

REFERENCES

1. Arey, L. B.: Developmental Anatomy, ed. 5, Philadelphia, Saunders, 1946.
2. Bass, M. H.: Diseases of the pregnant woman affecting the offspring, Advances Int. Md. 5:15-58, 1952. (Year Book Medical Publishers, Inc.)
3. Berkson, Joseph: Limitations of the application of fourfold table analysis to hospital data, Biometrics Bull. 2:47-53, 1946.
4. Berkson, Joseph: Smoking and lung cancer: some observations on two recent reports, J. Am. Stat. A. 53:28-38, 1958.
5. Böök, J. A.: Heredity and heart disease, Am. J. Pub. Health 50 (March, Part II): 1-10, 1960.
6. Böök, J. A., and Fraccaro, M.: Research on congenital malformations, Etudes néonatales 5:39-54, 1956.
7. Bross, I. D. J.: Therapy for intellectual obesity, Am. J. Obst. & Gynec. 69:372-378, 1955.
8. Dorn, H. F.: Philosophy of inferences from retrospective studies, Am. J. Pub. Health 43:677-683, 1953.
9. ———: Some applications of biometry in the collection and evaluation of medical data, J. Chron. Dis. 1:638-664, 1955.
10. ———: Some problems arising in prospective and retrospective studies of the etiology of disease, New England J. Med. 261:571-579, 1959.
11. Francis, Thomas, Jr.: Correlations in clinical and epidemiological investigation, Am. J. Md. Sc. 226:376-382, 1953.
12. Fraser, F. C.: Causes of congenital malformations in human beings, J. Chron. Dis. 10:97-110, 1959.
13. Frazier, T. M.: Error in reported date of last menstrual period, Am. J. Obst. & Gynec. 77:915-918, 1959.
14. Gentry, J. T., Parkhurst, Elizabeth, and Bulin, G. V., Jr.: An epidemiological study of congenital malformations in New York State, Am. J. Pub. Health 49:497-513, 1959.
15. Greenberg, Morris, Pellitteri, Ottavio, and Barton, Jerome: Frequency of defects in infants whose mothers had rubella during pregnancy, J. Am. M. A. 165:675-678, 1957.
16. Gregg, N. M.: Congenital cataract following German measles in the mother, Tr. Ophth. Soc. Australia 3:5-46, 1941.
17. Gruenwald, Peter: Developmental pathology, Am. J. Obst. & Gynec. 58:1-14, 1949.
18. ———: Environmental causes of abnormal embryonic development, Clin. Orthop. 8:13-19, 1956.
19. ———: Mechanisms of abnormal development: I. Causes of abnormal development in the embryo, Arch. Path. 44:398-436, 1947.
20. ———: *in* Prematurity, Congenital Malformations and Birth Injury, p. 160, New York, Association for the Aid of Crippled Children, 1953.
21. Grünfelder, Benno, and Lasch, Walter: Die Zeitpunkt einer embryonalen Entwicklungs störung als wesächliches Moment kongenitaler Anomalien, Ann. paediat. 173:388-404, 1949.
22. Haenszel, William: Some problems in the estimation of familial risks of disease, J. Nat. Cancer Inst. 23:487-505, 1959.
23. Hellman, Louis: *in* Prematurity, Congenital Malformations and Birth Injury, p. 191, New York, Association for the Aid of Crippled Children, 1953.
24. Ingalls, T. H.: Prenatal human ecology, Am. J. Pub. Health 50:50-54, 1960.
25. ———: The study of congenital anomalies by the epidemiologic method, New England J. Med. 243:67-74, 1950.
26. Kinsey, V. E., and Zacharias, Leona: Retrolental fibroplasia, J.A.M.A. 139:572-578, 1949.
27. Lilienfeld, A. M.: *in* Prematurity, Congenital Malformations and Birth Injury, pp. 178, 180, 181, New York, Association for the Aid of Crippled Children, 1953.
28. Lilienfeld, A. M., and Parkhurst, Elizabeth: A study of the association of factors of pregnancy and parturition with the development of cerebral palsy, Am. J. Hyg. 53:262-282, 1951.
29. Lilienfeld, A. M., Parkhurst, Elizabeth, Patton, Robert, and Schlesinger, E. R.: Accuracy of supplemental medical infor-

mation on birth certificates, Pub. Health Rep. **66**:191-198, 1951.

30. MacMahon, Brian: Statistical methods in medicine, New England J. Med. **253**:646-652, 688-693, 1955.

31. MacMahon, Brian, Pugh, T. F., and Ingalls, T. H.: Anencephalus, spina bifida and hydrocephalus. Incidence related to sex, race, season of birth, and incidence in siblings, Brit. J. Prev. & Social Med. **7**:211-219, 1953.

32. McIntosh, Rustin: The problem of congenital malformations, J. Chron. Dis. **10**:139-151, 1959.

33. McKeown, Thomas, MacMahon, Brian, and Parsons, C. G.: The familial incidence of congenital malformation of the heart, Brit. Heart J. **15**:273-277, 1953.

34. Mainland, Donald: The risk of fallacious conclusions from autopsy data on the incidence of diseases with application to heart disease, Am. Heart J. **45**:644-654, 1953.

35. Mantel, Nathan, and Haenszel, William: Statistical aspects of the analyses of data from retrospective studies of disease, J. Nat. Cancer Inst. **22**:719-748, 1959.

36. Masland, R. L.: A Collaborative Project for the Study of Cerebral Palsy, Mental Retardation and other Neurological and Sensory Disorders of Childhood, Washington, D. C., National Institute of Neurological Diseases and Blindness, (reproduced), 1958.

37. Muench, Hugo: Biostatistics—and why! Postgrad. Med. **13**:334-338, 1953.

38. Myrianthopoulos, N. C.: Genetics and public health, U.S. Pub. Health Rep. **74**:1098-1106, 1959.

39. Neel, J. V., and Schull, W. J.: Human Heredity, Chicago, Univ. Chicago Press, 1954.

40. Reid, D. D.: Statistics in clinical research, Ann. New York Acad. Sc. **52**:931-934, 1950.

41. Schwartz, Samuel, and West, Howard: Potentialities and limitations of medical data on official birth certificates, Am. J. Pub. Health **50**:338-345, 1960.

42. Shapiro, Sam: Pregnancy Study in H.I.P. (Summary of Objectives and Methodology), New York, Health Insurance Plan of Greater New York (mimeographed), 1958.

43. Siegel, Morris, and Greenberg, Morris: Fetal death, malformation and prematurity after maternal rubella, New England J. Med. **262**:389-393, 1960.

44. Simon, H. A.: Spurious correlation: A causal interpretation, J. Am. Stat. A. **49**:467-479, 1954.

45. Snyder, L. H.: Old and new pathways in human genetics, Am. J. Human Genet. **3**:1-16, 1951.

46. Stevenson, S. S., Worcester, Jane, and Rice, R. G.: Six hundred and seventy-seven congenitally malformed infants and associated gestational characteristics. I. General considerations, Pediatrics **6**:37-50, 1950.

47. Taylor, R. J.: Differences in Incidence Rates Detectable in the Collaborative Study of Cerebral Palsy, etc., Washington, D. C., National Institute of Neurological Diseases and Blindness, (Reproduced). 1960.

48. Wallis, W. A., and Roberts, H. V.: Statistics: A New Approach, Glencoe, Ill., The Free Press, 1956.

49. White, Colin: Sampling in medical research, Brit. M. J. **2**:1284-1288, 1953.

50. White, Colin, and Bailar, J. C., III: Retrospective and prospective methods of studying association in medicine, Am. J. Pub. Health **46**:35-44, 1956.

51. Wilson, J. G.: Experimental studies of congenital malformations, J. Chron. Dis. **10**:111-130, 1959.

52. Worcester, Jane: *in* Prematurity, Congenital Malformations and Birth Injury, p. 186, New York, Association for the Aid of Crippled Children, 1953.

53. Worcester, Jane, Stevenson, S. S., and Rice, R. G.: Six hundred and seventy-seven congenitally malformed infants and associated gestational characteristics II. Parental factors, Pediatrics **6**:208-220, 1950.

The Frequency of Congenital Malformations

PROFESSOR MAURICE LAMY AND JEAN FRÉZAL

Studies pertaining to the frequency of congenital malformations are doubly interesting because of their theoretic and practical value. They constitute an introduction to etiologic research and open up new perspectives on the problem of the structure and the evolution of human populations. They also furnish statistical information that is indispensable to the hygienist and to the physician.

In this paper, we shall consider first the over-all frequency of congenital malformations; then, their place in perinatal and infantile mortality; and, finally, the incidence of certain specific anomalies.

Before taking up these various points, it is necessary to point out the difficulty of such evaluations. These difficulties are of two kinds: the first pertains to the definition and the classification of the malformations; the second, to the method of establishing the statistics.

1. Traditionally, we distinguish between major malformations, which are either fatal or incapacitating, and minor anomalies, which have no effect on the viability of the individual. However, it is not always easy to draw the line between these two categories; it definitely varies from one statistic to the other, and this affects the over-all incidence. Moreover, the classification and the recording of "multiple" or "complex" malformations raises some delicate problems to which the authors have proposed very different solutions.

2. Inquiries pertaining to the incidence of malformations differ considerably in nature, but very few constitute really comprehensive studies.

The population statistics compiled by the WHO are based on death certificates as compared with the live births. Therefore, they fail to recognize everything connected with malformations in natimortality.

Most of the surveys are based on maternity files kept according to different methods: record of the first examination during pregnancy,[19] and women who have reserved beds in a maternity hospital,[9] consecutive births in most cases. Sometimes they consider only live births,[14] sometimes only stillbirths;[11] most of the time, they consider all births as a unit, and the proportion of anatomic examinations in the stillborn or in those infants who died in the neonatal period rarely is indicated clearly.

In certain series, the percentage of malformations is calculated not only from data collected during the neonatal period but also on the basis of a more-or-less long observation period. Furthermore, multiple methods are used. For example, the statistics of Murphy[25] are compiled on the basis of death certificates, some of which relate to subjects who died after 15 years. However, the only cases retained in the statistic were those in which the malformation was visible at birth or in which the diagnosis was confirmed by the anatomic examination; these represented only three-fifths (890 in 1,476) of the cases recorded.

In other surveys, (R. McIntosh, A. C. Stevenson, J. V. Neel),[19,26,35] a more or less large number of subjects were re-examined before the end of the first year. However, there was a gap, representing the deaths due to malformations, which occurred between the two recording periods, and certain malformations to which this stage of life admittedly is more susceptible.

Finally, an additional difficulty results from the fact that certain statistics encompass heterogeneous populations, of different racial or ethnic origin.

OVER-ALL INCIDENCE OF CONGENITAL MALFORMATIONS

The foregoing remarks clearly show how difficult it is, not to say arbitrary, to attempt an estimation of the over-all incidence of congenital malformations. In Table 1, we have assembled a certain number of statistics drawn up in different countries and specified the method of ascertainment. A reading of this table will show notable differences from one country to the other and even from one statistic to the other. However, it seems, that the over-all incidence of major malformations visible at birth and recognizable by anatomic examination of stillborn infants (after the 28th week of pregnancy) or of infants who die during the neonatal period, is in excess of 1 per cent and probably close to 1.5 per cent. Thus, in the statistics of Neel,[26] the percentages for single births are 1.02 according to the clinical data, and 1.3 according to the clinical and anatomic data.

The total percentage of major malformations for all infants born after the 28th week of pregnancy and with an observation period of 1 year after birth would seem to be about 4 to 5 per cent. Thus, Neel[26] reaches a figure of 3.12 per cent after a new examination of 16,144 infants of 9 months of age. Nevertheless, the condition of infants deceased between the 1st and the 9th months is not clearly reflected in his statistics. But, according to the data compiled by the WHO, about one quarter of the deaths due to congenital malformation occurs during this period. The absence of pyloric stenosis in these statistics is surprising. It may have

escaped the survey because this condition develops between the 3rd and the 6th weeks of life. McIntosh *et al.*[19] give a percentage of 7.5, which Neel[26] reduced to 5 per cent after eliminating certain minor anomalies.

However, this percentage of 4 to 5 per cent does not represent the totality of malformations. Indeed, some do not become manifest until later, during childhood, adolescence or even in adulthood, as in the case of many visceral malformations for example. Moreover, this figure does not take into account embryonic malformations (12% according to H. Streeter as reported by Davis[11] and 20 to 25% according to F. P. Mall as reported by Neel[26]). Hertig and Rock[15] noted that 42 per cent of the embyros removed during hysterectomy in pregnant women were deformed. However, interpretation of this observation calls for some reservations, because the representative character of such a sample is questionable. In addition, the diagnosis of embryonal malformation is extremely difficult.

Be that is it may, the over-all incidence of major malformations is higher than 5 per cent. It is hard to say if this rate varies according to race and population. It may possibly be lower in Negroes than in Caucasians. However, Neel[26] believes that the differences are not pronounced on the whole, whereas the relative frequency of the various specific malformations varies according to race.

The precise significance of this evaluation is difficult to grasp. In fact, it would be important to determine the role of malformations in abortions. Furthermore, among the so-called major malformations, some are curable and constitute a handicap for only a limited period of time. It would doubtless be of greater interest to appraise the importance of the role of malformations in permanent disability because this form of morbidity has the greatest social repercussions. Under present conditions, such a calculation is practically impossible with a sufficient degree of approximation.

TABLE 1

Authors	Number	Total Per Cent	Central Nervous System Per Cent	Circulatory System Per Cent	Digestive Tract Per Cent	Urogenital System Per Cent	Skeletal System Per Cent	
Murphy, D. P. Philadelphia, 1929–33	130,132	0.62	0.41	0.06	0.1	0.007	0.07	p.dc. (c +a)
Stevenson, S. S. et al. Boston, 1930–41	29,024	2.26	0.57	0.40	0.2	0.11	0.52	m.f.
Wallace, H. M. et al. New York, 1951		0.92	0.14	0.02	0.13	0.09	0.42	nv. bc. & dc. w + nw
McIntosh, R. et al. New York, 1946–53	5,739	7.5	1.3	0.9	1.0	1.0	3.0	m.e. c + a. r. w+nw
Davis, M. E. and Potter, E. L. Chicago, 1941–55	53,847	0.45	>0.18	>0.07	0.06	0.05	0.03	m.f. pnd. a.
Shapiro, R. N. et al. U.S.A., 1958	30,398	1.99	0.25	0.10	0.07	0.16	1.41	m.f. nv. w+tnw
Neel, J. V. Hiroshima, Nagasaki Kure, 1948–54	63,796	1.02 1.3 3.12	0.13 0.13 0.25	0.16 0.25 0.59	0.31 0.33 0.40	0.02 0.09 0.10	0.28[+] 0.28[+] 1.09	p.c. (+without hernias) + a (extrapolated) + f. (extrapolated)
Aresin, N. and Sommer, K. H. Leipzig, 1936–48	43,647	0.91	0.27	0.01	0.16	0.014	0.30	m.f.
Hegnauer, H. Munich	141,706	0.67	0.47		>0.09		0.34	m.f.
Buurman, G. et al. Born, Celle, Göttingen Leipzig, 1901–56	104,752 136,048	1.45 0.84	0.36		>0.14[+]	0.09	0.25	m.f. (+clefts)
Turpin, R. Paris, 1941–50	79,844	0.84	0.13		0.14	0.10	0.16	m.f.
Azer, V. Lyon, 1927–40	23,841	1.13	0.18	?	>0.13	?	0.21	m.f.

TABLE 1 (Continued)

Authors	Number	Total Per Cent	Central Nervous System Per Cent	Circulatory System Per Cent	Digestive Tract Per Cent	Urogenital System Per Cent	Skeletal System Per Cent	
Michiels-Simonnot Y. Dijon, 1950–58	13,403	1.21	0.23	0.1	0.24	0.13	0.33	m.f.
Coffey, V. P. and Jessop W. J. E. Dublin	12,552	1.63						m.f.
Carter, C. O. London, 1943–49	14,283	1.47	0.49	0.07	0.33	0.04 / 0.13+	0.25	m.b. + with hypospadias
Böök, J. A. and Fraccaro M. London, 1947–51	20,151	3.02	0.40	0.23	0.40	0.36+	0.51	m.f. with hypospadias and cryptorchidism
McDonald, A. C. England, 1957–8	3,216	1.5	0.55	0.48	>0.5	>0.2	>0.25	e.
Stevenson, A. C. et al. Belfast, 1957	8,519	1.41	0.83	0.25	0.13			p.c. + a(?) + r.
Böök, J. A. Lund, 1927–46	44,109	1.33	0.23	0.07	0.28	0.10	0.44	m.f.

Maternity Register = m { consecutive: f.
  { reservation: b.
  { prenatal registration: e.

Death certificates = dc.
Birth certificates = bc.
Live births = nv.
Perinatal deaths = pnd.
Medical examination = c.

Anatomical examination = a.
Population = p.
Re-examination after the first year = r.
Caucasians = w.
Non-Caucasians = nw.

MORTALITY DUE TO CONGENITAL MALFORMATIONS

The proportion of deaths due to congenital malformation in relation to infantile and neonatal mortality rates appears to vary greatly from country to country when based on population statistics (WHO). It is still, to a certain extent, inversely proportional to the mortality rate from exogenous causes. In countries where mortality due to infection or deficiency states has declined most, it represents between 15 and 20 per cent of infant mortality as a whole. Moreover, it does not seem that the incidence of congenital malformations, in absolute terms, has decreased in the last 10 years.

About one third of all deaths from malformation occur in the neonatal period, almost one half during the 1st month, and approximately 80 per cent during the 1st year. The number of male deaths and the male sex ratio at birth is higher among infants with malformations than in the population as a whole.

Actually, there are notable differences among the malformations themselves. Thus, anomalies of the circulatory and the digestive systems and the urogenital tract always are more frequent in the male. There is a definite prevalence of monstrosities, spina bifidae and meningoceles among females. Hydrocephalus is more prevalent in one sex or the other, depending on the country.

Table 2 shows the relative size of each group according to the statistics of the WHO. The mortality rates due to death from malformations of the circulatory system head the list at every age, and especially in the male (over 40%). In the female, it is sometimes preceded by death due to malformations of the central nervous system. The circulatory system malformations are most often in second place, followed by malfor-

TABLE 2. The Relative Incidence of Certain Congenital Malformations According to the WHO, 1956.

Position	Male				Female				
	1	2	3	4	1	2	3	4	
CNS		14	2		5	10	1		All ages
C.V.	16				11	5			
D.T.		2	14			1	15		
U.G.				16				16	
CNS	1	13	2		5	10	1		0–1 year
C.V.	15	1			11	5			
D.T.		2	14			1	15		
U.G.				16				16	
CNS	3	12			2	13			1–4 years
C.V.	12	3			13	2			
D.T.			15				15		
U.G.				15				15	
CNS		1	10	4		1	9	5	5 years or older
C.V.	15				15				
D.T.			5	10			6	9	
U.G.		14		1*		14		1	

* = Japan

The figure in each age group represents the number of countries.

CNS = Malformations and monstrosities of the central nervous system (750, 751, 752, 753)

C.V. = Circulatory system (754)

D.T. = Digestive system (756)

U.G. = Urogenital system (757)

The figures in parentheses are those of the detailed list of the international classification.

mations of the digestive tract, and finally by urogenital malformations.

Two noteworthy facts consistently emerge from these data: (1) The mortality curve following hydrocephalus reaches a peak between the 1st and the 4th years. One might wonder whether this phenomenon is not due to the fact that a large number of hydrocephalus cases are not really the result of malformations but of traumatic or infectious lesions during the neonatal period. (2) Malformations of the urogenital tract, which at first generally appear at the bottom of the list, increase in absolute number and in relative frequency after the 4th year and then occupy second place.

Similar characteristics in terms of sex and age are found in other statistics (maternity, study of a particular population group, etc.) However, these reflect a greater importance of malformations of the central nervous system, which are in 1st place. This is most probably due to the fact that such malformations quite often cause the death of the fetus in utero or are a factor in early perinatal death. In Scotland,[3] for example, the incidence of malformations of the central nervous system is 0.64 per cent in stillborn infants or in those who died during the neonatal period; the other malformations account for 0.39 per cent when all births are considered. Among live births (WHO), the relative number of malformations of the central nervous system is not as high (males 33.5% and females 50% of all deaths due to malformation in Scotland).

There are considerable divergencies in connection with malformations of the circulatory system, the relative incidence of which is lower than in the statistics of the WHO.

Thus, according to Murphy,[25] cardiac defects are responsible for only 8.6 per cent of all deaths from malformations (60% for the central nervous system). However, we have seen that this author has included only malformations visible at birth or those which were substantiated anatomically. In the statistics of Davis and Potter,[11] which

cover 240 cases of perinatal death, cardiac malformations appear in second place (16%), after the rate for malformations of the central nervous system (40%) and before those of the digestive and the urogenital tracts (9% and 9%, respectively).

At the *Ecole de Puériculture de Paris,* where premature infants are brought within a few hours of birth, out of close to 1,000 deaths (95% autopsies), major cardiac malformations totaled 3 per cent, or two thirds of all malformations.[32] Malformations of the central nervous system are much rarer there (less than 1%), but this is due to the manner in which cases are enlisted.

In short, the differences between the various statistics can be explained (apart from possible bias in compiling) if one considers (1) that malformations of the central nervous system are more frequently the cause of death in utero than are malformations of the circulatory system; (2) that they are rarely recognized at birth without an anatomic examination; and, finally, that (3) their proportion of the mortality rate due to malformations clearly increases after birth and the neonatal period. Thus, in the statistics of McIntosh[19] the percentage of central nervous system malformations is higher than that of cardiac malformations in the stillborn (7.2 and 5.4), but lower in children who die during the neonatal period (6.1 and 10.2).

It is still more difficult, and probably futile, to interpret the divergences observed in regard to malformations of the digestive and the urogenital tracts. The latter malformations seem to contribute, not unimportantly, to early mortality rates, as shown by the figures of McIntosh[19] and Sarrut[32] and by a comparison of anatomic and clinical data in the statistics of Neel.[26] The increase in their relative importance after 4 years (WHO) may be explained in the light of what is known of their course. Many of them do not become manifest or do not cause renal failure until after this age.

INCIDENCE OF CERTAIN
SPECIFIC MANIFESTATIONS

It would be interesting to follow up the comparisons made in the section or mortality by comparing the relative frequency of malformations according to system or apparatus (Table 1). Unfortunately, the differences in recording make any interpretation risky. The incidence calculated at birth hardly permits any evaluation of the actual incidence of certain malformations. Thus, the percentages calculated according to the statistics of Neel[26] increase from 0.16 at birth to 0.59 after a new examination in the 9th month in the case of cardiac malformations, and from 0.28 to 1.09 for skeletal anomalies, the difference between the two figures being explained here by the late diagnosis in the case of congenital dislocation of the hip.

On the whole, skeletal malformations occupy an important position, but the conditions for their diagnosis are not comparable. Also, it is preferable to limit comparison to a certain number of specific anomalies. The most favorable are those where the diagnosis is evident at birth and the incidence is sufficiently high.

The most remarkable observations relate to anencephaly, the frequency of which varies with both race and geographic location. In the statistics compiled by Penrose,[29] the incidence of anencephaly is higher among Caucasians than among Negroes. Searle[33] noted important differences among the various population groups living in Singapore, the highest rate (0.649%) being recorded among the Sikhs, in fact 9 times higher than among the other Indians (0.069). The incidence was zero in a group of Chinese (Hakka group).

In Europe, Penrose[29] found a decreasing gradient of frequency from northern Ireland and Scotland to southern England, where the rate is definitely higher than in continental Europe. In France, where the average incidence is 0.05 per cent, appreciable regional differences are observed (J. Frézal and M. Lamy).

A positive correlation exists between the incidence of anencephaly and that of spina bifida and meningoceles; this indicates an etiologic relationship which also is reflected by occurrence of these various malformations in the same family. Nevertheless, there are considerable variations in their relative frequency; for example, spina bifida is much more frequent than anencephaly in the 3 Swiss studies and in Sweden, but 3 times less common in Japan.[26]

The relative frequency of hydrocephaly appears to be much more variable and correlation with the preceding malformations is not as close.

According to Neel,[26] the incidence of anophthalmia-microphthalmia is significantly higher among the Japanese (0.002%) than among Caucasians (0.008%).

Polydactylia definitely is more common among Negroes than among members of the yellow race and even more than among Caucasians. On the other hand, the figures in Table 3 reveal a quite remarkable consistency in the incidence of achondroplasia (0.014%), a rate that is not very different from that calculated by Mörch[23] in Denmark (0.011%).

The incidence of harelip, whether alone or in conjunction with cleft palate, and that of cleft palate appear to vary little among the Caucasian population groups studied (about 0.13%, a figure close to that calculated by Fogh-Andersen,[13] i.e. 0.15%). However, it is higher among members of the yellow race (0.24% according to Neel[26]) and lower among Negroes (0.06% according to Davis[11]).

In the case of anal atresia there is no significant difference between the various series of statistics. The rate of pyloric stenosis is much more difficult to establish. It appears to be higher among Caucasians (0.3 to 0.4 per 100 live births, according to McMahon[21] and Laron[17]) than among Negroes or among members of the yellow race.

TABLE 3

Authors	Births	Anen-cephalia	Spina Bifida	Hydro-cephalus	Anoph-thalmia-micro-phthalmia	Anal Atresia	Poly-dactylia	Achon-droplasia	Harelip and/or Cleft Palate	Club Foot
Lucy, R. E. (in Neel) 1949	11,881	0.109	0.126			0.008	0.076		0.126	
Stevenson, S. S. Boston, 1930–41	29,024	0.23	0.034	0.28				0.014		
Harris, L. E., and Steinberg, A. G. 1944–50	8,716	0.06	0.24	0.13		0.03	0.05		0.14	0.38
Wallace, H. M. New York, 1951	Cau. Non Cau.	0.021	0.045	0.022		0.01	0.058 0.40		0.082 0.059	0.23 0.13
Shapiro, R. N. et al.	30,398	0.019	0.026	0.049		0.019	0.288 ++Negroes		0.285	0.405
McMahon, B. et al. Boston, 1936–52	168,654	0.193	0.253	0.09						
Murphy, D. C. 1929–33	130,132	0.075	0.016	0.138		0.007			0.035	
Mitani, S. (in Neel, J. V.) 1943	49,645	0.066	0.022		0.020	0.03	0.115		0.189	
Neel, J. V.	63,796	0.063	0.020		0.025	0.024	0.092	0.013	0.268	0.11
Hegnauer, H. Munich, 1951	141,706	0.082	0.076	0.08			0.03		0.09	0.11
Aresin, N., and Sommer, K. H. 1936–48	43,647	0.072	0.1	0.1	0.002(?)		0.045		0.11	0.128
Péron, R. Paris, 1894–1927	100,889								0.105	
Turpin, R. Paris, 1941–50	79,844								0.083	0.143

TABLE 3 (Continued)

Authors	Births	Anencephalia	Spina Bifida	Hydrocephalus	Anophthalmia-microphthalmia	Anal Atresia	Polydactylia	Achondroplasia	Harelip and/or Cleft Palate	Club Foot
Albertini, P. St. Denis, 1945–55	12,449	0.041	0.041	0.048		0.008	0.016		0.105	
Michiels-Simonnot, Y. Dijon, 1950–58	13,403	0.089	0.075	0.052			0.037	0.015	0.193	0.179
Azer, V. Lyon, 1927–41	23,841	0.042	0.046	0.080	0.004	0.021	0.034	0.025	0.117	0.117
Coffey, V. P., and Jessop, W. J. E. Dublin, 1953–54	12,252	0.52	0.43	0.36					0.18	0.29
Stevenson, A. C. et al. Belfast, 1957	8,519	0.46	0.293	0.293		0.011			0.05	0.05
Malpas, P. (in Neel) Liverpool, 1937	13,964	0.315	0.279			0.029	0.115		0.122	
Carter, C. O. London, 1943–49	14,283	0.189	0.190	0.056		0.014	0.048	0.014	0.133	0.14
Record, R. G., and McKeown, T. Birmingham, 1940–47	158,307	0.39	0.42	0.16						
Böök, J., and Fraccaro, M. London, 1947–51	20,151	0.15	0.12			0.044		0.005	0.11	0.34
Böök, J. Lund, Sweden, 1927–46	44,109	0.054	0.107	0.1	0.009	0.043	0.068	0.016	0.175	0.275
Erhat, R. (in Neel) Zurich, 1948	50,147	0.054	0.108		0.012	0.04	0.04		0.148	
Wertheimer, H. Geneva, 1936–55	27,732	0.076	0.141	0.087			0.08	0.014	0.133	
Doyle, T. V. Canton of Glaris, Switzerland, 1935–54	6,482	0.015	0.08	0.12			0.03		0.03	

Complex malformations pose a special problem. In the statistical calculations we have somewhat arbitrarily listed each malformation under its own heading. Actually, the study of these complex malformations should reveal specific associations and permit the identification of new syndromes, which is very important with a view to their etiologic investigation. Neel[26] has drawn attention to the frequent association of malformations of the central nervous system with harelip and/or cleft palate, on the one hand, and with omphalocele, on the other. In a study of aplasia of the ear, carried out with M. Ombredanne and A. Bérézin (unpublished), we have noticed the frequency with which malformations of the middle ear are associated with harelip. Such association seems to constitute a separate nosologic entity.

Among the known malformation syndromes, we should recall, in closing, the incidence of mongolism among Europeans (approximately 1 in 600 births). In addition, Klinefelter's syndrome with positive nuclear chromatin findings, which perhaps can be linked to congenital malformations, is believed to occur in 1 out of 1,000 subjects in the general population. It is much more frequent among subjects with mental deficiencies, reaching or exceeding a rate of 1 per cent.

CONCLUSIONS

As yet, we have only very fragmentary data on the incidence of congenital malformations. As such, however, their occurrence is frequent enough to show the scope of the problem confronting the physician and the hygienist. The data available are still too incomplete to permit comprehensive etiologic study.

It is desirable that such research be encouraged. It will be necessary for the different organizations involved to agree on definitions and on the type of surveys to be made. This is the only way to achieve rapid progress in this field.

REFERENCES

1. Albertini, P.: Statistique sur la proportion de malformations congénitales, Thèse méd. Paris, No. 59, 1957.
2. Alison, F., and Corone, Mme.: La mortalité des enfants de moins de 15 ans. Rôle des malformations congénitales, Bull. Inst. Nat. Hyg. 11:391, 1956.
3. Anderson, W. J. R., Baird, D., and Thomson, A. M.: Epidemiology of stillbirths and infant deaths due to congenital malformations, Lancet 1:1304, 1958.
4. Aresin, N., and Sommer, K. H.: Missbildungen und Umweltfaktoren, Zentralbl. Gynäk. 72:1329, 1950.
5. Azer, V.: Contribution à l'étude des malformations foetales et congénitales, Thèse méd. Lyon, No. 572, 1944.
6. Böök, J. A.: The incidence of congenital diseases and defects in a south Swedish population, Acta genet. 2:289, 1951.
7. Böök, J. A., and Fraccaro, M.: Research on congenital malformations, Etudes néonatales 5:39, 1956.
8. Buurman, G., Langendörfer, G., Noack, J., and Witt, H. J.: Vorkommen und Verteilung von Missbildungen in den letzten fünfundfünfzig Jahren, Zentralbl. Gynäk. 80:1432, 1958.
9. Carter, C. O.: Maternal states in relation to congenital malformations, J. Obst. & Gynaec. Brit. Emp. 57:897, 1950.
10. Coffey, V. P., and Jessop, W. J. E.: Congenital abnormalities, Irish J. M. Sc. 344:30, 1955.
11. Davis, M. E., and Potter, E. L.: Congenital malformations and obstetrics, Pediatrics 19:719, 1957.
12. Doyle, T. V.: Les malformations congénitales et leurs relations avec l'âge parental et l'ordre de naissance des enfants atteints, J. génét. hum. 8:179, 1959.
13. Fogh-Andersen, P.: Inheritance of harelip and cleft palate (Opera ex Domo.), Biol. hered. hum. Univ. Hafn., No. 4, 1948.
14. Harris, L. E., and Steinberg, A. G.: Abnormalities observed during the first six days of life in 8,716 live born infants, Pediatrics 14:314, 1954.
15. Hertig, A. T., and Rock, J.: Series of potentially abortive ova recovered from fertile women prior to first missed menstrual periods, Am. J. Obst. 58:968, 1949.
16. Hegnauer, H.: Missbildungshaüfigkeit und Gebäralter, Geburtsch & Frauenh. 11:777, 1951.

17. Laron, Z., and Horne, L. M.: The incidence of infantile pyloric stenosis, A.M.A. Am. J. Dis. Child. **94**:151, 1957.

18. McDonald, A. D.: Maternal health and congenital defect: a prospective investigation, New England J. Med. **258**:767, 1958.

19. McIntosh, R., Merritt, K. K., Richards, M. R., Samuels, M. H., and Bellows, M. T.: The incidence of congenital malformations: a study of 5,964 pregnancies, Pediatrics **14**:505, 1954.

20. McMahon, B., Pugh, T. F., and Ingalls, T. H.: Anencephalus, spina bifida and hydrocephalus, Brit. J. Prev. & Social Med. **7**:211, 1953.

21. McMahon, B., Record, R. G., and McKeown, T.: Congenital pyloric stenosis, an investigation of 578 cases, Brit. J. Social Med. **5**:185, 1951.

22. Michiels-Simonnot, Y.: A propos de 162 cas de malformations congénitales: Considérations étiologiques et statistiques, Thèse méd. Lyon, 1959.

23. Mörch, E. T.: Chondrodystrophic dwarfs in Denmark (Opera ex Domo.), Biol. hered. hum. Univ. Hafn., No. 3, 1941.

24. Mosier, H. D., and Scott, L. W.: The incidence of the female sex-chromatin pattern in mentally defective males, A.M.A. Am. J. Dis. Child. **98**:447, 1959.

25. Murphy, D. P.: Congenital Malformations, Philadelphia, Lippincott, 1947.

26. Neel, J. V.: A study of major congenital defects in Japanese infants, Am. J. Human Genet. **10**:398, 1958.

27. O. M. S. (W. H. O.): Rapp. épidém. démogr. **9**:410, 1956.

28. Penrose, L. S.: Observations on the aetiology of mongolism, Lancet **2**:505, 1954.

29. ———: Genetics of anencephaly, J. Ment. Def. Res. **1**:4, 1957.

30. Péron, R. H. M.: Fréquence des fissures congénitales de la lèvre et du palais, Thèse méd. Paris, 1929.

31. Record, R. G., and McKeown, T.: Congenital malformations of the central nervous system, Brit. J. Social Med. **3**:183, 1949.

32. Sarrut, S.: Personal communication, 1960.

33. Searle, A. G.: The incidence of anencephaly in a polytypic population, Ann. Human Genet., London **23**:279, 1959.

34. Shapiro, R. N., Eddy, W., Fitzgibbon, J., and O'Brien, G.: The incidence in congenital anomalies discovered in the neonatal period, Am. J. Surg. **96**:396, 1958.

35. Stevenson, A. C., and Warnock, H. A.: Observations on the results of pregnancies in women resident in Belfast: I. Data relating to all pregnancies ending in 1957, Ann. Human Genet., London **23**:382, 1959.

36. Stevenson, S. S., Worcester, J., and Rice, R. G.: Six hundred and seventy-seven congenitally malformed infants and associated gestational characteristics, Pediatrics **6**:37, 1950.

37. Turpin, R.: Essai sur l'étiologie des malformations congénitales, Presse méd. **63**:857, 1955.

38. Wallace, H. M., Baumgartner, L., and Rich, H.: Congenital malformations and birth injuries in New York City, Pediatrics **12**:525, 1953.

39. Wertheimer, H.: Relations des malformations congénitales avec l'âge parental et l'ordre de naissance et répartition du sexe des enfants atteints, J. Génét. hum. **6**:49, 1957.

Sources of Variation in the Incidence of Malformations

THOMAS McKEOWN, M.D., Ph.D., D.phil., F.R.C.P., B.A., M.B., B.S.

There are several reasons for thinking that environmental influences play a significant part in the etiology of malformations. In the first place, there is no reason to suppose that the effects of selection operate less powerfully on lethal conditions manifested before birth than they clearly do on those manifested after birth and before the end of reproductive life. Secondly, for most malformations for which the evidence is available, the degree of concordance appears to be little, if any, higher in monozygotic than in dizygotic twins. Finally, there is direct evidence in respect of one environmental influence (rubella) and indirect evidence in respect of a number of others. It is with this indirect evidence that we are concerned here. It is proposed to restrict discussion to five indices: maternal age; birth order; season of birth; social class; and secular variation. Because they are highly correlated, two of these variables will be considered together.

MATERNAL AGE AND BIRTH ORDER

There are two ways in which the relationship of a malformation or a disease to maternal age and birth order can be investigated: by comparison of its distribution with that of the related population of unaffected births; and by examination of its distribution within sibships of the affected. The first method requires information which can be acquired soon after birth, but is very difficult to obtain in later years; therefore, it is suitable for investigation of conditions manifested at or within a few years of birth. The second method, described by Greenwood and Yule,[4] is applicable in later life when

sibships are complete and may give very misleading results when they are not. Since most major malformations are recognized soon after birth, the first is evidently the appropriate method. Difficulty arises in its application largely because the age and the birth order of related births (in practice the total population of births) are not published for suitable areas in national statistics.

Tables 1 and 2 give the relative incidence of a number of malformations in consecutive years in Birmingham according to birth rank and to maternal age. They include all of the most common malformations (whose incidence was at least 1 per 1,000 total births) with the exception of talipes, as well as 4 of the less common ones—congenital dislocation of the hip, patent ductus arteriosus, harelip (with or without cleft palate) and cleft palate (without harelip)—for which data were also available. An attempt was made to identify all examples of each condition in Birmingham during a number of years (indicated in Table 1) and the age and the birth rank of those affected were compared with observations on a control series drawn from the population of unaffected births of the same years.

The effect of birth rank has been separated from that of age by indirect standardization (Table 1). The number in each cell represents the ratio of the number of malformations in the birth rank specified to the number which would have been expected if the malformations in each maternal age group had had the same birth rank distribution as the control series. Therefore, the estimates give the relative incidence in each birth rank, the incidence in all birth ranks

TABLE 1. Relative Incidence of Malformations Related to Birth Rank* (Birmingham Data)

Type of Malformation	Birth Rank		
	1	2 and 3	4 and Over
Anencephalus 1940–47 (305)......................	1.4	0.7	0.9
Spina bifida 1940–47 (309).......................	1.3	0.8	1.0
Hydrocephalus 1940–47 (118).....................	1.3	0.9	0.9
Mongolism 1942–52 (217)........................	1.4	0.9	0.9
Harelip with or without cleft palate 1940–50 (153)....	1.1	1.0	0.9
Cleft palate without harelip 1940–50 (95)...........	1.0	1.1	0.8
Patent ductus arteriosus 1936–52 (152).............	1.2	0.9	0.7
Pyloric stenosis 1940–49 (478)....................	1.3	0.9	0.5
Congenital dislocation of the hip 1942–52 (136)......	1.4	0.7	1.0

*The effect of maternal age has been removed by a process of indirect standardization described in the text.

being 1. A similar procedure was followed in separating the effect of age from that of birth rank (Table 2). The results in respect of each malformation are as follows:

Anencephalus. The most conspicuous feature is the raised incidence in first-born and a slight increase with maternal age.

Spina Bifida. Primogeniture is again significant, but there is no evidence of association with age.

Hydrocephalus. Increased frequency with age is marked, but the risk to first-born is also present.

Patent Ductus Arteriosus. Incidence decreases with increasing birth rank and is apparently unrelated to maternal age.

Congenital Dislocation of Hip. There is a marked primogeniture effect and possibly a slight increase with age.

Mongolism. The increased incidence with increasing age is more marked in mongolism, in which it was first convincingly demon-

strated (Penrose[13]) than in any other malformation. There is also evidence of some increased risk to first-born.

Pyloric Stenosis. The incidence of this condition, manifested and probably also developed after birth, decreases regularly with increasing birth rank and possibly increases slightly with maternal age.

Harelip (With or Without Cleft Palate). The effect of birth rank is probably trivial, but there is a sharp rise at late ages.

Cleft Palate (Without Harelip). There is no evidence of association with either age or parity.

Perhaps the most striking feature of these observations, viewed collectively, is that when the effects of age and birth rank are separated there are only two common trends: increased incidence associated with primogeniture; and increased incidence associated with increasing age. (The possible exceptions are patent ductus arteriosus and py-

TABLE 2. Relative Incidence of Malformations Related to Maternal Age* (Birmingham Data)

Type of Malformation	Maternal Age		
	Under 25	25 to 34	35 and Over
Anencephalus.....................................	0.9	1.0	1.1
Spina bifida.....................................	1.0	1.0	1.0
Hydrocephalus...................................	0.7	1 0	1.3
Mongolism.......................................	0.3	0 6	2.5
Harelip with or without cleft palate................	0.9	0.9	1.4
Cleft palate without harelip.......................	0.9	1.1	0.8
Patent ductus arteriosus..........................	1.1	0.9	0.9
Pyloric stenosis..................................	0.9	1.0	1.1
Congenital dislocation of the hip...................	0.9	1.0	1.1

*The effect of birth rank has been removed by a process of indirect standardization described in the text.

loric stenosis, for which the relationship to parity appears to be present also in birth ranks after the first.) A malformation may exhibit both effects (as in hydrocephalus and mongolism, and possibly also anencephalus, congenital dislocation of the hip, and pyloric stenosis), only one (spina bifida, patent ductus arteriosus, and harelip) or neither (cleft palate). Therefore, it is understandable, that when the effects of age and parity are not separated, the trend in relation to either variable is commonly U-shaped.

In considering the possible interpretation of this relationship to primogeniture and increasing age, it must be remembered that the same association may have very different significance in different malformations. This is probable because the influences (reflected in trend with birth rank and age) must operate at different periods throughout, and even after, gestation. For example, in anencephalus the influence associated with primogeniture must take effect within a few weeks after fertilization. In patent ductus arteriosus, it may be manifested immediately before and after birth. (It has been suggested, on experimental and clinical grounds, that failure of the ductus to close may be due to deficient oxygenation of the blood, and that therefore the increased frequency in first-born may be due to respiratory difficulties which are more common in offspring of primigravidae: Record and McKeown.[9]) In infantile hypertrophic pyloric stenosis, the effect probably occurs after birth, for the tumor is not present at birth and develops in the neonatal period.[7]

SEASON OF BIRTH

Until recently, results of attempts to relate the incidence of malformations to the season of their birth or conception were largely negative. The relevant literature consisted of conflicting reports in which numbers were small (Dittrich[2]) or in which insufficient account was taken of seasonal fluctuations in numbers of related births.[12,14,15] There are now three conditions

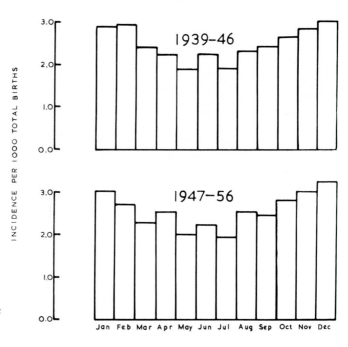

MONTHLY INCIDENCE OF ANENCEPHALIC STILLBIRTHS IN SCOTLAND

1939–46

1947–56

INCIDENCE PER 1000 TOTAL BIRTHS

Jan Feb Mar Apr May Jun Jul Aug Sep Oct Nov Dec

FIG. 1. Incidence of anencephalic stillbirths in Scotland.

whose occurrence has been shown to be related to season. They are anencephalus, congenital dislocation of the hip and patent ductus arteriosus.

ANENCEPHALUS

The incidence of anencephalus in Birmingham was approximately 50 per cent higher in children born in the half-year, October to March, than in those born in the half-year, April to September[9] This relationship also has been a feature of Scottish anencephalic stillbirth rates in every year since 1939 when they were first recorded (Fig. 1), but was not observed in a Rhode Island series examined by MacMahon, Pugh and Ingalls.[10] The month with the highest incidence of affected births in Scotland and Birmingham is December. The variation is not explained by changes in the proportions of first- and later-births, a possibility which arises because anencephalus is more common in first- than in later-born.

CONGENITAL DISLOCATION OF THE HIP

Record and Edwards[16] showed that in Birmingham the incidence of congenital dislocation of the hip in children born in winter was approximately twice as great as in children born in summer. A similar relationship was observed in Japan, where the reported incidence of this condition is many times greater than in Western communities.[11] The association was not attributable to variation in proportions of first- and later-births.

PATENT DUCTUS ARTERIOSUS

Patent ductus arteriosus is both less common and less completely recorded than the other two malformations, and the evidence of seasonal variation, though suggestive, is less secure. Rutstein, Nickerson and Heald[19]

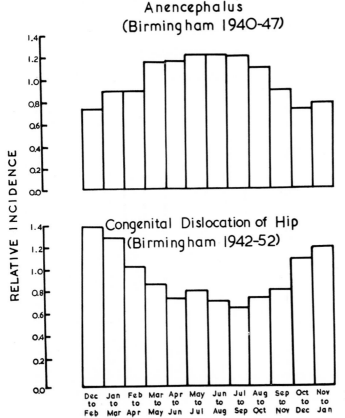

FIG. 2. Period of operation of seasonal influence.

reported that incidence was lower from February to August than from October to January, and that the seasonal fluctuation corresponded roughly with rubella notifications of 7 months earlier. Record and McKeown[17] found a sharp rise in incidence in Birmingham during the summer months (May to August) which appeared to be unrelated to the occurrence of rubella and was more marked for girls than for boys.

INTERPRETATION OF SEASONAL VARIATION

Because the evidence of seasonal variation of the incidence of patent ductus arteriosus is different in the two series in which it has been reported, we shall refer here only to the other two malformations. In anencephalus, the lesion occurs within a few weeks after conception, that is approximately 6 to 7 months before birth. (Mean duration of gestation of anencephalus is 7 to 8 months.) For a Birmingham series of anencephalics

born in the years 1940 to 47, both the date of the last menstrual period and the date of birth were known. Figure 2 gives the period of probable operation of the environmental influence reflected in the seasonal fluctuation on the assumption that it occurred 1 month after the 1st day of the last menstrual period. This date was calculated separately for each mother. The seasonal effect is most marked in midsummer and least marked in midwinter.

In congenital dislocation of the hip, Record and Edwards[16] suggested that the environmental influence reflected in the seasonal variation might be the weight or the tightness of clothing to which the infant is subjected shortly after birth. If this is so, its occurrence is fairly reflected by the seasonal distribution of births (Fig. 2).

Two features of Figure 2 are particularly striking: (1) the seasonal distribution of one malformation is almost the mirror image

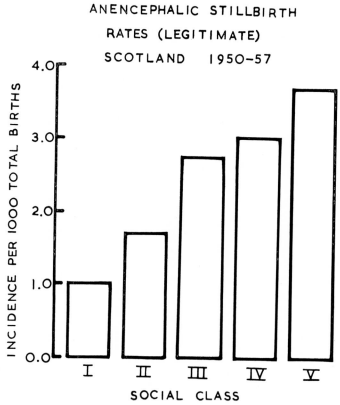

FIG. 3. Anencephalic stillbirth rates according to social class, Scotland, 1950 to 1957.

of that of the other; and (2) incidence increases (or decreases) very regularly from one period to another (a feature also of Scottish stillborn anencephalic rates in Fig. 1). The trends are suggestive, not of an influence (such as an infection) whose effect is limited to a season, but of one which waxes and wanes regularly throughout the year. For example, the monthly incidence of both malformations is evidently highly correlated with such variables as the amount of sunlight, the number of daylight hours, the temperature, etc. While some of these relationships are no doubt fortuitous, they suggest the direction in which it may be profitable to look. Record and Edwards[16] showed that there was a negative correlation between relative incidence of congenital dislocation of the hip and mean temperature. This observation makes somewhat more credible their suggestion that dislocation may be influenced by clothing, which would vary with temperature and with season.

SOCIAL CIRCUMSTANCES

Anencephalus is the only malformation whose incidence has been shown convincingly to be associated with social circumstances; the relationship is very striking indeed.[1,3] Scottish stillborn anencephalics (Fig. 3) are nearly 4 times more common in births to parents in Class V (unskilled workers) than in births to parents in Class I (professional and related classes). The relationship between the frequency of the malformation and social circumstances was not observed in Birmingham data,[17] a surprising result in view of the strength of the association in Scotland. As published, Scottish stillbirth data do not permit separation of the influence of social class from that of season of birth.

SECULAR VARIATION

In order to examine secular variation, we evidently need good observations on incidence over a considerable period; few malformations meet this simple but exacting requirement. The best data are for anencephalus.

Figure 4 shows the incidence of anencephalus in Scotland (stillbirths only) and Birmingham (stillbirths and live births) for the period 1940 to 1957. Since there are considerable fluctuations from year to year, the data are presented in triennia. They suggest three conclusions: (1) incidence is consistently lower in Birmingham than in Scotland (the difference is a little greater than the figure indicates because the Scottish rates exclude the small proportion of liveborn anencephalics); (2) there is considerable secular variation in incidence, which was about 20 to 30 per cent lower in 1946 to 1948 than in 1955 to 1957; and (3) the secular trend is similar in the two series, the correlation coefficient based on the triennal data being 0.57.

DISCUSSION

In the foregoing discussion we have attempted to summarize the positive findings in respect to the variables in relation to which the incidence of malformations has been shown to fluctuate. Needless to say, their chief interest is in the possibility that when considered in relation to clinical and pathologic evdence, they may suggest the nature of significant environmental influences. The best example so far available is perhaps infantile hypertrophic pyloric stenosis, in which it is clear that whatever the genetic basis of the condition, its manifestation is largely determined by something in the postnatal environment to which first-born children are more commonly exposed than later-born. The grounds for this conclusion are (1) that the tumor develops after birth[7] and (2) that onset is earlier in domiciliary than in hospital births.[8] However, the fact that the risk is relatively much greater when the mother (rather than the father) has had the abnormality as a child[6] cannot be explained on any simple genetic hypothesis[5] and may indicate that the risk, related to primogeniture, is associated with the mother.

It is by piecing together the evidence concerning malformations in some such way that our hopes for unraveling their etiology must largely rest. For this purpose, one of the most significant, and hitherto neglected, pieces of evidence is seasonal incidence. So far, it has had much less attention than maternal age and birth order; ultimately, it may prove to be more rewarding. But, in respect of all these variables the main requirement is undoubtedly good data from a number of different areas, preferably in such a form that the influences can be examined separately. Anencephalus, with its conspicuous association with season of birth, primogeniture and social class, is an example of a malformation in which it is by no means impossible that further enquiry may reveal the nature of environmental influences which can be controlled. The grounds for thinking so are at least as good as they were 20 years ago for cancer of the lung.

REFERENCES

1. Anderson, W. J. R., Baird, D., and Thomson, A. M.: Epidemiology of stillbirths and infant deaths due to congenital malformation, Lancet 1:1304, 1958.
2. Dittrich, R. J.: Congenital anomalies: contribution to study of etiology, Human Biol. 1:278, 1929.
3. Edwards, J. H.: Congenital malformations of the central nervous system in Scotland, Brit. J. Prev. & Social Med. 12:115, 1958.
4. Greenwood, M., and Yule, U.: On the determination of size of family and of the distribution of characters in order of birth, J. Statist. Soc. 77:179, 1914.
5. Knox, G.: On the nature of the determinants of congenital pyloric stenosis, Brit. J. Prev. & Social Med. 12:188, 1958.
6. McKeown, T., and MacMahon, B.: Infantile hypertrophic pyloric stenosis in parent and child, Arch. Dis. Childhood 30:497, 1955.
7. McKeown, T., MacMahon, B., and Record, R. G.: Size of tumour in infantile pyloric stenosis related to age at operation, Lancet 2:556, 1951.
8. ———: Evidence of postnatal environ-

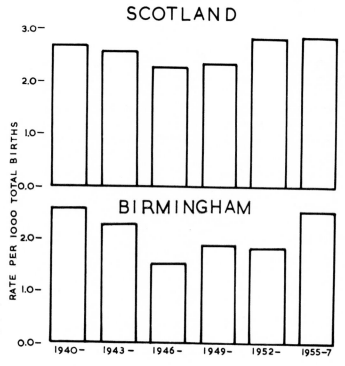

FIG. 4. Secular trend of anencephalus in Scotland (stillbirths only) and Birmingham (stillbirths and live births).

mental influence in the aetiology of infantile pyloric stenosis, Arch. Dis. Childhood 27:386, 1952.

9. McKeown, T., and Record, R. G.: Seasonal incidence of congenital malformations of the central nervous system, Lancet 1:192, 1951.

10. MacMahon, B., Pugh, T. F., and Ingalls, T. H.: Anencephalus, spina bifida, and hydrocephalus: Incidence related to sex, race, and season of birth, and incidence in siblings, Brit. J. Prev. & Social Med. 7:211, 1953.

11. Mizuno: Personal communication cited by Record, R. G., and Edwards, J. H.: *in* Environmental influences related to the aetiology of congenital dislocation of the hip, Brit. J. Prev. & Social Med. 12:8, 1957.

12. Murphy, D. P.: The month of conception of 935 congenitally malformed individuals, Am. J. Obst. & Gynec. 31:106, 1936.

13. Penrose, L. S.: A method of separating the relative aetiological effects of birth order and maternal age with special reference to mongolian imbecility, Ann. Eugen. (Camb.) 6:108, 1934.

14. Petersen, W. F.: The distribution of congenital malformations in the United States, Am. J. Obst. & Gynec. 28:70, 1934.

15. ———: The seasonal trend in the conception of malformations, Am. J. Obst. & Gynec. 28:443, 1934.

16. Record, R. G., and Edwards, J. H.: Environmental influences related to the aetiology of congenital dislocation of the hip, Brit. J. Prev. & Social Med. 12:8, 1958.

17. Record, R. G., and McKeown, T.: Congenital malformations of the central nervous system: I—A survey of 930 cases, Brit. J. Social Med. 3:183, 1949.

18. ———: Observations relating to the aetiology of patent ductus arteriosus, Brit. Heart J. 15:376, 1953.

19. Rutstein, D. D., Nickerson, R. J., and Heald, F. P.: Seasonal incidence of patent ductus arteriosus and maternal rubella, A.M.A. Am. J. Dis. Child. 84:199, 1952.

SESSION I

Discussion

Moderator

PROFESSOR A. BRADFORD HILL, C.B.D., D.S.C., F.R.S.

Statistical Research Unit, London School of Hygiene and Tropical Medicine,
Keppel Street, London, W. C. 1, United Kingdom

Panel Members

EDITH L. POTTER, M.D.

Department of Obstetrics and Gynecology, University of Chicago
School of Medicine, Chicago, Illinois, U.S.A.

PROFESSOR DAVID KLEIN

Service de Génétique, Clinique d'Ophthalmologie, Université de Genève
Geneva, Switzerland

GILBERT W. MELLIN, M.D.

Assistant Professor of Pediatrics, Columbia University
New York, New York, U.S.A.

LOUIS M. HELLMAN, M.D.

Department of Obstetrics and Gynecology, State University of New York
College of Medicine, Brooklyn, New York, U.S.A.

DR. POTTER: The three papers have provided an excellent background. To estimate incidence we must have a definition of the conditions which we are including. Having read that 5 or 10 per cent of all children are malformed, mothers sometimes ask: "Does that mean that I have 1 chance in 10 or in 20 of having a malformed child?" I tell them that among our acquaintances we could invariably find something that might be regarded as a malformation and that we should attempt to include only those conditions outside the general range of variability. This is extremely difficult to do. The frequency with which a malformation causes death might be thought to be a suitable basis for estimates of incidence. However, this is perhaps unacceptable, for we are concerned about prevention of malformations and must know the frequency with which a conceptus is born abnormal.

In very early pregnancy, the only way that the embryo can react to disturbance is by a change in growth pattern. Therefore, malformations are to be expected as a result of any disturbance, whether genetic or environmental. Probably at least 20 per cent of all conceptions terminate prior to the time when reporting is necessary in most countries. In the first 3 or 4 months of pregnancy, it is extremely uncommon to find a normal abortus. Thus, we get a better idea of the size of this problem than when we consider only children who are born with a specific malformation. I have examined nearly 10,000 abortuses, and fewer than 25 per cent of recognizable embryos were normal. Therefore, the frequency of abnormal development is extremely high and must account for a large proportion of abortions.

If attention is restricted to stillbirths or early infant deaths, the figure is much lower. Our own material is based on approximately 100,000 births at the Chicago Lying-in Hospital; the incidence of malformations which caused stillbirth or early infant death was 0.4 per cent. The frequency of potentially lethal malformations in surviving children was about 0.6 per cent, so that in the material which I have been able to study for the last 25 years, death from malformations occurred or was averted by operative interference in only approximately 1.0 per cent of fetuses present at 20 weeks gestation. However, malformations which do not cause stillbirth or early death may profoundly affect the life expectation of the child.

Much less has been heard about variations in frequency in different parts of the world; anencephalus is an outstanding example. I was interested in a recent unpublished paper from Africa in which among 2,000 consecutive deliveries no case of anencephalus was observed. However, the frequency of prehelicine fistulae was 2.5 per cent and of polydactyly 1.5 per cent. Four per cent of all births had these anomalies. As we look back on the papers of the afternoon, we must be impressed by this variation. These differences between populations provide a good starting point for further studies on malformations.

DR. KLEIN: I was intrigued by the report of Mr. Erhardt, who demonstrated once again that the problems encountered in different countries are similar. Like him, we were impressed by variation in the incidence of rubella obtained by the prospective and the retrospective methods. The retrospective method may show that 100 per cent of offspring of mothers who have contracted rubella have cataract; however, using the prospective method estimates of incidence may not exceed 10 per cent. Although statisticians assure us that the prospective method is preferable, there are those who prefer the retrospective method.

It is sometimes stated that, if a mother contracts rubella, the risk of giving birth to a child suffering from cataract, idiocy or microcephaly is minimal. This may have grave consequences later. In Switzerland, it is possible to undergo a legal abortion upon a psychiatric certificate. In Bel Air, Geneva, we have a child with idiocy due to rubella of the mother. This mother lived only 3 miles from Geneva at Douvenne. When she wanted to go to Geneva for advice, her family doctor advised her not to go because "it was not worth the trouble."

At Professor Franceschetti's Ophthalmologic Clinic in Geneva, we have collected all cases of maternal rubella in which permission to perform an abortion was granted. As Dr. Babel has reported, we found cataract in 57 per cent of 24 embryos and 4 neonates whose mothers had had rubella. Thus, we have a third method—histologic verification in the fetus—which proves that the retrospective method has its value. Therefore, I welcome the emphasis on the importance of the retrospective method in Mr. Erhardt's report.

I have little to add to Professor Lamy's admirable report. I should like only to ask whether he, too, has observed an increase in the frequency of association of nervous with other conditions. We have the impression that malformations are associated more frequently in the same individual than would be expected by chance. I have read that Dr. Neel has made a similar observation in Japan. However, other authors refute the possibility of the manifestation of one gene favoring the manifestation of another. We see no such objection. In the case of ophthalmologic malformations and also in mongolism, we often see associated malformations, e.g., keratoconus, cataract, etc., which appear to be unrelated to the fundamental disturbance.

I was also interested in Dr. McKeown's report. The work in Geneva confirms his results. In 1957, Dr. Bertheimer published a report on 27,732 children examined by us at the Geneva maternity clinic of Professor de Watteville. We encountered 204 affected children. Although our numbers are smaller, our results are consistent with those obtained by Dr. McKeown. For example, in anencephaly we also found an increased frequency in first-born and no correlation with maternal age; in hydrocephaly, we found a slight increase with increasing parental age

and a tendency for the first-born to be affected; in harelip and cleft palate, we likewise found an increased risk with increasing parental age. His reference to the influence of season opens new prospects in this field of investigation.

DR. MELLIN: I represent the Fetal Life Study which was begun by Dr. McIntosh in 1946 and carried on by Dr. Katherine Merritt. We have now observed over 10,000 pregnancies, starting within 4 weeks of the last menstrual period preceding pregnancy and following the mothers and the children continuously until the end of the 1st year of life. Some of the figures already have been referred to. As has been pointed out, incidence of congenital malformations requires the establishment of a numerator and a denominator. For the numerator we must have definition and classification, and the primary things we must ask are "what, when and how?" "What" has been discussed in reference to major or minor malformations. "When" is another question because we must consider the problem longitudinally. So far, we have discussed primarily postconceptional and postnatal phases of life; but, we must also consider the preconceptional phase.

We have attempted to discover when early pregnancies terminate. This is difficult to do. We have tried also to examine all early abortions. Many of our specimens were sent to the Carnegie Institution in Washington. Many of them were inadequate for examination, so that this approach is not wholly satisfactory for epidemiologic purposes. We are now attempting to establish "fetal life tables." That is to say, we are trying to assess for a woman at a certain stage of pregnancy the chances of a full-term baby. It is by no means easy to determine when a woman has actually lost a pregnancy, particularly in the early months.

We have mentioned already that recognition of a malformation may be related to survival. For example, should diagnosis of patent ductus arteriosus be accepted in stillbirths? Similarly, in the diagnosis of congenital dislocation of the hip! There are many who treat children on presumptive evidence of congenital dislocation of the hip. If all clinical diagnoses are accepted, some normal children are included.

There is also the question of "how." We start with clinical observation; we try to collect all macerated fetuses, and in medical centers we use technics, such as cardiac catheterization and routine roentgenograms. Finally, there is the question of "what." The point has already been brought out in relation to confusion between association and cause-and-effect.

About definition and diagnosis, I speak primarily as a clinician. We must classify malformations in some way, and this requires knowledge of the material we are to classify. Similar malformations may arise from the same causes.

Timing also has been referred to. We have based our estimate of time of conception on the last menstrual period, but this is not the time of conception. Moreover, if the cycle is irregular, our estimates are subject to error.

To reconcile statistical and medical considerations in classification is often difficult, and some compromise is needed between the unique observation of the individual case offered by the physician and the definition and the classification used by the statistician. Therefore, I suggest that we cannot use a statistical record as a medical record.

All samples are in some degree biased; it is important to recognize this while eliminating bias so far as possible. Some sources of biases have been mentioned: others are detail of observation and of ethnic groups. In our own series, we have had both Negro and white populations. This has enabled us to make some useful cross-correlations in populations which geographically and economically are similar but differ in respect of race.

The nature of an observation depends on the motives of the observer and his ability to compromise between the unique observation and the statistical classification or definition. Retrospective data cannot be as valid as prospective data, since classification and definition often are not established at the time of the observation. As classification and definition of any specific item becomes more difficult, the retrospective observations lose their validity. And, if classification and definition are not established before prospective observations are made, even prospective data lose some of their velocity. Results obtained for rubella, for example, may be entirely different by prospective and by retrospective methods. When children are followed for only 1 year after birth, many cases of deafness may be missed.

In the statistics obtained in our study, the incidence of anencephaly was 2.4 and 17.7 per 10,000 in Negro and white populations, respectively. These populations were from the same social and geographic background. We found no seasonal variation, but there were only 11 cases in our series. For polydactyly, the incidence in Negroes was 106 per 10,000; in the white population, only 15. Congenital dislocation of the hip also was less common among the Negroes, but the incidence of accessory nipples and preauricular fistulae was raised.

DR. HELLMAN: About 2 years ago, I discussed with Dr. Neel the difference between occurrence rates in white and colored populations. Foolishly, I suggested that I could answer this problem simply and quickly, as I had in my hands two well-controlled populations. In the King's County Hospital in Brooklyn, there are 6,000 deliveries a year, for which information regarding congenital malformations and race was recorded on punch cards with strict definition. For the city of Hartford, Connecticut, we also had information about the births recorded by special investigators working in the hospitals. I did not believe that the use of birth certificates in New York City was adequate for the solution of this problem, because the error in birth certification in New York City may be of the order of 20 per cent. However, we soon became aware of the difficulties. There were 20,000 deliveries in Connecticut and about the same number in King's County Hospital. Unfortunately, the population in Hartford was almost entirely white, whereas that of King's County Hospital had about 85 per cent of colored. Moreover, although the samples were large, the incidence of the malformations was relatively small, and it was necessary to group malformations.

We have three groups for the Hartford figures, based on pregnancies of more than 28 weeks. The first group is composed of malformations incompatible with life: those affected were stillborn or died within the 1st week of life. A second group consists of major malformations, referred to as consequential, which either would cause death in the 1st year of life, or about which something had to be done if the individual were to survive and to live a useful life. The third group includes inconsequential malformations, such as polydactyly and extra nipples. The total incidence of the inconsequential and the consequential malformations and those incompatible with life was 1.6 per cent. I would remind you that these results were obtained in a white population, well-off economically. We divided the data for King's County by race: the incidence of congenital malformations for white and nonwhite was 2.1 and 1.5 per cent, respectively. The standard deviation of the difference of these figures is 0.2, so that they are significantly different. The results show that the incidence of malformations in the white population in Hartford is roughly similar to that in the nonwhite population in New York. Therefore, whether the colored have more or fewer congenital malformations remains an open question.

MODERATOR HILL: Three questions addressed to Professor McKeown all deal with mongolism. The first comes from Dr. Carter, United Kingdom: Mongolism now is known to be due to a defect in the germ plasm and shows the most definite maternal age effect. Why, then, does Professor McKeown suggest that an effect of this kind usually is to be attributed to variation in environment?

Dr. Markert of the U.S.A. asks: Can the relative frequencies of mongolism with reference to birth order and maternal age, be explained within the framework of a single primary, genetic cause?

From Dr. Clarke Fraser: Would Professor McKeown elaborate on why he thinks that the sources of variability he mentioned suggest an environmental etiology, commenting particularly on the maternal age effect in mongolism and the failure of the malformations rate to fall with improving environmental conditions.

DR. MCKEOWN: I suggested that the sources of variation to which I referred should broadly, but with reservations, be interpreted as environmental in origin. The maternal age association in mongolism is the reservation that I had in mind.

I do not think that it is likely that we shall be able to explain the association with both age and birth rank in mongolism by any single genetic hypothesis.

The third question is whether the association with age could be environmental, since there has been no decline in the frequency of mongolism with improvement in the living conditions. This question reflects the idea that all environmental influences are attributable to social circumstances. Social circumstances have, of course, improved immensely during the past century. But, if the age association in mongolism is attributable to environmental influence, it is more likely to be of biologic than of social origin. For example, it might be due to the changing condition of the uterus with increasing age.

MODERATOR HILL: Dr. Bern Dortfort of Hungary asks: World-wide statistics concerning both live and stillbirths indicate that the figure for malformations has increased since 1951 by 15 to 20 per cent. Are the speakers able to confirm these figures and can they explain them?

PROFESSOR LAMY: I am not sure that there has been an increase in the incidence of congenital malformations of the order of 15 to 20 per cent. I have attempted to show in my report how difficult it is to establish statistics of this type, and that different and even contradictory results may be obtained according to the population considered; according to whether stillborn or liveborn are included; according to whether the liveborn are studied at birth, or at age 2, 3 or 4. Possibly only apparent changes are involved. For example, we know that, with improved hygiene, new methods of immunization, antibiotics, etc., the importance of infectious diseases among causes of death diminished enormously. Certainly, the relative importance of deaths due to malformations has increased. But has there been an absolute increase? At the present state of our knowledge, we cannot give a definite answer to this question. Therefore, I should like to refrain from answering the second question, since I cannot furnish a satisfactory answer to the first.

MODERATOR HILL: Dr. Kissler from the U.S.A.: What is the incidence of major congenital malformations in succeeding pregnancies after their appearance in the first-born?

PROFESSOR LAMY: The physician cannot give an answer unless he knows what malformation is involved, and its mode of transmission. For example: when a first-born child has a malformation of the hand of the brachydactylia type, we know that a hereditary malformation is involved with a genetic mechanism which is manifested in subjects who are heterozygotes for a dominant gene. In cases of this type, one of the parents must be so affected, while the other is unaffected, unless a recent mutation is involved. On the basis of this hypothesis, the parents may be told that there is a 50 per cent chance that succeeding pregnancies will end in the birth of a normal or a malformed child. An-

other example is a recessive affection, such as deaf-mutism which, in its usual form, is a consequence of malformation of the internal ear. Such cases involve a recessive condition which becomes manifested in subjects homozygotic to the gene, the 2 parents being heterozygotes. Here, we can give an exact answer: there is 1 chance in 4 of having a child with malformation, and 3 chances of having a normal child. In many other affections, we do not know how the condition is transmitted. In yet other cases, we know the cause. For example, if a child is born with a cataract because the mother contracted rubella during the first 3 months of pregnancy, we know that there is virtually no risk of subsequent birth of other malformed children among the brothers and the sisters of such a child.

MODERATOR HILL: Dr. Wildervanck from The Netherlands asks: Is anything known about the frequency of concordance in twins with cataract, deafness and congenital heart diseases, when the mother suffered from rubella?

DR. WARKANY:* In a joint paper, Drs. Beswick and Warner and I referred to one instance of nonidentical twins, a male and a female, exposed to rubella; both had the postrubella syndrome. In his New York study, Dr. Mellin also reported a pair of nonidentical twins who were both affected by prenatal rubella.

MODERATOR HILL: From Dr. Horsfall, U.S.A.: Are we to assume that reported differences in incidence between males and females are significant?

DR. HELLMAN: Since the sex-ratio at birth is roughly 1.06 to 1.00 and the primary sex-ratio differs substantially from this, clearly many males are killed. Recently, we have published results of examination of abortions in which the sex was determined by the sex-chromatin of the placenta before

---

* Dr. Josef Warkany, Professor of Research Pediatrics, University of Cincinnati College of Medicine, Children's Hospital Research Foundation, Cincinnati, Ohio, U.S.A.

the fetus was old enough or when not enough fetus was present for recognition of sex. The ratio of males to females was 165 to 100.

DR. POTTER: We have found a considerably higher total death rate for males than for females in our hospital, the mortality rate for males being twice as high as for females. Also, we have found that when all major malformations are grouped together, the rate is somewhat higher for males. However, there are remarkable differences between different conditions. Two outstanding examples are anencephalus and complete bilateral renal agenesis. In our own material, about 80 per cent of the anencephalics are female, and in bilateral renal agenesis, approximately 80 per cent are male. These are the only conditions so sharply related to sex.

May I also comment on an earlier question, related to the change in frequency of malformations? We calculated annual rates for the 30 years that our hospital has been open and found variation between 1.5 and 5.5 per cent. For the 5 years, 1930 to 1935, the rate was 4.4 per 1,000 total births, for Dr. Hellman's groups 1 and 2, and in the last 5-year period, 3.3. There appears to have been a reduction. I recently examined national figures for the United States and, although open to question, they show no increase.

MODERATOR HILL: Dr. Kessim, United Kingdom, asks Professor McKeown: Have you a graph showing the birth order for normal Birmingham children and was the increased incidence of patent ductus arteriosus in first-born significant statistically?

PROFESSOR MCKEOWN: The material which I showed for age and birth order was based on a comparison between affected and controls, and the data for the control population were obtained from a random sample of the general population of births. It has been suggested that our controls have too low a proportion of first-born and may exaggerate the importance of primogeniture. For the years in which our data from a sample now overlap with our information for all births, there is no serious discrepancy. The proportion of first-born in Birmingham, is, in fact, substantially higher than for the population of Great Britain as a whole.

The incidence of patent ductus arteriosus in first-born was significantly increased. This observation led us to explore the frequency of association of patent ductus arteriosus with difficult labor. We had in mind the experimental work of Kennedy and Clark, who showed in the guinea pig that the condition of the ductus could be modified by variation in the levels of carbon dioxide and oxygen. We found that there was a substantial increase in the frequency of difficult labor in children who had patent ductus arteriosus. Taken with the experimental evidence and with reports of increased frequency of patent ductus arteriosus at high altitudes in the Andes, these results are suggestive.

MODERATOR HILL: Dr. Doll, United Kingdom, asks Professor McKeown: Does the occurrence of an abnormality in a first-born child influence the number of children in the family?

PROFESSOR MCKEOWN: Most people who have examined the relationship of malformations to age and birth order have been acutely aware of the importance of fertility. I referred earlier to limitations of the Greenwood-Yule method, but one of its advantages is that it is not plagued by this complication, because it examines completed sibships. But it is a difficulty in the use of a population at birth for purposes of comparison. Therefore, we have tried to assess fertility, using such indices as the total numbers of children born and the spacing between births. We have never found any evidence that mothers curtail the size of their families after having had a malformed child.

MODERATOR HILL: Dr. Hillsome, United Kingdom, asks: Have the health habits and the environmental factors affecting fathers of malformed infants been adequately studied; for example, age, drugs, smoking, alcohol, venereal disease, etc.? If not, are such studies likely to be practicable and profitable?

DR. MELLIN: I believe that today there are no data large enough to permit assessment of the effect of father's age or health.

DR. KLEIN: In cases of chondrodystrophy, a definite correlation has been established with the advanced age of the mother and the father. Fathers who have sired children with chondrodystrophy are generally of advanced age, that is, at an age over 35. The risk for a father over 35 years of age is about 4 times as high as the normal risk.

MODERATOR HILL: Dr. Kirkland, United Kingdom, asks: Would the panel comment on the incidence of single or multiple congenital abnormalities?

PROFESSOR LAMY: Physicians frequently are confronted with children with multiple malformations. I do not know the ratio of multiple to single malformations, and I doubt whether reliable statistics are available. However, the presence of multiple malformations may call attention to a different mechanism. We know that a child suffering from a rubella embryopathy may at the same time have a cataract, a malformation of the internal ear, and a malformation of the heart. This phenomenon also manifests itself when there is a hereditary malformation controlled by genes. For example, we know that some skeletal changes (osteogenesis imperfecta or osteopsathyrosis) are manifested not only by fragility of the bone but also by a special bluish aspect of the conjunctiva and by deafness. In cases of this type, the question arises as to whether they involve the action of a single gene which has a pleotropic effect, or whether the action of two genes is involved, which are close together and adjacent on the same chromosome.

DR. HELLMAN: I have some data on the frequency of multiple malformations and the perinatal mortality associated with them. In the Hartford figures, of a total of 596 patients with malformations, 38 had multiple malformations. For those with multiple malformations, the perinatal mortality was 71 per cent compared with the perinatal mortality for the total group with malformations of 20 per cent. The Kings County figures are very similar: Of a total of 476 malformations, 26 were multiple with a perinatal mortality of 57 per cent, compared with 25 per cent for the total series.

SESSION II

Intrinsic Factors (Genetics)

Moderator

PROFESSOR E. HADORN

Zoologisch-vergleichend-Anatomisches Institut, Universitat Zurich, Zurich, Switzerland

SOME GENETIC ASPECTS OF CONGENITAL DEFECT

JAMES V. NEEL, A.B., M.D., Ph.D.

*Institute of Human Biology, University of Michigan School of Medicine,
Ann Arbor, Michigan, U.S.A.*

CONGENITAL HUMAN ANOMALIES DUE TO CHROMOSOME ABERRATIONS

PROFESSOR RAYMOND TURPIN, M.D.

*Clinical Professor of Infant Paediatrics, Director, Institut de Progenese,
Faculté de Médecine, Paris, France*

THE INTERACTION BETWEEN GENES AND ENVIRONMENT IN DEVELOPMENT

PROFESSOR HANS NACHTSCHEIM

Freie Universitat, Ehrenbergstrasse 26/28, Berlin-Dahlem, Germany

SEX CHROMOSOME ABNORMALITIES

DR. W. M. COURT BROWN, O.B.E., B.Sc., M.B., Ch.B.

*Group for Research on General Effects of Radiation, Department of Radiotherapy,
Western General Hospital, Edinburgh 4, Scotland, United Kingdom*

Some Genetic Aspects of Congenital Defect

JAMES V. NEEL, A.B., M.D., Ph.D.

INTRODUCTION

Nowhere in all the field of human biology has the relative etiologic importance of ex-trinsic (nongenetic) factors as contrasted with intrinsic (genetic) factors been debated more vigorously down through the years and right up to the present than with respect to congenital malformations. Accordingly, it seems appropriate at the very outset of this presentation that as a geneticist I acknowl-edge my deep respect for the role of non-genetic factors in eliciting congenital defects, and the complexity of the interplay between these factors and the genetic. My apparent preoccupation with the intrinsic in what fol-lows should be received for what it is—an attempt to examine today the role of genetic factors when tomorrow brings a similar evaluation of the nongenetic.

The principle that from the etiologic standpoint, genetic and otherwise, congenital malformations are a very mixed group in-deed has been enunciated frequently in re-cent years.[9,18,20,24,33] The task which lies ahead is that of defining for each specific defect the precise nature of the nongenetic precipitants and/or genetic systems respon-sible for the defect. In this knowledge lies the possibility of prevention. On the basis of our present information, it seems quite unlikely that one simple formula which may be applied to all defects will be found. Ac-cordingly, very detailed studies of specific defects are called for. Nevertheless, as I hope to demonstrate shortly, there is still an important role for studies which view mal-formation patterns and certain related phe-nomena as population characteristics.

Having implied, in effect, in my opening remarks the dangers of generalization in this complex field, I should like now, in the in-terests of orientation, to make several very sweeping statements which it would be dif-ficult to document in detail at the present time. First, when congenital defects are viewed as a whole, it is difficult to implicate the mechanisms of simple, fully penetrant dominant or recessive inheritance in the eti-ology of more than approximately 20 per cent. Achondroplasia and congenital ich-thyosis provide well-known examples of simply inherited congenital abnormalities. Second, on the basis of our very new, very fragmentary and very rapidly evolving knowledge of chromosomal aberrations as a cause of congenital defect, it seems unlikely that these ultimately will be found to ac-count for much more than 10 per cent of the total. Finally, that virus infections alone and unaided—in the sense that neither the genotype of the mother or the fetus plays any modulating influence—account for more than 10 per cent of all congenital defects seems to be unlikely at this writing. By this reckoning at least 60 per cent of congenital defects remain to be accounted for.

SUMMARIZATION OF SOME STUDIES ON CONGENITAL DEFECT IN JAPAN

The various lines of observation which can be brought to bear on the problem of unraveling the etiology of this remaining 60 per cent have been very adequately sum-marized recently by Fraser.[9] Shortly after World War II, my associates and I found ourselves in a position to collect in Japan extensive data on congenital defect under

63

circumstances which permitted many of the types of related observations enumerated by Fraser (*loc. cit.*). Perhaps the most striking finding of this study, which provided the first data for an Oriental population that met the requirements of modern sampling procedures, was the great similarity in the total impact of congenital malformations on Oriental and Caucasian populations, despite the very obvious differences in diet and disease experience between them. However, when the details of the picture were scrutinized, it was apparent that as regards the occurrence of specific defects, there were many differences between the two populations. Under these circumstances, it is difficult to avoid the concept that some regulatory system is at work which holds the impact of congenital defect at a certain level in all populations, although, as regards specific defects, each population is subject to internal adjustments.

The data gathered in Japan, as well as the existing information on Caucasian populations, provide a number of possible clues concerning the nature of the postulated systems. Some of these clues, which have been discussed in detail elsewhere,[21,23,27] may be enumerated briefly as follows:

1. With only a few possible exceptions, each of the congenital defects adequately studied to date is associated with a significantly increased recurrence risk for subsequent children within the sibship in which it is found. This recurrence risk appears to be predominantly, if not entirely, type specific, i.e., there is involved not a general predisposition to defects of all types but a very specific predisposition.

2. In Japan, consanguineous marriages result in children with congenital defects significantly more often than nonconsanguineous marriages. This consanguinity effect varies from defect to defect, being negligible in the case of some of the more common, but emerging most strongly where rare or complex and multiple defects in a single child are involved. However, Stevenson[31] was unable to demonstrate a similar consanguinity effect in a smaller series of Caucasian births.

3. It is a well-known fact that children with multiple major defects occur more frequently than can be explained on the basis of chance alone. It has not been generally appreciated to what extent these associations mirror population patterns. For instance, in Japan, harelip and/or cleft palate is a significantly more common defect than in most Caucasian populations studied to date. On the other hand, the major defect in the abdominal wall variously termed omphalocele or gastroschisis is less common in Japanese than in the Caucasian populations for which we have data. Consider, now, a series of children with one or more of the common defects of the central nervous system: anencephaly, spina bifida, or hydrocephaly. In Japan, these central nervous system defects are more often associated with harelip than in Caucasian populations, but less often associated with gastroschisis. This association is disproportionate, in that it goes well beyond the association to be expected simply on the basis of the relative frequency of the defects in the two populations. Otherwise stated, the individual defective child reflects in an exaggerated form certain population characteristics, a fact which has profound implications from the etiologic standpoint.

4. Although the twin data are admittedly scanty, they indicate a rather low concordance rate between identical twins with respect to specific defects.

5. Finally, there is a clear tendency for an increase in the frequency of congenital defects with advancing maternal age and parity, an increase particularly striking in mothers over the age of 40. This increase is greater than can be accounted for by the well-known maternal age relationship of mongolism.[4,14]

THE ROLE OF BALANCED POLYMORPHIC SYSTEMS IN CONGENITAL DEFECT

Elsewhere,[21] I have suggested that the foregoing facts may best be accounted for on the hypothesis that a substantial proportion of congenital defects of ambiguous etiology are the segregants or phenodeviants resulting from complex genetic systems with a positive adaptive value, of a type commonly referred to as "homeostatic" or "balanced polymorphic." The characteristics of such systems have been explored in some detail, *inter alia*.[8,15] Other causes of these congenital defects which of course require consideration are such well-known and simpler phenomena as genes of irregular penetrance, so-called polygenes, dominant mutations responsible for early death or sterility (and hence not susceptible to genetic analysis), maternal-fetal serologic incompatibility, and developmental accidents on a purely random basis. My apparent preoccupation in this presentation with only one of the several genetic mechanisms we could consider springs from the conviction that the possible role of these "homeostatic" systems has thus far received all too little attention.

Undoubtedly, the best known and at the same time simplest example of a polymorphic system in man concerns the gene responsible for the sickling phenomenon. In this system, a single abnormal gene is responsible for a qualitative change in the amino acid composition of hemoglobin. In individuals heterozygous for this gene, only 30 to 40 per cent of the hemoglobin is abnormal, and there are no apparent ill-effects. In homozygous individuals, on the other hand, virtually all the hemoglobin is abnormal, and there results a severe, chronic hemolytic anemia, known as sickle cell anemia, which usually terminates fatally before the age of 20. Diseases of such severity inherited in this fashion usually are very rare, but in this instance, in certain parts of Africa as many as 4 per cent of all infants suffer from the anemia, while some 40 per cent of the population are heterozygotes. The explanation of this paradox apparently lies in large part in the fact that in regions where falciparum malaria is hyperendemic, the heterozygote for this gene, for reasons not entirely clear, less frequently dies from falciparum malaria than the normal individual. Thereby, a balance is established between the loss of abnormal genes from the population due to the early death of children with sickle cell anemia, and the loss of normal genes due to the greater death rate from malaria among normal individuals than among heterozygotes for this gene. Children with sickle cell anemia are the price the population pays for the ability of a substantial proportion of its members to resist malaria. This is as simple an example of a balanced polymorphic system as can occur. (For recent reviews of this subject, with particular reference to balanced polymorphism, see Allison[1,2]; Neel[19]; Lehmann[12]; Jonxis and Delafresnaye[11]; Rucknagel and Neel[25].)

The polymorphic systems thought to play a role in human malformations are visualized as incorporating this general principle but are much more complex in several different ways. First, in general, not just one but several different genetic loci may be involved, with the malformation phenotype resulting from any one of several possible genotypes with respect to these loci. Secondly, the age-parity effects referred to earlier strongly implicate the role of what may broadly be termed environmental factors in the expression of these systems. The low concordance rate among identical twins suggests that these environmental influences may be quite specific in time and place, obtaining in one part of the female reproductive tract, but not in closely adjacent areas. For instance, the highly localized circumstances surrounding implantation might be quite critical.

It is worthy of emphasis that to the extent that this hypothesis is correct, congenital defects must be regarded not so much as nature's mistakes as the concession populations must make for possessing certain types of genetically adaptive systems. The conceptual basis for malformations is thus quite different in a polymorphic system than in other types of systems.

Systems of this type do not so easily lend themselves to the experimental approach as

the simpler systems of classic mendelian genetics, a fact which undoubtedly accounts
for the limited attention they have received
in the past. A really tidy demonstration of
the precise role of such systems in the etiology of congenital defect in man or in
laboratory organisms will be difficult. However, there are, at least two lines of investigation, until now insufficiently pursued,
capable of yielding important and possibly
even critical evidence.

The first of these is concerned with inbreeding effects. From the genetic standpoint, once dominant inheritance has been
excluded, recessive inheritance is the chief
alternative to balanced polymorphism in the
etiology of congenital defect. As a generalization, inbreeding effects will tend to differ
for recessive inheritance with or without
complete penetrance and for a balanced
polymorphic system.[6] However, the precise
magnitude of the consanguinity effects to be
expected with either system is determined
by many facts—the number of alleles which
exist for any locus, the frequency of each
allele in the population, and, in the case of
a polymorphic trait, the number of loci par-
ticipating in the system. Unfortunately, our
knowledge of the allelic structure of populations, human or otherwise, is still most
incomplete. Accordingly, a final interpretation of consanguinity effects must await advances in basic genetics. Some insight into
the potential complexity of evaluating inbreeding effects is again supplied by the
locus associated with the sickling phenomenon. In addition to the sickle cell gene,
several other alleles of this locus are known
which undoubtedly enter into polymorphic
systems, but in addition there are very probably a considerable number of other rare
alleles which do not appear to confer an advantageous effect when heterozygous. Of
course, such alleles would contribute rather
markedly to an inbreeding effect. Thus the
same locus may participate in both the
"polymorphic" and what is sometimes
termed the "classic" genetic model. This

very simple example underlines the danger
of thinking in terms of all-or-none models
for either a particular locus or a particular
trait.

The second line of investigation capable
of yielding critical data on the relative importance of polymorphic systems is the study
of the effects on malformation frequency of
hybridizing lines which have long been separated. Surprisingly little data are available
for man or for experimental organisms.
Here, in general, the result should be the
disturbance of long-established genetic equilibria, with a temporary decrease in the frequency of the segregants associated with
these systems. It is noteworthy that the very
inadequate data available concerning the frequency of congenital defect in the American
Negro, who of course is the product of much
hybridization, suggest a lower frequency of
major congenital defect than in his Caucasian contemporaries. Unfortunately, no
adequate data are yet available for the
African Negro.

TYPE SPECIFIC STUDIES:
CONGENITAL HYPOTHYROIDISM

The relative etiologic importance of genetic and nongenetic factors undoubtedly
will vary widely from defect to defect. Accordingly, a necessary step toward a definitive understanding of the etiology of congenital defect must involve many extensive
studies oriented around specific defects. My
associates and I have completed recently
such a study of congenital hypothyroidism.[22]
This particular defect was selected for espe-
cial study for two reasons. First, absence of
the gland is compatible with life, so that the
clinical entity, congenital hypothyroidism,
stems from etiologies as diverse as absence
of the gland, at one extreme, or a highly
specific biochemical lesion, at the other. Second, recent technical advances involving
primarily the use of isotopes and chromatog-
raphy have made it possible to define with
a high degree of accuracy the precise nature
of the biochemical defect in congenital hy-

pothyroidism associated with the presence of thyroid tissue. Five such biochemical lesions have been identified at this writing.[7,16,17,28,29,30] On the basis of intensive studies of 54 congenitally hypothyroid children and their families, we concluded that approximately 35 per cent of such children possess readily demonstrable thyroid tissue. Although as technics improve, we may find that some of the remaining 65 per cent possess very feebly functional thyroid tissue, certainly, in the great majority, the thyroid gland is to all intents and purposes completely absent. We have been impressed by the fact that where there is evidence for the presence of imperfectly functioning thyroid tissue, i.e., a "biochemical lesion," the distribution of the disease within the sibship and the increase in consanguinity among the parents strongly implicate simple recessive inheritance as the major etiologic factor. Where, on the other hand, there is no evidence for the presence of thyroid tissue, there are many features such as a disturbed sex ratio, low recurrence risks, associated defects, and slight increases in consanguinity among the parents which tend to identify these children with that 60 per cent of congenital defect into whose etiology we have just been inquiring. Under these circumstances, it is tempting indeed to speculate

that the grand sweep of organogenesis, from which a departure has such disastrous consequences for the individual, has come under the control of genetic systems wherein it is extremely difficult to identify the role of individual genes, whereas the details of the biochemical functioning of these same organs, details often phylogenetically more recent, tend to be under the control of much simpler systems, wherein the role of the individual gene becomes apparent through the appearance of biochemical mutants.[22]

PROBLEMS IN DEFINING ENVIRONMENTAL FACTORS

In both my introductory remarks and in the body of this presentation, I have emphasized my respect for the role of environ-

mental factors in the production of congenital defect. In particular, the geneticist is concerned with those nongenetic factors operating during development in such a manner as to modify the expression of the genotype. However, the problem of disentangling cause and effect in this area will not always be solved easily. For instance, in June of 1958, Stott,[32] on the basis of a carefully executed retrospective study, reported an increased frequency of a variety of "shocks" during the early prenatal development (largely 1st trimester of gestation) of children with mongolism. Several previous investigators already had commented on an apparent increase in the frequency of abnormal bleeding during the 1st trimester of the pregnancies that resulted in mongols.[3,26] Some 7 months after Stott's report, Lejeune, Gautier and Turpin[13] reported that mongolism was associated with the presence of an extra chromosome, and hence determined at the moment of conception. Stott's findings would seem to provide a vivid demonstration of the weaknesses of even the most carefully planned and executed retrospective studies in an emotionally charged situation. While the older reports on abnormal bleeding also could be accounted for in this fashion, an alternative interpretation is that those portions of the placenta of fetal origin also participate in the tissue defect of mongolism, a participation which carries with it a predisposition to the kind of intra-uterine accidents which result in abnormal bleeding. In this case, what had been interpreted as cause is really effect.

CONCLUDING REMARKS

The very high frequency of serious disorders of development, only a fraction of which survive to the late stages of pregnancy and then are labeled congenital defects, has long been recognized for many mammals,[5] but only recently documented for man.[10] A major concern of the geneticist in the next several decades will undoubtedly be appropriate studies in this broad field of teratogenesis. The potentiality for significant genetic investigation in this area is still largely to be realized.

REFERENCES

1. Allison, A. C.: Aspects of polymorphism in man, Cold Spring Harbor Symp. on Quant. Biol. **20**:239-252, 1955.
2. ———: Population genetics of abnormal human haemoglobins, Acta genet. **6**:430-434, 1957.
3. Benda, C. E.: Mongolism and Cretinism, pp. xv and 310, New York, Grune & Stratton, 1946.
4. Böök, J. A., Fraccaro, M., Hagert, C. G., and Lindsten, J.: Congenital malformations in children of mothers aged 42 and over, Nature **181**:1545-1546, 1958.
5. Corner, G. W.: The problem of embryonic pathology in mammals, with observations upon intra-uterine mortality in the pig, Am. J. Anat. **31**:523-545, 1923.
6. Crow, J. F.: Some possibilities for measuring selection intensities in man, Human Biol. **30**:1-13, 1958.
7. DeGroot, L. J., and Stanbury, J. B.: The syndrome of congenital goiter with butanol-insoluble serum iodide, Am. J. Med. **27**:586-595, 1959.
8. Dobzhansky, Th.: A review of some fundamental concepts and problems of population genetics, Cold Spring Harbor Symp. on Quant. Biol. **20**:1-15, 1955.
9. Fraser, F. C.: Causes of congenital malformations in human beings, J. Chron. Dis: **2**:97-110, 1959.
10. Hertig, A. T.: Pathological aspects *in* Ville, C. A. (ed.): The Placenta and Fetal Membranes, pp. 109-124, 222, Baltimore, Williams & Wilkins, 1960.
11. Jonxis, J. H. P., and Delafresnaye, J. F. (eds.): Abnormal Haemoglobins, pp. ix and 427, Oxford, Blackwell, 1959.
12. Lehmann, H.: Variations in human haemoglobin synthesis and factors governing their inheritance, Brit. M. Bull. **15**:40-46, 1959.
13. Lejeune, J., Gautier, M., and Turpin, R.: Les chromosomes humains en culture de tissues, Compt. rend. Soc. Biol. **248**:602-603, 1959.
14. Lenz, W.: Der Einfluss des Alters der Eltern und der Geburtennummer auf angeborene pathologische Zustände beim Kind, Acta Genet. Stat. Med. **9**:169-201, 1959.
15. Lerner, I. M.: Genetic Homeostasis, pp. vii and 134, New York, Wiley, 1954.
16. McGirr, E. M., and Hutchison, J. H.: Radioactive iodine studies in nonendemic goitrous cretinism, Lancet **1**:1117-1120, 1953.
17. Morgans, M. E., and Trotter, W. R.: Association of congenital deafness with goiter. The nature of the thyroid defect, Lancet **1**:607-609, 1958.
18. Nachtsheim, H.: Betrachtungen zur Atiologie und Prophylaxe angeborener Anomalien, Deutsche med. Wchnschr. **41**:1845-1851, 1959.
19. Neel, J. V.: The genetics of human hemoglobin differences: problems and perspectives, Ann. Human Genet. **21**:1-30, 1956.
20. ———: Genetics and human congenital malformations, Pediatrics **19**:749-754, 1957.
21. ———: A study of major congenital defects in Japanese infants, Am. J. Human Genet. **10**:398-445, 1958.
22. Neel, J. V., Carr, E. A., Beierwaltes, W. H., and Davidson, R. T.: Genetic studies on the congenitally hypothyroid, Pediatrics **27**:269-285, 1961.
23. Neel, J. V., and Schull, W. J.: The effect of exposure to the atomic bombs on pregnancy termination in Hiroshima and Nagasaki, pp. xvi and 241, Washington, National Academy of Sciences-National Research Council Pub. 461, 1956.
24. Penrose, L. S.: Heredity and environment in the causation of foetal malformations, Practitioner **166**:429, 1951.
25. Rucknagel, D. L., and Neel, J. V.: The hemoglobinopathies, *in*: Progr. in Med. Genet. **1**:In press.
26. Schröder, H.: Haben gynäkologische Erkrankungen eine Bedeutung für die Genese des Mongolismus, Ztschr. ges. Neurol. u. Psychiat. **163**:390-396, 1938.
27. Schull, W. J.: Empirical risks in consanguineous marriages: sex ratio, malformation, and viability, Am. J. Human Genet. **10**:294-343, 1958.
28. Stanbury, J. B., and Hedge, A. N.: A study of a family of goitrous cretins, J. Clin. Endocrinol. **10**:1471-1484, 1950.
29. Stanbury, J. B., Kassenaar, A. A. H., Meijer, J. W. A., and Terpstra, J.: The occurrence of mono- and diiodotyrosine in the blood of a patient with congenital goiter, J. Clin. Endocrinol. **15**:1216-1227, 1955.

30. Stanbury, J. B., Ohela, K., and Pitt-Rivers, R.: The metabolism of iodine in 2 goitrous cretins compared with that in 2 patients receiving methimazole, J. Clin. Endocrinol. **15:**54-72, 1955.

31. Stevenson, A. C., and Warnock, H. A.: Observations on the results of pregnancies in women residents in Belfast: I. Data relating to all pregnancies ending in 1957. Ann. Human Genet. **23:**382-394, 1959.

32. Stott, D. H.: Some psychosomatic aspects of casualty in reproduction, J. Psychosom. Res. **3:**42-55, 1958.

33. Warkany, J.: Etiology of congenital malformations, Advances in Pediatrics **2:**1-63, 1947.

Congenital Human Anomalies
Due to Chromosome Aberrations

RAYMOND TURPIN, M.D.

JÉRÔME LEJEUNE, M.D.

Only in the past year and a half or so have congenital diseases due to chromosome aberrations taken their place in the nosology of human medicine. Their discovery was made possible by technical advances and especially by the in-vitro cytologic cultures of Alexis Carrel. These methods first enabled the number of human chromosomes to be calculated as $2n - 46$.[33] Regardless of the races studied and the technics used, this basic observation has not been disputed.

The arrangement of chromosomes observed in mitosis (late prophase or prometaphase) allows us to distinguish the following criteria for each:

1. Ratio of total length to that of the neuter genome $(A + X)$;

2. Ratio of the length of its shortest arm to its total length (centromerel index);

3. Presence or absence of trabants (called "satellites" by some authors). In the calculation of the above-mentioned ratios, this factor has not been taken into account, nor has the heterochromatic support of these trabants.

On the basis of a critical study of the data furnished by Buckton, Jacobs and Harnden; Chu and Giles; Fraccaro and Lindsten; Lejeune and Turpin; Levan and Hsu; and Tjio and Puck, a committee meeting in Denver in April, 1960, proposed a numerical system for the nomenclature of human chromosomes from 1 to 22, the X and the Y chromosomes retaining their literal designation. This system has the advantage of being internationally understandable and is not the creation of one author. In comparison with the nomenclature by means of letters, it has the disadvantage of not being figurative. In the course of this paper we shall follow the original designation by its international equivalent, in accordance with the tables established in Denver.

At present, human chromosome aberrations fall into 2 major categories: anomalies of number and translocations.

Anomalies of number, which are comparable with those anomalies that occur experimentally in accordance with the mechanism of nondisjunction, comprise trisomic individuals $(2n + 1)$ and deficient individuals $(2n - 1)$; these are the poikilosomic anomalies.

The translocations known at the present time involve whole chromosomes more often than segments of chromosomes.

ABERRATIONS OF NUMBER
(POIKILOSOMIAS)

This type of aberration may involve either autosomes or gonosomes.

AUTOSOMES

The prime example of a human chromosome aberration that is responsible for a congenital disease is trisomic mongolism.[22,23] This discovery confirmed a theory that had been advanced independently by several authors.[3,6,36,42] According to the nomenclature used by the French authors,[22] this is a Vh trisomia (*21*). In rapid succession, this aberration was confirmed in a child presenting Klinefelter's syndrome and mongolism,[7] then in 5 mongoloid infants,[18] and finally in 3 others.[4] Each author made use of his own personal technic. The samples for the laboratory tests were taken from the fascia lata, the skin or the bone marrow.

At present, trisomic mongolism, so far as we know, has been established every time confirmation of the diagnosis was sought. Further on, however, we shall see that it can be masked by a translocation.

While opening a new chapter in the classification of human disease, trisomic mongolism also has disclosed the conditions for the appearance of the disease:

1. An incidence of approximately 20 per 10,000 births, which is more in line with that of experimental nondisjunctions (6 to 7 per 10,000) than with that of punctual mutations (20 per 1,000,000);

2. Consistent concurrence in identical twins, but usually lack of concurrance in fraternal twins;

3. Unusual recurrence of the disease in siblings,[40] the reason for which might lie in the mosaic development of siblings or in a translocation;

4. Increased incidence with aging of the mother, a fact which is in accord with experimental findings, since the incidence of nondisjunctions induced by x-rays increases with aging of the ovules;

5. The risk that a mongoloid mother and a nonmongoloid father will produce a mongoloid child as readily as a nonmongoloid one, since the ovocyte $44A + 2X + Vh$ must in principle produce $22A + X + Vh$ and $22A + X$ ovules in equivalent proportion. This possible transmission is the first clinical example of a chromosome aberration being inherited.

Moreover, the hypothesis of a genetic imbalance induced by trisomia, promoting by its action upon the modifying genes the resurgence in mongoloids of certain derma-toglyphic characteristics that are closer to those of the lower primates than to those of the previously evolved hand of the anthropoids, merits mention.[38,39] We would propose a neologism to describe this phenomenon, i.e. "phyloteny" (*phyle,* tribe or race; and *teino,* retain).

With regard to the greater incidence of the minor signs of the so-called "mongolism series" (mucocutaneous signs) among the nonmongoloid collateral relatives and ascendants of mongoloid individuals,[30,35] it is a subject which up to the present time has been interpreted in two different ways that are not mutually exclusive.

For some authors the phenomenon is obviously the result of a statistical bias, as the only individuals counted are allegedly precisely those retarded ones which have the mucocutaneous stigmata transmitted to them by their parents. Quite obviously, if one were to discover retarded individuals with trisomic mongolism but without mucocutaneous stigmata, this would be proof of a statistical bias, but such subjects remain to be found.

For other authors the phenomenon is a genuine one which they believe to be the expression of a certain genetic predisposition to chromosome aberrations. In fact, there is a case of mongolism and Klinefelter's syndrome coexisting in the same subject[7]; the simultaneous presence of mongolism, Klinefelter's syndrome[24] and Turner's syndrome[1] has been observed in siblings. Also, it is known that in *Drosophila melanogaster* the presence of a minute gene on the X-chromosome frequently causes the loss of this chromosome in the course of development.

In addition to trisomic mongolism, other examples of autosome trisomia have been reported. These are isolated observations combining complex malformations and retardation of intellectual awakening from the earliest months of life.

One girl who attracted attention because of her numerous minor anomalies, congenital heart disease and retarded mental development was found to have chromosome 17 (*17*) represented 3 times[5]; the specimen for the cytologic examination had been taken 3 hours after death intervened at the age of 4 months and 10 days.

Another girl, in whom mental retardation was accompanied by harelip and cleft palate, apparent congenital absence of the eyes and polydactylism of the left foot had a medium acrocentric chromosome represented 3 times.[29] Prior to recording this case history, the same authors had studied a boy and a girl, both with multiple malformations, heart disease and mental retardation, and had found an extra chromosome that "seemed to belong to group E" of their classification.

The discovery of trisomic mongolism raised two questions from the very start: the nature of the chromosome identified and the reason for its appearance. The nature of the chromosome hardly lent itself to discussion, since it was identified as chromosome Vh (*21*), and the "accessory" chromosomes (B of Zea Mays, for example) are genetically inactive and of variable size.

Its origin was suggestive, by experimental analogy, of the nondisjunction responsible for the appearance of the triploid IV fly. The proof of this would be furnished by the observation of a trivalent at meiosis in an individual with monogolism. On the other hand, the karyotype study of the progenitors of mongoloid subjects and of those with Klinefelter's or with Turner's syndrome does not appear to have brought out, according to the published data, anomalies of their karyotype,[10] although there are examples of 2A-X female mice that may be fertile. Upon investigation, the karyotype of the normal fraternal twin brother of a mongoloid child appeared to be normal.[42]

On the other hand, in order to explain the repeated birth of mongoloid children—for example, 4 or even 5 out of 8 children born to parents neither of whom is mongoloid[40]—a germinal mosaic or a translocation would be a highly acceptable answer.

GONOSOMES

After the discovery of mongolism as an autosome aberration, there followed that of the gonosome aberrations.

These aberrations could be anticipated, since we knew of individuals with gonadal dysgenesis of female morphology contradictorily endowed with a male sex-chromatin pattern (negative chromatin) (80% of the cases of Turner's syndrome), and also of individuals with gonadal dysgenesis of male morphology contradictorily endowed with a female sex-chromatin pattern (positive chromatin) (80% of the cases of Klinefelter's syndrome).

First there was a case of Klinefelter's syndrome with positive chromatin and the genetic formula 44A + XXY, published by Jacobs and Strong.[21] This fact was quickly confirmed, and we ourselves have collected 10 personal examples.

Next, a case of Turner's syndrome with negative chromatin and the genetic formula 44A + X, published by Ford, Jones, Polani, de Almeida and Briggs.[8]

Then, justifying the theory of nondisjunction, so to speak, Jacobs *et al.*[19] published the case history of a woman whose female morphology was not very pronounced, who had experienced her menopause very early and had a "super-female" karyotype (44A + XXX).

Complementary studies carried out in subsequent months disclosed the following specific findings:

1. The gonosome formula opposes two etiologic varieties of Turner's syndrome: the 44A + X variety, with negative chromatin, and the 44A + XX variety, with positive chromatin.

2. There are cases on hand[12] of 44A + X individuals with positive chromatin that reopen the question of the interpretation of the chromatin corpuscle.

3. The gonosome formula XXY of Klinefelter's syndrome proves that the masculinizing effect of the human Y-chromosome is

superior to that of the Y-chromosome of Drosophila, since the XXY fly is a fertile female. A case of possible Vh/Y translocation[43] described below does not contradict this observation.

4. In the study of the bone marrow of a case of Klinefelter's syndrome, an XX/XXY mosaic formula was found.[9] In another case, examinations showed that about two thirds of the karyotypes had 47 chromosomes and one third had 48 or 49 (skin biopsy).[2] Examination by means of tissue culture of the bone marrow of an intersexual revealed an XY/XO mosaic with a Y-chromosome of abnormal dimensions.[16]

5. The karyotype study of intersexuals has the great advantage of making it possible to separate the above varieties with abnormal gonosome formulae from the following varieties: male pseudohermaphrodites with the formula 44A + XY,[20,25,32] female pseudohermaphrodites with the formula 44A + XX,[44] true hermaphrodites with the formula 44A + XX[13,17,45] and without mosaicism.

In a clinical case of female eunuchoidism, confirmed after discussion as a case of "pure gonadal dysgenesis," the karyotype led to this pathologic condition being assigned the genetic formula 44A + XY.[15] According to the authors of another case history, which was difficult to interpret but in this instance was of an anatomicoclinical nature, the pattern was that of a "gonadal dysgenesis with the formula 44A + XY."[28]

TRANSLOCATIONS

The human karyotype can be modified by means of translocations that are compatible with life. In the cases known up to now this involves translocations among acrocentric chromosomes (centromere fusions). The pathologic consequences of such translocations seem to be apparent in some cases but not in others. This variability probably depends on the extent of the loss of genetic material that accompanies the elimination of a centromere.

The possibility of clinically unapparent translocations poses the problem of a possible morphologic variability of the human karyotype. Considering the very high number of normal human karyotypes that already have been identified, it does not appear that this variability could be very great.

Translocations are either isolated or are associated with karyotype anomalies, the pathologic effects of which are known.

ISOLATED TRANSLOCATIONS

The first translocation[41] was discovered in the karyotype of a child 4½ years old, in whom trophic failure (abiotrophy), complicated by a moderate but definite retardation of psychic development, was accompanied by complex vertebrocostal malformations. We gave this complex condition the name of "polydysspondylia."

In the absence of any other demonstrable etiology, a cause-and-effect relationship between the translocation and the syndrome observed was discussed. Only the discovery of a new example of this pathologic condition can confirm this hypothesis. A centromere fusion $T_1{\sim}Vs$ (*13-22*) gave the karyotype an apparent 42A + Vs + ($T_1{\sim}Vs$) + XY formula.

Another variety of translocation[43] was observed in the karyotype of a child who was, to all appearances, afflicted with a gonadal dysgenesis "of the seminiferous tubules" as described by Grumbach[13]: clitoris in the form of a penis; urogenital sinus; intra-abdominal male genital apparatus; involution of Sertoli's cells in the seminiferous tubules with no spermatogenic activity; a small retrovesicular mass reminiscent of an exceedingly hypoplastic uterus; positive chromatin (55%); dextrocardia. Following discussion, the most reasonable interpretation of the karyotype anomaly appeared to be that of a terminal translocation of a Vh segment (*21*) on the Y-chromosome. The segmental deficiency of the Y-chromosome accompanying the loss of the centromere is believed to have led to the upsetting of the balance between the masculinizing and the feminizing factors in favor of the latter.

ASSOCIATED TRANSLOCATIONS

The chromosome aberrations that are responsible for mongolism or for Klinefelter's syndrome can be accompanied by translocations.

An example of the first possibility[10] gave an apparent chromosome number of 46 to a mongoloid karyotype, trisomia being masked by a translocation between Vh and T (*21* and *13, 14* or *15*).

An example of the second possibility[24] gave an apparent chromosome number of 46, by virtue of centromere T ~ T fusion (*14-15*), to a 44A + XXY karyotype characteristic of Klinefelter's syndrome.

In either case, no mention is made of pathologic signs connected with the translocation. The problem unquestionably deserves further, more detailed study. It cannot be resolved unreservedly in the negative.

Moreover, it is not impossible that a nondisjunction which is already complicated by another (mongolism and Klinefelter's syndrome) may also promote a translocation.

FURTHER POSSIBILITIES

In all likelihood, the list of congenital diseases due to chromosome aberrations is not yet complete. To the examples of aberrations that can be explained in terms of nondisjunction or of terminal translocation, perhaps it will be possible to add examples of other gross anomalies (numerical anomalies and significant omissions or duplications). The present-day methods of analysis being what they are, the alterations that do not cause significant morphologic anomalies (intercalary translocations, minor duplications or omissions, inversions) may easily escape notice.

In addition, these analyses must take two difficulties into consideration. The first involves the possible coincidence of two aberrations: for example, a translocation masking a trisomia. The other involves the possible

appearance of anomalies in the culture medium; the often numerous polyploid cells; the development of a clone with a 2n-1 karyotype; even the appearance of a slight but definite polyteny that doubles the length of all the elements of the genome and allows one to discern a periodic structure of associated chromatids.[46]

Up to the present time, aberrations of number have been found to be responsible for semifatal or fatal conditions. They cause severe alterations of bodily development and more or less severe disorders of mental development.

The consequences of translocations are in proportion to the genetic density of the segment that has been eliminated. This principle of experimental genetics still remains to be demonstrated as valid in man. Certain facts are conducive to accepting rather than rejecting it.

The systematic investigation of sex-linked characteristics (achromatopsia, for instance) in families comprising an individual with a gonosome aberration would permit the identifications of the parent responsible for the nondisjunction. The accumulation of data would even make it possible to discover the relative fertility of the various chromosome types of gametes.[31]

Following the example of mongolism, some chromosome aberrations are perhaps capable of causing anomalies in the nuclear cytoplasm with morphologic repercussions. It is known that the nuclear segmentation index* of the polynuclear cells in mongolism[34] is abnormally low, and significantly so. This peculiarity, the consequence of which is a shift to the left in Arneth's formula, is a further justification for karyotype analysis if the condition is accompanied by a congenital malformation.

Chromosome aberrations have opened a new nosologic chapter in human medicine. The initial results are tending to overcome

---

* The nuclear segmentation index is equal to the mean number of nuclear segments per polynuclear neutrophil.

a significant lag in the study of human heredity as compared with that of experimental heredity.

REFERENCES

1. Bassoe, H. H.: Familial congenital muscular dystrophy with gonadal dysgenesis, J. Clin. Endocrinol. **16:**1614, 1956.
2. Bergman, S., Reitalu, J., Nowakowski, H., and Lenz, W.: The chromosomes in two patients with Klinefelter syndrome, Ann. Human Genet. **24:**81, 1960.
3. Bleyer, A.: Indication that mongoloid imbecility is a gametic mutation of degressive type, Am. J. Dis. Child. **47:**342, 1934.
4. Böök, J. A., Fraccaro, M., and Lindsten, J.: Cytogenetical observations in mongolism, Acta paediat. **48:**453, 1959.
5. Edwards, J. H., Harnden, D. G., Cameron, A. H., Crosse, M., Wolff, O. H.: A new trisomic syndrome, Lancet **1:**787, 1960.
6. Fanconi, G.: Die mutationstheorie des Mongolismus (M.), Schweiz. med. Wchnschr. **43:**81, 1939.
7. Ford, C. E., Jones, K. W., Miller, O. J., Mittwoch, U., Penrose, L. S., Ridler, M., and Shapiro, A.: The chromosomes in a patient showing both mongolism and the Klinefelter syndrome, Lancet **1:**709, 1959.
8. Ford, C. E., Jones, K. W., Polani, P. E., de Almeida, J. C., and Briggs, J. H.: A sex chromosome anomaly in a case of gonadal dysgenesis (Turner's syndrome), Lancet **1:**711, 1959.
9. Ford, C. E., Polani, P. E., Briggs, J. H., and Bishop, P. M. F.: A presumptive human XXY/XX mosaic, Nature (Lond.) **183:**1030, 1959.
10. Ford, C. E., Polani, P. E., *et al.:* Presentation at Am. Ass. for Mental and Nerv. Dis. Research, New York, December, 1959.
11. Fraccaro, M., Kaijser, K., and Lindsten, J.: Chromosome complement in parents of patient with gonadal dysgenesis (Turner's syndrome), Lancet **2:**1090, 1959.
12. ————: Somatic chromosome complement in continuously cultured cells of two individuals with gonadal dysgenesis, Ann. Human Genet. **24:**45, 1960.
13. Grumbach, M. M., Morishima, A., and Chu, E. M. Y.: Personal communication.
14. Harnden, D. G., and Armstrong, C. N.: Chromosomes of a true hermaprodite, Brit. M. J. **2:**1287, 1959.
15. Harnden, D. G., and Stewart, J. S. S.: Chromosomes in a case of pure gonadal dysgenesis, Brit. M. J. **2:**1285, 1959.
16. Hirschhorn, K., Cooper, H. S., and Decker, W.: A case of inter-sex with XY/XO mosaicism, Annual meeting Am. Soc. Human Genet., April 28-30, 1960.
17. Hungerford, D. A., Donnelly, A. J., Nowell, P. C., and Beck, S.: The chromosome constitution of a human phenotype intersex, Am. J. Human Genet. **11:**215, 1959.
18. Jacobs, P. A., Baikie, A. G., Court Brown, W. M., and Strong, J. A.: The somatic chromosomes in mongolism, Lancet **1:**710, 1959.
19. Jacobs, P. A., Baikie, A. G., Court Brown, W. M., MacGregor, T. N., Maclean, N., and Harnden, D. G.: Evidence for the existence of the human "super female," Lancet **2:**423, 1959.
20. Jacobs, P. A., Baikie, A. G., Court Brown, W. M., Forest, H., Roy, J. R., Stewart, J. S., and Lennox, B.: Chromosomal sex in the syndrome of testicular feminization, Lancet **2:**591, 1959.
21. Jacobs, P. A., and Strong, J. A.: A case of human intersexuality having a possible XXY sex-determining mechanism, Nature, **183:**302, 1959.
22. Lejeune, J., Gautier, M., and Turpin, R.: Etude des chromosomes somatiques de neuf enfants mongoliens, Compt. rend. Acad. Sc. **248:**1721, 1959.
23. ————: Les chromosomes humains en culture de tissus, Compt. rend. Acad. Sc. **248:**602, 1959.
24. Lejeune, J., Turpin, R., and Decourt, J.: Abérrations chromosomiques et maladies humaines. Syndrôme de Klinefelter XXY à 46 chromosomes par fusion centromérique T∼t, Compt. rend. Acad. Sc. **250:**2468, 1960.
25. Lejeune, J., Turpin, R., and Gautier, M.: Analyse caryotypique trois pseudohermaphrodites masculins, Compt. rend. Acad. Sc. **250:**618, 1960.
26. ————: Le mongolisme, premier exemple d'aberration autosomique humaine, Ann. Génét. **1:**41, 1959.
27. Mosier, H. D., Scott, L. W., and Cotter, L. H.: The frequency of positive sex-chromatin pattern in males with mental deficiency, Pediatrics **25:**291, 1960.
28. Netter, A., Lambert, A., Lumbroso, P., Trevoux, R., Delzant, G., De Grouchy, and Lamy, M.: Dysgenesis gonadique avec chromosomes XY: premier cas, Bull. et mém. Soc. med. hôp. Paris 7-8, 275, 1960.
29. Patau K., Smith, D. W., Therman, E., Inhorn, S. L., and Wagner, H. P.: Multiple

congenital anomaly caused by an extra autosome, Lancet **1**:790, 1960.

30. Penrose, L. S.: The distal triradius on the hands of parents and sibs of mongol imbeciles, Ann. Human Genet. **19**:10, 1954.

31. Polani, P. E., Briggs, J. H., and Ford, C. E.: Chromosomes of man, Brit. M. J. **2**:1330, 1959.

32. Sternberg, W. H., and Kloepfer, H. W.: Genetic and pathologic study of simulant females (testicular feminization syndrome), Annual meeting Am. Soc. of Human Genet., April 28-30, 1960.

33. Tjio, J. H., and Levan, A.: The chromosome number of man, Hereditas **42**:1, 1956.

34. Turpin, R., and Bernyer, G.: De l'influence de l'hérédité sur la formule d'Arneth (cas particulier du mongolisme), Rev. hémat. **2**:189, 1947.

35. Turpin, R., Bernyer, G., and Tissier, C.: Mongolisme et stigmates familiaux de la série mongolienne, Presse méd. **53**:597, 1947.

36. Turpin, R., Caratzali, A., and Rogier, H.: Etude étiologique de cent quatre cas de mongolisme et considérations sur la pathogénie de cette maladie, Premier Congrès de la Féd. Internat. Latine des Stés d'Eugénique, vol. I, Paris, Masson, 1937.

37. Turpin, R., and Lejeune, J.: Analogies entre le type dermatoglyphique palmaire des singes inférieurs et celui des enfants atteints de mongolisme, Compt. rend. Acad. Sc. **258**:395, 1954.

38. ———: Etude comparée des dermatoglyphes de la partie distale de la paume de la main, chez l'homme normal, les enfants mongoliens et les simiens inférieurs, Compt. rend. Acad. Sc. **258**:1449, 1954.

39. ———: Etude dermatoglyphique des paumes des mongoliens et de leurs parents et germains, Semaine hôp. Paris **76**:3955, 1953.

40. ———: Etude d'une famille compartant quatre frères et soeurs mongoliens, Semaine hôp. Paris **76**:3979, 1953.

41. Turpin, R., Lejeune, J., Lafourcade, J., and Gautier, M.: Abérrations chromosomiques et maladies humaines. La polydysspondylie à 45 chromosomes, Compt. rend. Acad. Sc. **248**:3636, 1959.

42. Waardenburg, P. J.: Mongolismus *in* Das Menschliche Auge und seine Erhanlagen, vol. 1, pp. 44-48, The Hague, Nighoff, 1932.

43. Personal observation No. 36.

44. Personal observation No. 121.

45. Personal observation Nos. 81 and 92.

46. Personal observation No. 127 (malade de le Dr. Hepp, Brésil).

47. Personal observation No. 40.

The Interaction Between Genes and Environment in Development

PROFESSOR HANS NACHTSHEIM

In the course of a conference on congenital malformations which was held in 1959 in the United States, Dr. F. Clarke Fraser,[6] at the close of a lecture on the causes of congenital malformations in human beings, summed up his statements in 3 sentences:

1. A minority of congenital malformations have a major *genetic* cause.

2. A minority of congenital malformations have a major *environmental* cause.

3. Most malformations probably result from complicated interactions between genetic predispositions and subtle factors of the intra-uterine environment.

By such a clear and concise formulation, Fraser has well summarized the present state of our knowledge. It serves no useful purpose to discuss whether genetic malformations in man are more frequent than those due to the environment, or vice versa. We do not know. Nor would it make any sense to try to express as a percentage the frequency of one or the other type of malformation arising as the result of genetic causes or of the environment.

Any further discussion must be based on the fact that *every* individual is the product of a close interplay between genes and the environment; and that the formation of a specific malformation may in one case be mainly attributable to endogenous factors, in another mainly to the environment, and in yet another case to a more or less complicated interplay between endogenous and exogenous factors. In man, it is often difficult or impossible to distinguish between these situations.

For an understanding of such situations in man, we must time and again have recourse to animal material. I intend to discuss here several examples, mainly from my own work and that of my co-workers, which will demonstrate the origin of anomalies by the complex interplay between endogenous and exogenous factors and are similar to situations encountered in man.

Let us start with a seemingly simple case. Albinism, or the complete inability to form pigment, is a mutation familiar in most domesticated and many wild species of mammals. All germ layers lack an enzyme necessary for pigment formation; hence, the skin, the hair and the eyes of the complete albinos are devoid of pigment. Depending on the thickness of the iris and the state of contraction of the pupil, the eyes appear more or less pink due to the translucence of the blood vessels.

In all mammals in which a genetic analysis has been made, such as the rabbit and the mouse, total albinism is inherited as a simple recessive condition; the gene responsible has the symbol c. Penetrance and expressivity are complete in all homozygotes (cc), and following crosses of albinos with normal, fully pigmented animals (CC), albinism segregates out according to mendelian expectation in subsequent generations. Exogenous factors have no influence on the manifestation of the albino gene. It has never been possible to induce the formation of even a trace of pigment in a real albino (cc) animal. Hence, total albinism belongs to that group of conditions which is entirely dependent on gene action.

However, mutation from the normal allele (C) does not always give rise to the albino gene (c) which suppresses pigmentation completely. C may mutate to less extreme alleles which reduce pigmentation to a greater or a lesser extent. Usually genes causing more pigmentation tend to dominate over genes causing less pigmentation. An interesting feature which has been known for a long time is the fact that some of these alleles are temperature-dependent in their manifestation. The classic example is the so-called Himalayan rabbit (c^h) which lacks pigment on most of its body and in the eyes but is pigmented on the most exposed parts of the body, such as on ears, nose, feet and tail (acromelanism). However, in contrast with the complete albino, the Himalayan rabbit can form pigment in any part of the body, even in the eye, if that part of the body is exposed to cold temperature during the growth of hair, etc. Conversely, by the application of a high temperature, pigmentation of Himalayan rabbits can be suppressed in those parts of the body which normally are pigmented.

Thus we are able, with the aid of an exogenous factor (temperature), to change a $c^h c^h$ or $c^h c$ animal phenotypically into a cc animal. Of course, such a transformation is only temporary, as during the next moult the acromelanic pigmentation will reappear unless we keep the animal permanently in a hot environment.

However, with the aid of another gene, the acromelanism of the Himalayan rabbit can be eliminated permanently. I first produced such a "synthetic albino" in the rabbit some 30 years ago.[12]

In addition to albinism, the rabbit has a gene for leucism (x) which, in homozygous condition, suppresses the formation of fur pigment, though in a different manner. This type is called Vienna white by the rabbit breeders. As the name implies, the hairs are white, but the eyes are blue; this is due to the fact that pigment is present in the ectodermal parts of retina and iris but not in the mesodermal stroma of the iris (color of opaque media). If a Vienna white (xx) rabbit is crossed with a Himalayan ($c^h c^h$) rabbit, one can obtain in the F_2 generation a double recessive $xx c^h c^h$ rabbit which is a "synthetic" albino. The gene for Vienna white suppresses pigmentation in nose, ears, feet and tail, and the Himalayan gene suppresses pigmentation in the eye. Such synthetic albinos breed true when mated with each other. However, if we mate such a synthetic ($xx c^h c^h$) with a true (XXcc) albino, all the F_1 animals ($Xx c^h c$) show acromelanism like the Himalayan rabbit. In F_2 there is a bifactorial segregation which, on account of the interaction of the genes, gives a ratio of 9 Himalayan rabbits: 7 albinos. Four of the latter are true albinos, the rest are "synthetic."

In the living animal, true and synthetic albinos cannot be distinguished phenotypically. However, apart from the breeding test, synthetic albinos can be recognized in tissue culture. If iris or retinal tissue of such an animal is grown in vitro at a low temperature, some pigment is formed in the ectodermal derivatives but not in the mesodermal tissue of the iris which, under the influence of xx, remains unpigmented. Neither iris nor retina of a true albino forms any pigment in vitro.

However, a synthetic albino may be distinguished from a true one if it contains not the ordinary Vienna white allele x but x^e, which combines the effect on pigmentation with an increased disposition to convulsions. $x^e x^e$ Rabbits, particularly when they are young, suffer from epileptiform convulsions which occur in $x^e x^e c^h c^h$ synthetic albinos but not in true (XXcc) albinos.

There is yet another way of making a synthetic albino in the rabbit without the use of any albino allele at all. Some years ago, Karin Magnussen[11] discovered an isolated albinism of the eye in the rabbit. This simple recessive trait (symbol ra = red eye) completely suppresses the ectodermal and also considerably reduces the mesodermal eye pigment. Unlike ordinary albinism, this gene does not act through blocking an enzyme system; it can be shown histologically that the pigment cells of the eye degenerate. The gene has nearly no effect on the pigment cells of skin and hair. However, when the two genes for Vienna white and for albinism of the eye are brought together, the double recessives (raraxx) are synthetic albinos as the sole remaining ectodermal eye pigment of Vienna white animals is removed by the action of the ra gene.

When we compare the situation in animals, particularly in the rabbit, with what is known about albinism in man, it is obvious that the differential diagnosis in man is still in a very unsatisfactory state. Often, no distinction is made between albinism, leucism and even spotting. For instance, Walter Tietz[15] recently described in man a dominant albinism associated with deaf-mutism, but stated himself that these people have blue eyes; he compared the case with blue-eyed white deaf cats which are "Vienna white" rather than albinos. We also know in man complete and partial albinism attributable to the gene c or its alleles, as well as a recessive isolated albinism of the eye.

Let us visualize what the picture in man would be if the situation regarding albinism and similar phenotypes would be exactly the same as we now know it in the rabbit. In relation to complete albinism or the isolated albinism of the eye, adequate family investigations would establish the simple recessive inheritance with reasonable certainty. However, where a phenotype is due to the interaction of several recessive genes, as in our synthetic albinos, the chances of its successful analysis would be remote. Double recessive combinations would be very rare events due to the breeding structure of human populations and due to the small size of human families, especially if the genes in question have not been analyzed individually, as in animals. It would be very difficult to decide whether and to what extent such occurrences are genetic in nature.

A second example is offered from my own work. In most domestic animals the difference in size between the largest and the smallest individuals is much greater than in man. In rabbits the "German Giant" with an average weight of 5,000 grams and the "Ermine" with an average of 1,000 grams differ as 5:1. The difference is so great that a natural mating between the giant and the midget is impossible. However, living offspring in crosses in both directions can be obtained by artificial insemination. A number of genes participate in the determination of size, some acting one way, some the other.

In combination with the other midget genes of the "ermine" rabbit this incompletely recessive midget gene, (symbol dw = dwarf), reduces still further the small size of that breed. Rabbits which carry this gene in single dose are fully viable though somewhat smaller than homozygous normal animals. However, rabbits which carry this gene in double dose are inviable superdwarfs; although the dwdw homozygotes usually are born alive, they invariably die within a few days of birth. The breeders of "ermine" rabbits who want their animals as small as possible are usually quite prepared to accept the loss of the lethal superdwarfs for the sake of the effect of the gene in heterozygous condition. Hence, prize-winning "ermine" rabbits often are heterozygous for the dw gene.

Now we can introduce into the genotype of the "ermine" breed certain genes which are not exactly genes for dwarfism but nevertheless have a more or less retarding influence on prenatal development. This applies, for instance, to the so-called Rex or short-hair genes which in the rabbit are inherited as simple recessives. If we produce an "ermine" which is also homozygous for one of these short-hair genes, it is completely viable. But if we introduce into this short-haired "ermine" even a single dose of the dw gene, this is enough to produce a nonviable superdwarf. The dw gene is thus a recessive lethal in the ordinary "ermine" but a dominant lethal in the short-haired "ermine."

But what will happen if we remove the dw gene from the other genes for small size in the "ermine" and put it into rabbits of normal size or even into giants? I made such tests during the last war, but unfortunately I was not able to complete the experiments on account of unfavorable conditions in connection with the war. Nonetheless, the experiments progressed far enough to justify the statement that the larger the animal into which we introduce the dw gene, the less the resulting effect, and we may assume that in the giant it becomes cryptogenic which can no longer prevail over the genes for large size in the giant. The gene for lethal dwarfism is thus a good example for the dependence of the effect of a gene on the genetic background or the gene association in which it finds itself with its action and counteraction, a situation which in man undoubtedly plays a much bigger role than we can fathom at present.

The third example demonstrates the increasing importance of exogenous factors. In man, there exists a whole series of hereditary cataracts. The type of opacity of the lens is extremely characteristic in nearly all of these inherited forms. They appear mostly monosymptomatically, but several form part of a more complex syndrome. On the other hand, however, it is well known that the most varied exogenous factors may lead to opacity of the lens, such as infections, toxic effects, errors of metabolism and radiant energy (infrared etc.). In our laboratory animals we have also made numerous observations on hereditary and nonhereditary cataracts. I select once more a case out of my own experience with rabbits which during the past few years has been particularly analyzed and demonstrates very well the interplay between heredity and the environment.

In 1939, I described jointly with the ophthalmologist H. Gürich[14] a hereditary opacity of the sutural lines of the lens of the rabbit which usually later develops into a nuclear cataract. The development takes place in 3 stages. At birth there is always a bilateral cloudiness of the posterior raphe of the lens. It is not difficult to demonstrate this with the aid of the ophthalmoscope and the slit lamp after the eyes of the newborn animal have opened. This initial opacity probably hardly impairs vision. The cataract *could* remain in this stage throughout life. However, at the age of 6 to 8 weeks a turbidity of the posterior cortex of the lens begins to develop which subsequently leads quickly to the third stage of total opacity. The condition is inherited as a simple recessive character (symbol=cat I); segregation in F_2 and backcross generations is close to the mendelian expectation. Penetrance and expressivity are complete; among many hundreds of animals in the pure strain which we have bred for 20 years, there has never been an animal in which bilateral turbidity of the posterior raphe has not been clearly discernible.

Whether the cataractous degeneration of the lens progresses beyond the first stage depends entirely upon exogenous factors. The genetically determined lesion of the raphe allows the penetration of water into the raphe system. The entry of water leads to the denaturation of the lens proteins with consequent turbidity of the cortex. With the total decomposition of the colloidal lens protein the development of the cataract reaches its peak. On the normal diet which contains much water this is the usual course of events. However, as shown by my assistant U. Ehling in 1957,[1] if, during the sensitive period of lens development, namely the 2nd and the 3rd months, the animals are kept on a dehydrated diet, the cataract, in most of the animals, remains stationary in its first stage.

In recent years, Ehling and Krokowski[2,9] have succeeded in producing a cataract similar to the first stage of the inherited one on a purely phenotypic basis. Following irradiation of 20 to 23-day-old animals with a dose of 350 rad, the same turbidity of the raphe appears as a radiocataract. As in the case of the inherited cataract, the further development of the radiocataract depends on the water content of the lens, stages 2 and 3 being capable of being suppressed by a dehydrated diet. However, there is *one* outstanding difference between the genetic and the radiation-induced cataract. In the case of the hereditary cataract, new lens fibers may be formed after complete turbidity of the lens has developed, and these fibers remain free from turbidity; in the case of the radiocataract, the destruction of the germinative zone by the ionizing radiation renders the formation of new fibers impossible.

However, these investigations[3,5] uncovered a connection between the effects of radiation and the genotype. By accident, the rabbits used for the irradiation experiments included some albinos. These proved to be more resistant to irradiation than the pigmented animals. The experiments were repeated on 30 animals which included several stages of the albino series. Some were fully pigmented, others had a reduction of melanin formation, still others were Himalayan (acromelanic) rabbits, while some were complete albinos. As the result of the increasing reduction in pigment and the associated decrease in the amount of C-enzyme, there developed a definite and gradual increase in radiation resistance.

In view of these results, it was only logical to examine the influence of cataract genes on irradiation sensitivity of the lens.[4] Animals heterozygous and homozygous for the cat-I gene were irradiated; the latter already showed the turbidity of the posterior raphe due to the cat-I gene. However, the radiation sensitivity of the lens is not increased by the cataract gene in heterozygous or homozygous condition nor by the resulting turbidity of the posterior raphe.

The last example showed us how an anomaly may be produced both by a gene and, as a "phenocopy," by an environmental factor. The following example will show the possibility that one allele of a gene, together with a peristatic factor, may produce the same phenotype as two alleles of that genes (i.e., the homozygote). The case is particularly instructive because of the parallel between man and animal.

The main characteristic of the Pelger anomaly in the rabbit as well as in man is a reduction of segmentation of the nuclei of neutrophil white blood cells. In man, as in rabbit, the condition is due to a simple dominant gene with complete penetrance and expressivity.[13] In heterozygotes, nuclei with 2 segments ("pince-nez" types) are the typical Pelger cells; segmentation is completely suppressed in the homozygotes, and the nuclei remain round or ovoid. Now with the aid of a colchicine injection, one can obtain a phenocopy of the homozygote in the heterozygous Pelger rabbit; that is to say, 1 dose of the Pelger gene + colchicine has the same phenotypic effect as 2 Pelger genes. Of course, this is only a transitory phenocopy which persists as long as the colchicine is circulating in the blood.[8]

We can observe the same phenocopy in human heterozygous for the Pelger gene during an illness accompanied by a high temperature, the white blood picture then corresponding to that of a homozygous Pelger. After the illness has subsided, the blood picture reverts to that typical of the heterozygous Pelger condition.[10]

The last example comes from man.[7] In collaboration with my own department, Dr. W. Fuhrmann of the Paediatric Hospital of the Free University of Berlin has examined 122 patients suffering from congenital heart diseases with special reference to the genetic and the exogenous factors which are behind these congenital malformations of the heart and the big vessels. The congenital heart defects in particular always are quoted as being only rarely genetically determined while, in by far the majority of cases, exogenous disturbances during the mother's pregnancy are thought to be the causative factor. It is said that in mothers of affected children, disturbances during pregnancy are particularly frequent. However, it should not be overlooked that nearly every mother of a child that has some kind of malformation at birth will be inclined to place the blame on some irregularity during pregnancy. Thus all such statements are to be accepted with caution. Therefore, Fuhrmann did not limit himself in his investigations to the 122 propositi and their families but extended his investigations to healthy children and their parents. The result of this very careful investigation is noteworthy: "teratogenic" environmental factors are reported by the mothers in established congenital heart defects and in control cases to about the same extent. Only in the case of hemorrhages early in pregnancy were there definite differences between the mothers of patients and the mothers of control children. While it is possible that in some cases disturbances of pregnancy may cause malformations, the frequently encountered consanguineous marriages of the parents of malformed children point to the participation of the genotype in the malformation.

CONCLUSION

Though we could quote only a few examples out of our own field of research, they illustrate the complexity, the intimacy and the complications in the interaction between genes and exogenous factors. In our investigations as to the causes of congenital malformations we always must consider *primarily* the effectiveness of the genotype. As an experimental investigator, one cannot warn sufficiently not to jump to conclusions in the case of isolated human malformations and attribute them to exogenous conditions. Where several specific genes have to interact to produce an abnormality, where an abnormality is due to a new mutation or to a chromosomal aberration, the abnormality may be expected as a sporadic event and not with familial repetition. Nonetheless, the genotype in all these cases may be 100 per cent responsible for the malformation. In dealing

with man, one has to be careful not to overestimate the importance of the phenocopies of hereditary traits obtained by many exogenous factors in animals. As interesting and as valuable as these animal experiments may be, they still do not give any indication as to the numerical incidence of this type of malformation in man.

REFERENCES

1. Ehling, U.: Untersuchungen zur kausalen Genese erblicher Katarakte beim Kaninchen (Investigations on the causal genesis of hereditary cataract in the rabbit), Z. Menschl. Vererb. Konstitutionsl. 34:77-104, 1957.
2. Ehling, U., and Krokowski, E.: Die Entwicklung der Radiokatarakt in Abhängigkeit vom Wassergehalt der Linse (Evolution of radiocataract as a function of water content of the lens), Fortschr. Geb. Röentgenstrahlen 88:360-365, 1958.
3. ———: Die Entwicklung der Radiokatarakt in Abhängigkeit vom Genotypus. Eine Untersuchung am Kaninchenauge (Evolution of radiocataract as a function of genotype. Researches on the leporine eye), Z. Naturforsch. 14b:201-205, 1959.
4. ———: Der Einfluss von Kataraktgenen auf die Strahlenempfindlichkeit der Linse (Influence of cataract genes on radiation sensitivity of the crystalline lens), *ibid.* 15b:110-115, 1960.
5. Ehling, U., Mex, A., and Krokowski, E.: Die Strahlenempfindlichkeit der Kaninchenlinse und ihre Abhängigkeit von spezifischen Genen (Radiation sensitivity of the leporine lens, and its dependence on specific genes), Naturw. 46:633-634, 1959.
6. Fraser, F. C.: Causes of congenital malformations in human beings, J. Chron. Dis. 10:97-110, 1959.
7. Fuhrmann, W.: Untersuchungen über ätiologische Faktoren bei angeborenen Herzmissbildungen (Studies on etiological factors in congenital malformations of the heart). In press.
8. Harm, H.: Beeinflussung des weissen Blutbildes von Pelger- und Nicht-Pelger-Kaninchen durch Colchicin (The white blood picture of Pelger and non-Pelger rabbits as affected by colchicine), Acta haemat. 10:95-105, 1953.
9. Krokowski, E., and Ehling, U.: Die Entwicklung der Radiokatarakt in Abhängig-

keit vom Alter (Evolution of radiocataract as a function of age), Fortschr. Geb. Röentgenstrahlen **88**:591-595, 1958.

10. Lüers, T., Nachtsheim, H., and Petzel, G.: Phänokopie des Blutbildes des homozygoten Pelgers infolge reaktiver Linksverschiebung bei einem heterozygoten Pelger (Phenocopy of the blood picture of a homozygous Pelger owing to reactive shift to the left in a heterozygous Pelger), Blut **2**:177-187, 1956.

11. Magnussen, K.: Beitrag zur Genetik und Histologie eines isolierten Augenalbinismus beim Kaninchen. I-V (On the genetics and histology of an isolated ocular albinism in the rabbit. I-V), Z. morph. Anthrop. **44**:127-135, 1952; **46**:24-29, 1954; **49**:306-311, 1959; **50**:103-120, 1959; **51**:81-88, 1960.

12. Nachtsheim, H.: Die genetischen Beziehungen zwischen Körperfarbe und Augenfarbe beim Kaninchen (The genetic relationships between body color and eye color in the rabbit), Biol. Zentralbl. **53**:99-109, 1933.

13. ————: Vergleichende Erbpathologie der Blutkrankheiten—am Beispiel der Pelger-Anomalie betrachtet (Comparative hereditary pathology of diseases of the blood, as seen in the example of Pelger's anomaly), Arch. Klaus-Stift. Vererb. forsch. **25**:566-585, 1950.

14. Nachtsheim, H., and Gürich, H.: Erbleiden des Kaninchenauges. I. Erbliche Nahtbändchentrübung der Linse mit nachfolgendem Kernstar (Hereditary disorders of the leporine eye. I. Hereditary suturo-fasciolar opacity of the lens with subsequent nuclear cataract), Z. Menschl. Vererb. Konstitutionsl. **23**:463-483, 1939.

15. Tietz, W.: Dominant albinism associated with deaf-mutism, Am. Soc. Human Genet. (abstract), April, 1960.

Sex Chromosome Abnormalities

W. M. COURT BROWN, O.B.E., B.Sc., M.B., Ch.B.

In January, 1959, the first evidence for a human sex chromosome abnormality was published by Jacobs and Strong:[3] it has become apparent since then that abnormalities involving the sex chromosomes are not uncommon and, indeed, that their frequency in the population may well be as great or greater than that of abnormalities involving the autosomes.

An important preliminary to the discovery of sex chromosome aberrations was the work on sex chromatin, dating from the original description of the sex chromatin body by Barr and Bertram.[2] This work led to the recognition of three clinical states in which the sex as determined by sex chromatin, the nuclear sex, was at variance with the phenotypic sex. These states were (1) some cases of Klinefelter's syndrome, (2) some of Turner's syndrome and (3) some cases of testicular feminization. Until chromosome analysis became possible it was believed that all three states were examples of sex-reversal, but as is now known this appears to be true only of testicular feminization.

The analysis of sex chromatin plays an important part, in the search for and the diagnoses of sex chromosome abnormalities; therefore, I would like to summarize the present state of knowledge regarding sex chromatin in relation to both normal human beings and to disease states (Table 1).

In our experience the sex chromatin body can be seen in about 41 per cent of the cells in suitably stained preparations of buccal mucosal smears from normal women. The absence of such a body in phenotypic females occurs in some cases of Turner's syndrome, in some of gonadal dysgenesis and in cases of testicular feminization. A sex chromatin body is not seen in normal males, and its presence in phenotypic males is associated with a chromosomal sex of XXY. Two other types of patient have been described who do not conform to the normal pattern. In the first type, some cells show 2 sex chromatin bodies, and so far such individuals have been found to possess 3 X chromosomes. The second type of patient is one in whom sex chromatin is seen in an unusually small number of cells, and the chromatin bodies themselves appear to be smaller than normal. In this latter instance, the findings have been associated with the presence of 1 X chromosome which is normal in appearance and 1 from which a segment has been deleted. The great value of the buccal smear technic lies in its use as a

TABLE 1. Nuclear Sex. Percentage Distribution of Sex Chromatin Bodies in Buccal Mucosal Cells

	Per Cent No Sex Chromatin	Per Cent 1 Sex Chromatin Body	Per Cent 2 Sex Chromatin Bodies
Normal Males.....................	100	0	0
Normal females (20 individuals)........	59	41 (S.D.±3.4)	0
Individuals with 3 X Chromosomes (4 patients)....................	18 to 37	43 to 57	14 to 36
Partial deletion of an X Chromosome (1 patient).....................	93	7	0

method for the screening of large numbers of people in the search for sex chromosome abnormalities.

We can now turn to the various abnormalities which are known at the present date. These can be subdivided into: (1) abnormalities considered to result from errors occurring in the parents prior to the conception of the child; (2) those presumed to follow errors subsequent to conception at any time from the first cleavage-division onward and possibly into postnatal life; and (3) those in which gametogenesis and sex determination appear to be normal but sex differentiation is abnormal. While this classification has the merit of simplicity, it must be realized that in some conditions errors of both the first and the second types may occur in the same individual, and attention will be drawn to this in the discussion on mosaics.

The abnormalities of the first type (Table 2) are listed in order of ascending chromosome number. The first to be considered is that in which the chromosome number is 45, the nuclear sex apparently male, and the chromosomal sex XO. These individuals are the chromatin-negative cases of Turner's syndrome, characterized in most instances by short stature, neck webbing, immature development of the breasts and the genitalia with amenorrhea, primitive "streaklike" gonads in the infundibulopelvic ligaments, and sometimes coarctation of the aorta. However, amenorrhea, is not invariable, and one patient has been described who has conceived and given birth to a living male child.[1] The second abnormality was found in a phenotypic female. In this woman, a significantly small proportion of the buccal mucosal cells showed sex chromatin bodies, her chromosome count was 46, but one of the X chromosomes was partially deleted. So far, only one example of this type of abnormality has been reported, the individual presenting with primary amenorrhea and immaturity of the breasts and the external genitalia. The appearances of the gonads were those associated with Turner's syndrome, but none of the other stigmata usually associated with Turner's syndrome was found. In the third abnormality, the chromosome count is 47, double sex chromatin bodies are found, and chromosome analysis reveals the presence of 3 X chromosomes. The first such individual to be described had developed secondary amenorrhea some 2 to 3 years after the menarche. Others have since been found in which sexual development appears to be normal; details have been published of one who has given birth to 4 male children.[4] The last two abnormalities occur in phenotypic males. In the most common one, the chromosome count is 47, the nuclear sex female, and the chromosomal sex XXY. In the other, the chromosome count is 48, the nuclear sex is characterized by the presence of double chromatin bodies, and the chromosomal sex features of Klinefelter's syndrome, i.e., undersized testes with evidence of deficient or absent spermatogenesis and seminiferous tubule dysgenesis, and in some instances gynecomastia. The little that is known about the clinical features of XXXY individuals suggests that they represent a more even variant of Klinefelter's syndrome

TABLE 2. Conditions Presumed Due to an Error Occurring Prior to Conception

Chromosome Number	Chromosome Sex	Phenotypic Sex	Nuclear Sex	Clinical State
45	XO	F	−	Turner's syndrome
46	X^x	F	±	Primary amenorrhoea
47	XXX	F	++	"Super-female"*
47	XXY	M	+	Klinefelter's syndrome
48	XXXY	M	++	? Klinefelter's syndrome

*Some examples are now known in which no physical abnormality is detectable.

TABLE 3. Conditions Presumed Due to an Error Occurring Subsequent to Conception

Chromosome Number	Chromosome Sex	Phenotypic Sex	Nuclear Sex	Clinical State
45/46	XO/XX	F	?*	Turner's syndrome
45/47	XO/XXX	F	++	?
46/47	XX/XXY	M	+	Klinefelter's syndrome

*The nuclear sex findings will depend on the degree of admixture of the two stem-lines.

than individuals with an XX Y sex chromosome complement.

The second group of abnormalities of the sex chromosomes which have been published (Table 3) is comprised of aberrations which are presumed to have arisen subsequent to fertilization. In each of these, there are two lines of cells present in the body, the one distinguished from the other by its chromosome number, i.e., they represent one of the two main possible forms of chromosome mosaics. The first type is a mosaic with cell-lines containing chromosome numbers of 45 and 46, the chromosomal sex being respectively XO and XX. The phenotype is female, and the clinical state that of Turner's syndrome. Presumably, the findings on sex chromatin analysis may vary, depending on the degree of admixture of the two stem-lines in the various tissues. The second type of mosaic is one in which the chromosome numbers are 45 and 47, and the chromosomal sex respectively XO and XXX. In this instance, double sex chromatin bodies were noted in the buccal mucosal cells. The phenotype was female, the external genitalia were undeveloped, the vagina was absent, and no breast development had occurred. The third type of mosaic to be described is one in which the chromosome numbers were 46 and 47, and the chromosomal sex respectively XX and XXY. The nuclear sex was female, and the clinical state that of Klinefelter's syndrome. A fourth type has been described with stem-lines of 45 and 46 and sex chromosome complements of respectively XO and XY. This type of mosaicism appears to be one cause of true hermaphroditism.

The third group of abnormalities (Table 4) are not errors of sex determination but of sex differentiation, and perhaps strictly speaking should not be included in this paper. They are so because they fall within the broad definition of congenital abnormalities. In the first two examples, the chromosome number is 46, the nuclear sex male, and the chromosomal sex XY, i.e., individuals displaying one or the other clinical state were conceived as males, but due to abnormal differentiation they have developed into phenotypic females. The first abnormality is testicular feminization in which many of the phenotypic expressions of female sex are well developed, although the gonads are of the male type. The second example of abnormal sex differentiation is pure gonadal dysgenesis. The clinical state is that of a tall eunochoid female with primary amenorrhoea, underdeveloped genitalia and breasts, and primitive "streaklike" gonads. The third abnormality of sex differentiation occurs in a number of cases of

TABLE 4. Conditions in Which Sex Determination Is Normal But Sex Differentiation Is Abnormal

Chromosome Number	Chromosome Sex	Phenotypic Sex	Nuclear Sex	Clinical State
46	XY	F	−	Testicular feminization
46	XY	F	−	Gonadal dysgenesis
46	XX	?	+	True hermaphroditism (some examples)

true hermaphroditism which have been examined and in which the chromosome count has been 46, the nuclear sex female, and the chromosomal sex XX. These individuals possess phenotypic features of either sex, and also both ovarian and testicular tissue.

In such a short communication it is possible only to deal briefly with the probable cases of the chromosome abnormalities that have been described. Most of those abnormalities believed to be due to an error in the parental gonads can be explained by the occurrence of nondisjunction. In meiosis this error occurs when 2 chromosomes, instead of separating during anaphase to the opposite poles of the cell, remain together and both go to the same pole, and such an error produces gametes with 22 and 24 chromosomes. However, such an explanation, is inadequate to account for the occurrence of a partial deletion of one sex chromosome. While other mechanisms for this might be postulated, the error most probably occurs during the prophase of the first miotic division when the chromosomes are elongated, looped and somewhat diffuse. The occurrence of a double chromosome break with faulty union of the broken ends could lead to the loss of a segment of the chromosome. It should be noted that these errors can occur in the gonad of either parent, and a study of sex-linked characters such as color blindness may enable one to deduce in which parent the error has taken place.

Chromosome mosaics may rise in two general ways: (1) as a result of errors in division of the cytoplasm of the ovum prior to fertilization; and (2) due to errors, such as nondisjunction or anaphase-lagging, taking place subsequent to fertilization. The first error, if it occurs at all in man, probably is extremely rare and will involve an abnormality of cleavage during meiotic division with the production of 2 ova, which are independently fertilized, in place of an ovum and a polar body. If, after independent fertilization, the 2 ova develop into

a single individual, this individual could be a chromosome mosaic. The second type of error, involving either nondisjunction or anaphase-lagging during somatic cell division, can in theory occur at any stage of development from the first cleavage-division of the fertilized ovum into postnatal life. While the mosaics which are detailed in Table 3 may be explained in this way, I mentioned earlier that the classification adopted in this paper is rather oversimplified, and it is in relation to mosaics that this is the case. The most reasonable explanation for both XO/XXX and XO/XY mosaics postulates the occurrence of an abnormal chromosome distribution at an early cleavage division after fertilization. However, it can be argued that this explanation may be insufficient for the other two forms of mosaicism, and the possibility must be envisaged that these arise as a result of errors subsequent to the conception of an individual who at conception was abnormal due to an error occurring in the parents' gonads. For example, the XO/XX mosaic may be the result of a divisional error subsequent to the conception of an individual with an XO chromosomal sex, giving rise to a cell line with a normal female chromosome sex of XX.

Before going on to discuss the limited knowledge available on the frequency of sex chromosome abnormalities in the population, it is necessary to make a few remarks about the manner in which a diagnosis of a chromosome abnormality is established. The salient feature in this problem is that the X chromosome is similar to the larger autosomes of the group 6, 7 and 8 (Denver classification). Using the present technics, there is no specific feature of the X chromosome which will clearly distinguish it from these autosomes. In diagnosing an abnormality involving this chromosome therefore, it is necessary to take into account all the available data, including the chromosome count, the chromosome analysis, the nuclear sex and the clinical findings. It seems apparent that abnormalities of the sex chromosomes cause less disturbance to development than abnormalities of the autosomes, a published exception to this being the autosomal abnormality which has been described in the apparently normal parent of a mongol. Among the sex chromosome aberrations, Turner's syndrome so far is the clinical state showing the most widespread changes, and in the others most of the physical changes have been limited, as far as can be seen to the genital tract and the breasts. Therefore, in summary, if an individual is found to have an abnormal chromosome number; if analysis reveals that the additional or absent chromosome (or chromosomes) corresponds in size to the group of chromosomes which includes the X; and, if the nuclear sex is either at variance with the phenotypic sex or shows some abnormality such as the presence of double chromatin bodies, then it is reasonable to believe that a sex chromosome is involved and not an autosome. This belief is substantiated further if the main and perhaps the only physical abnormality is related to sexual development. Of course, exactly the same principle will hold if the chromosome number is normal, but there is evidence for a morphologic change such as a partial deletion. The situation is more complex where it is suspected that the patient is a mosaic. Here it becomes necessary first to demonstrate that the unusual chromosome count distribution is unlikely to be due simply to the play of chance and second, that within each suspected modal number there is a significant constancy of karyotype.

During the past 18 months, the accent in human cytogenetics has been on the recognition of individual types of chromosome abnormality. However, now that a high degree of systematization has been established in the search for and the recognition of these abnormalities, investigators are becoming increasingly concerned with discovering their frequency in the human population, and the extent to which they contribute to the incidence of various diseases. Before the advent of the technics in chromosome analysis, 4 surveys were undertaken using the technic of nuclear sexing: (1) This was done on liveborn male children and suggested that in approximately 1 child in 400 the nuclear sex was at variance with sexual phenotype. (2) This was done on the male inmates of a mental defective institution and suggested that in just over 1 per cent the nuclear sex was of the female type. (3) This survey was carried out on children attending special schools for the mentally handicapped and again indicated a frequency among the males of a disparate nuclear sex of about 1 per cent. Many workers now are conducting similar surveys among mental defectives, and it well may be that the frequency of sex chromosome abnormalities among male defectives lies between 1 and 3 per cent. (4) This survey, on males with azoospermia, suggested that about 10 per cent of these were chromatin-positive. Much less information is available on the frequency of nuclear sex aberrations among females.

REFERENCES

1. Bahner, F., Schwarz, G., Harnden, D. G., Jacobs, P. A., Heinz, H. A., and Walter, K.: A fertile female with an XO sex Chromosome constitution, Lancet 2:101, 1960.
2. Barr, M. L., and Bertram, E. G.: Nature, London 163:676, 1949.
3. Jacobs, P. A., and Strong, J. A.: A case of human inter-sexuality having a possible XXY sex-determining mechanism, Nature, London 183:802, 1959.
4. Stewart, J. S. S., and Sanderson, A. R.: Fertility and oligophrenia in apparent tuinto -X female, Lancet 2:21, 1960.

SESSION II

Discussion

Moderator
PROFESSOR E. HADORN
Zoologisch-vergleichend-Anatomisches Institut, Universitat Zurich, Zurich, Switzerland

Panel Members

DR. SALOME G. WAELSCH
*Professor of Genetics (in Anatomy), Albert Einstein College of Medicine,
Eastchester Road and Morris Park Avenue, New York 61, New York, U.S.A.*

DR. JAMES V. NEEL
*Department of Human Genetics, University of Michigan School of Medicine,
Ann Arbor, Michigan, U.S.A.*

PROFESSOR HANS GRÜNEBERG
Biometry Department, University College, Gower Street, London, England

PROFESSOR HANS NACHTSHEIM
Freie Universitat, Ehrenbergstrasse 26/28, Berlin-Dahlem, Germany

DR. JAN BÖÖK
Director, Institute for Medical Genetics, University of Uppsala, Uppsala, Sweden

DR. PAUL E. POLANI
*Director, Medical Research Unit, National Spastics Society, Department of Child Health,
Guy's Hospital, London, S.E. 1, England*

PROFESSOR RAYMOND TURPIN
*Clinical Professor of Infant Pediatrics, Director, Institüt de Progenese,
Faculté de Médecine, Paris, France*

DR. W. M. COURT BROWN
*Group for Research on the General Effects of Radiation, Department of Radiotherapy,
Western General Hospital, Edinburgh 4, Scotland*

DR. ETIENNE WOLFF
*Laboratories d'Embryologie Experimentale, College de France,
Nogent-sur-Marne, Seine, France*

MODERATOR HADORN: First, we shall discuss the papers of Dr. Nachtsheim and Dr. Neel; and, second, the chromosomal problems.

DR. WAELSCH: The papers of both Dr. Neel and Professor Nachtscheim stressed the problem that has been foremost in the minds of all, namely, the role of genes and environment in the etiology of congenital malformations. Dr. Neel's paper made a most significant contribution to this problem by introducing a new concept. The apparent dichotomy between genes and environment in the etiology of malformations is, of course, unreal. But the interrelationship between genes and environment is another question. Dr. Neel's scheme is extremely promising. It involves the idea of a delicate balance between individual genes, the rest of the genome, that is, the so-called residual genotype, and the environment. This balance controls the normal pattern of development. Any disturbance results in abnormal development, no matter whether it originates in a particular gene locus or in the residual genotype or in the environment. Could Dr. Neel define more specifically how he envisages the balanced polymorphic system to act in the control of congenital abnormalities? In the analogy which he draws to the problem of sickle cell anemia and malaria, I am not quite clear which genotype would be subject to malformations. The answer to this question would also affect the expectancy in respect to hybridized populations, for depending on which genotypes are assumed to be subject to malformations in this balanced polymorphic system, the expected number of abnormalities would either decrease or increase.

Professor Nachtsheim's paper dealt with the interaction of genes and environment in development. When one studies the development of a genetically controlled abnormality, the object is to identify the primary site of action of the particular abnormal gene. This is done by study of the individual stages and steps by which the abnormal-

ity arises in the embryo. That is, one studies a chain of events A, B and C, which show a temporal sequence. It is tempting to interpret this sequence in causal terms. But, it is not justified to assume that abnormality B follows abnormality A causally just because it appears later. Perhaps the system which gives rise to B is sensitive to whatever produces the abnormal effect at a slightly later stage and a common cause may produce both abnormalities.

Equally dangerous is the conclusion from this type of study that the first observed abnormality represents the site of gene action. A wide gap of knowledge still prevails between the primary action of the gene which underlies an abnormality and the first observable effect in the embryo.

DR. NEEL: The essence of the concept of a polymorphic system is that there is an advantage to heterozygosity and that the greater the degree of genetic heterozygosity the greater the advantage. This contrasts with what we might call the classic model, for the advantage rests with the organism which has become homozygous for a certain allele which in itself confers an advantage. To reduce this to its simplest terms, let us consider a 2-locus system in which at each locus we have 2 alternative forms of the gene, let us say, A, a, B, b. In a polymorphic system, the normal would be the most heterozygous organism with respect to these 2 loci, namely AaBb. The individual predisposed to a malformation, as it were, would be the homozygote, no matter whether this was aabb or AABB. The distinction between this and the classic model which has dominated much of our thinking until now is fairly clear.

PROFESSOR GRÜNEBERG: In the introduction to his paper, Dr. Neel suggested that no more than 20 per cent of all congenital malformations can be attributed to simple dominant or recessive genes, no more than 10 per cent may be due to chromosomal aberrations, and no more than 10 per cent to various infections, leaving some 60 per cent to be accounted for in other ways. When we analyze the causation of a single type of congenital abnormality in animals— this was first done by Sewell Wright in the guinea pig and has since been done extensively in the mouse by various investigators —an equally large or larger part of the total variance cannot be attributed either to genetic or to specifiable environmental causes. Evidently, we are approaching the dimension in development where typical causal explanations cannot account for more than a fraction of the total effect—where indeterminate or purely accidental events become increasingly important. Many congenital anomalies come into being when the developing system is quite small, in fact, so small that fluctuations of molecular dimensions can make themselves felt. But, unlike similar events in physics, some of these accidental deviations seem to become perpetuated and to grow to macroscopic dimensions.

The evidence for the accidental nature of much of the phenotypic variance in animals comes from the analysis of inbred strains. In these, the genetic variance has been largely eliminated by the process of inbreeding, and the total picture which emerges cannot be directly compared with the situation prevailing in mixed human populations. Nevertheless, the fact that harelip and cleft palate occur in some 10 per cent of mice of the A strain, which do not have a balanced polymorphic system, suggests that this also may be true for many human malformations which cannot be attributed either to simple genetic or specifiable environmental conditions. However, I agree with Dr. Neel that balanced polymorphic systems probably are responsible for a much greater proportion of malformations than hitherto has been realized.

Professor Nachtsheim mentioned the widespread occurrence of the Pelger anomaly, both in humans and in rabbits. So far as is known, in the heterozygote the Pelger anomaly is not pathologic. But, perhaps, he can give us some information as to the effect, if any, on viability which occurs in the homozygous Pelger.

PROFESSOR NACHTSHEIM: Professor Grüneberg asked me about the viability of homozygous Pelgers. Some time ago, when I tried experimentally to produce the first homozygous Pelgers in rabbits, I found the ratio between normal and heterozygous Pelgers to be 1:2. From this I inferred that homozygous Pelgers obviously are not viable and die during early gestation. However, it has been found, that only a little more than 80 per cent of the homozygotes die so early. The rest survive until birth, but, then, as a rule, die during the first days of postpartum life.

We can accept the expression used by Professor Hadorn who describes such exceptional cases as "bolters." However, only some female rabbits have bolter offspring. Others never give birth to a homozygous Pelger. We have found recently that among the offspring of female rabbits that give birth to viable homozygotes, the percentage of homozygotes approximately corresponds to what is to be expected theoretically. All of the offspring of these rabbits survive, not only one occasional homozygote. Also, we have attempted to breed the homozygotes and, by so doing, to increase the percentage of liveborn homozygotes. In this, however, we have not yet succeeded. Obviously, we are concerned here with a special factor, probably an exogenous factor.

When I made these observations, I suggested that we may expect human homozygotes, when found, to exhibit the special nuclear design of the neutrophils. This prediction has since been corroborated. What has not been corroborated is my second prediction that human homozygotes most probably would be lethal.

MODERATOR HADORN: We should now like to have the comments of two specialists in the study of chromosomes.

DR. BÖÖK: Our experience with human karyotype studies is based on material from over 400 primary cell cultures and their derivatives from biopsies of approximately 120 individuals. We also have studied over 100 primary cultures with material from human fetuses. Dr. Turpin mentioned briefly some problems of the present technic of karyotyping. Time will not allow a full consideration of methodologic problems, but I should like to bring out a few points. With cell culture technic it is not possible to prove directly that the karyotype determined for the cells in vitro is exactly the same as for those in the donor body. The findings have to be corroborated by circumstantial evidence. For conclusions concerning an abnormal karyotype we require, in our laboratory, consistency with regard to several sets of primary cultures derived from at least 2 different biopsies. If possible, this evidence should be supplemented by genetic data.

In view of the present great enthusiasm for clinical cytogenetics perhaps also it should be pointed out that human karyotyping is not yet a routine screening procedure that can be applied easily with statistical numbers. The total number of individuals who have been karyotyped is still very limited. The largest unselected series I know of is that of Dr. Makino in Japan which comprises about 40 individuals. Other series like our own are biased in too many ways to give any hints about possible variations in nonclinical material. It is doubtful whether the total number of individuals who so far have been karyotyped approaches 1,000. This should be kept in mind when we talk about the normal human karyotype as well as chromosomal variations which are associated with pathologic conditions.

Finally, to my knowledge, more than 25 different chromosomal aberrations associated with pathologic conditions in man have been discovered during the last 2 years. One half of them concern the sex chromosomes; about one half the autosomes. Some of them have not yet been officially reported or need confirmation. This may justify a prediction that clinical cytogenetics is not only a new and important branch of human pathology but is bound to have important implications for the clinician.

At the present time, diagnostic karyotyping is indicated only for a particular group of patients. These are the patients for whom the diagnosis of mongolism needs confirmation and all of the patients with abnormal sexual development. The value of this work is shown, for instance, by our diagnostic series of 29 cases of suspected mongolism: 20 were trisomic for chromosome number 21, as explained by Dr. Turpin; 3 had other variations; and 6 had apparently normal karyotypes and the diagnosis could be dismissed. Finally, the fact that chromosomal variations associated with congenital malformations appear to occur in appreciable quantities and that they may even be transmitted to further generations merits some reconsideration from the point of view of radiation effects on human populations.

DR. POLANI: Dr. Turpin has commented on the association of Klinefelter's syndrome and mongolism in the same individual and the association of Klinefelter's syndrome and Turner's syndrome in one sibship. In this sibship, unfortunately, the male was chromatin-negative and the female chromatin-positive. Concerning chromatin-positive Turner's syndrome, in the 5 cases studied by us and about whose diagnosis we were in no doubt clinically, we have never seen a normal female complement of sex chromosomes. Instead, we found evidence of XO/XX mosaicism, as Dr. Court Brown has stated. I think this may well be a matter of semantics, and I will not belabor the point.

Concerning the inadequacy of present-day technics in the detection of some structural anomalies of chromosomes, to which Dr. Turpin referred, considerable hope should come from studies by the testicular squash technic, in males with active spermatogenesis at any rate. This technic should allow us to pick up not only translocations but also deletions and inversions, at least those of a certain size.

I would like to underline Dr. Court Brown's remarks about the presence of conspicuous somatic anomalies in only a proportion of chromatin-negative XO females. About one third of them had only smallness of stature and some very inconspicuous anomalies. To clarify the question raised by Dr. Court Brown, I would like to say that the clinical diagnosis in our 5 chromatin-positive patients (XO/XX mosaics) was ovarian dysgenesis. Except for small stature and absent secondary sex characters they were unremarkable and of normal intelligence.

It has been pointed out that studies of color blindness can help in assessing the origin, maternal or paternal, of anomalous numbers of sex chromosomes. In chromatin-negative ovarian dysgenesis there is reasonable evidence, from such studies, that a presumably single X can be from either parent. As Dr. Court Brown has said, "An ovular origin of chromosome mosaicism in chromatin positive ovarian dysgenesis is highly improbable." Much more likely is a postsyngamic mitotic origin through nondisjunction with or without loss of 1 X chromosome, depending on the type of mosaic produced.

Dr. Court Brown and Professor Böök have stressed the fact that there are *no* definite and *no* positive identifying features which distinguish the X chromosome from the larger autosomes of group 6 to 12. Dr. Court Brown also has emphasized the necessity of taking account of all available data, such as chromosome count and morphology, clinical features and nuclear sex. For the presumably XO group of females with 45 chromosomes, statistical support for the interpretation of the missing chromosome as one of the sex pair again comes from color-blindness studies. Thus, in chromatin-negative females with ovarian dysgenesis or with Turner's syndrome, the frequency of red-green color blindness suggests the presence of only 1 X chromosome, as in normal males. The corroborative finding of a chromosome number of 45, in women of his group where the missing chromosome is one of the larger members of the group which includes the X chromosome, strongly suggest that this indeed is the missing chromosome. I think the same could be said for individual cases when the proper genetic situation applies.

MODERATOR HADORN: There are two questions for Professor Turpin. The first, from Dr. Stott (United Kingdom) is: Has the trisomic chromosome in mongolism also been found in the cells of the skin and the blood?

PROFESSOR TURPIN: All our observations on mongolism have been made on the basis of fascia lata cultures. These were obtained under general anesthesia. Other authors have diagnosed mongolian idiocy on the basis of skin and/or bone marrow findings. I have no knowledge of this diagnosis being made on the basis of the blood picture.

MODERATOR HADORN: There is a second question. Dr. Brent, U.S.A., asks: How can we be certain that the extra chromosome in mongolism is the cause of mongolism rather than merely another associated anomaly?

PROFESSOR TURPIN: I think Dr. Brent's question would not have been put had his attention not been drawn to a degree of clinical polymorphism in mongolism. It is an indisputable fact that mongoloids show considerable polymorphism, both somatically and psychologically. The average IQ of mongoloid children is approximately 45, or with variations of about 50 per cent either way. Therefore, in a population of mongoloids, some show very marked and others show less marked oligophrenia. This can be understood to mean that the polymorphism of mongolism expresses a polymorphism of the genome. As to the importance and the consequences of mongoloid trisomia, it entails an overdosage of genes, but this overdosage must be regarded in association with the individual genome. All mongoloids have an essentially different genome in addition to the trisomia, and each reacts to the trisomia in his own way. Consequently, this association between mongoloid trisomia and the particular individual genome may involve considerable variations, both psychological and somatic. That, I think, is why it is not surprising that associated malformations introduce a marked degree of polymorphism in mongolism.

MODERATOR HADORN: Dr. Hockstrom of Sweden asks: Can chromosome aberration be due to chemical agents, for example to contraceptives acting upon the mature sperm cells or the unfertilized ovum? I think the answer to this question is that we don't know. Of course, any substance which may act on the spindle mechanism could lead to nondisjunction. But we are only at the beginning of the investigation of the effect of chemicals on chromosomal aberrations.

Dr. Willemse, Holland, asks: As there is a true and a false Klinefelter syndrome with no clinical distinction, except positive and negative sex chromatin, is it possible that the Klinefelter with 43 autosomes and an XXY chromosome sex is in fact one with 44 autosomes and an XY, also a false Klinefelter? Or, is the chromosomal technic so perfect that such a mistake cannot occur?

DR. COURT BROWN: It is difficult to answer this question, because I know of no Klinefelter syndrome patient who is chromatin-positive with a chromosome count of 43 autosomes and XXY. The questioner may be confused by the facility with which the diagnosis of a chromosomal abnormality which involves the X chromosome can be made and he asks: Is the chromosomal technic so perfect that such a mistake cannot occur? I think the answer is no, but I believe that if we take all of the available data into consideration the chances of such a mistake are reduced very considerably.

MODERATOR HADORN: Dr. Horn (United Kingdom) asks: There is considerable variation in background radiation in different parts of this country and of the world. Is this variation reflected by fluctuation in the incidence of congenital defects of genetic origin?

DR. NEEL: I know of two studies which bear on this question. The first was published in the *American Journal of Public Health* a few months ago. The investigators demonstrated a higher frequency of congenital defect in the northern part of New York State than in the southern part. The second report is a technical bulletin of the Atomic Energy Commission in which an attempt has been made to compare the malformation frequency in the high and the low radiation background areas of the United States. The second report appears to confirm the New York State report. However, the choice of a statistic in the second report is rather unfortunate. The statistic used is "Proportion of deaths due to congenital defect per thousand deaths." This is a statistic which is very susceptible to local differences in the age composition of the population, and I have satisfied myself that such differences do exist. The first report does not seem to be open to this criticism. However, in addition to differences in radiation, there are many differences between the areas contrasted. The areas of relatively high radiation are often mountainous or plateau areas, very poor from the agricultural standpoint and primarily devoted to the raising of sheep and other animals or to mining. Already, we have seen evidence that the frequency of congenital malformations is sensitive to certain environmental factors, and before concluding that radiation and the frequency of congenital defect are associated, one would have to assess the possible role of these other factors.

MODERATOR HADORN: Dr. Fraser Roberts, United Kingdom, asks: Would the panel agree that apart from other considerations the discovery of XXXY individuals makes the use of the term "super female" inappropriate for XXX? Why not simply triple X and triple XY?

DR. COURT BROWN: When our group in Edinburgh first found an individual with 3 X chromosomes we felt it to be quite reasonable to christen this woman the "super female," even though phenotypically she lacked some of the qualities one might expect. From experience with Drosophila, I believe that genetically this was the correct thing to do. The situation now has become confused, with the finding of the triple XY male, and we may have to start talking about triple X females and triple XY males.

MODERATOR HADORN: I may mention in this connection that my collaborator Anders has found a boy having up to 3 or 4 sex chromatin bodies in the nuclei, 4 chromosomes of the type X and, in some cells, 2 small chromosomes corresponding to the Y's.

PROFESSOR NACHTSHEIM: I want to emphasize that the seeming differences between Dr. Waelsch and myself are due to a misunderstanding, viz., an incorrect translation of the German title chosen by me in the final program. I gave the title of my report as: "Zusammenspiel und Gegenspiel von Genen und exogenen Factoren bei der Entstehung angeborener Anomalien." This was translated as: "The interaction between genes and environment in development." It was not my intention to speak about embryology, but I wished to speak about the development of characteristics during the formative processes, a modification which was not expressed in the translation. For the rest, I agree completely with Dr. Waelsch.

DR. POLANI: I am very glad that Dr. Court Brown has agreed to the use of terms such as "triple X female." Otherwise, we might have to use the phrase "diminutive super female" to describe a woman known to me who has secondary amenorrhea, double chromatin masses in the oral mucosa, and a karyotype of 44 autosomes, 2 X chromosomes and what may be a small fragment of a third X chromosome.

DR. BÖÖK: I would like to comment on the association between mongolism and the extra chromosome. We will have to do some rethinking about morphology and nomenclature. There are several clinical conditions which look like mongolism, and although the pediatrician can recognize trisomic patients as typical mongols, he may be unable to distinguish them from some cases where the chromosomal condition is different, for example, a combination of trisomial and monosomial or translocation. However, other patients with these translocations would not be regarded clinically as typical mongols. Therefore, the classification must be revised in the light of knowledge of the chromosomal conditions, and the possibility that mongols with different karyotypes differ clinically and biochemically must be explored.

DR. WAELSCH: This discussion recalls the beautiful work of Boveri who, at the end of the last century, used abnormalities of chromosomal numbers to prove the effect of chromosomes on development and to show the qualitative differences between chromosomes. He was well aware of the fact that a normal chromosome complement is necessary for normal development and differentiation.

DR. WOLFF: I should like to focus attention on a phenogenetic problem. In connection with the remarks made by Dr. Waelsch on Dr. Nachtsheim's report, I would point out that, in a system which leads to a particular malformation, the genetic factor may act on several simultaneous factors of the same reaction. My co-worker Segnel, for example, has demonstrated the mechanism underlying the lack of pigmentation in a Leghorn chicken showing partial albinism. In the Leghorn breed, a few chromatoblasts are known to be pigmented at the start of development; they rapidly degenerate but, by in-vitro cultivation of the Leghorn skin, it is possible to produce intensive pigmentation by influencing the milieu, particularly when the skin is cultivated on synthetic media. This pigmental system is dependent on three conditions: a precursor (dihydroxyphenylalanine or tyrosine), the enzyme (tyrosinase) and an oxidizing factor. Segnel demonstrated that it is the precursor which is lacking in this system in normal Leghorns. The demonstration was possible only by cultures in synthetic media in the presence or the absence of tyrosine. Other amino-acids may replace tyrosine in its absence. Addition of tyrosinase causes no appearance of pigment in the Leghorn skin unless the medium contains tyrosine. Cultivation in the presence of oxygen or an oxidizing agent, such as methylene blue, may intensify but is not sufficient to provoke pigmentation of Leghorn feathers.

MODERATOR HADORN: This morning's discussion has shown the multiplicity of factors which the student of congenital malformations has to consider. We heard first of the action of single genes. Then, we discussed the interaction between genes and environment. Next, we considered what is necessary for normal development, and the extent to which it depends on genic balance which becomes dangerously disturbed in cases of chromosomal aberrations. We heard also that the genic make-up of a population can influence the rate and alter the character of the malformations. Finally, we saw some fatal malformations in a new light as the price paid by a population in order to gain adaptive qualities within a system of balanced polymorphism. We can also consider malformations due to mutations as part of the price paid to secure the plasticity of the hereditary substance.

SESSION III

Extrinsic Factors (Environment)

Moderator

SIR DUGALD BAIRD, M.D., F.R.C.O.G.

*Professor of Midwifery and Gynaecology, University of Aberdeen,
Aberdeen, Scotland, United Kingdom*

Speakers

ENVIRONMENTAL TERATOGENIC FACTORS

JOSEF WARKANY, M.D.

*Professor of Research Pediatrics, University of Cincinnati College of Medicine,
Children's Hospital Research Foundation, Cincinnati, Ohio, U.S.A.*

VIRUS INFECTIONS AND CONGENITAL MALFORMATIONS

A. J. RHODES, M.D., F.R.C.P. (EDIN.), F.R.S.C.

*Director and Head, Department of Microbiology, School of Hygiene,
University of Toronto, 150 College Street, Toronto, Canada*

THE INTERPLAY OF INTRINSIC AND EXTRINSIC FACTORS
IN THE ORIGIN OF CONGENITAL MALFORMATIONS

WALTER LANDAUER, Dr. phil. nat.

*Department of Animal Genetics, Storrs Agricultural Experiment Station,
University of Connecticut, Storrs, Connecticut, U.S.A.*

Environmental Teratogenic Factors

JOSEPH WARKANY, M.D.

In common usage, environmental teratogenic factors signify agents, events or circumstances which are capable of deforming an embryo or a fetus which at conception had good potentialities of growth and differentiation. "Exogenous" forces were early considered as possible sources of intrauterine mutilation, while "endogenous" tendencies to abnormal development were identified more recently. Now one speaks usually of nongenetic teratogenic factors as opposed to genetic factors. Thus, at the present time, the terms "environmental," "exogenous," "external" and "nongenetic" often are used synonymously and interchangeably. It will be pointed out later that this laxity of usage may be confusing and misleading at times but, at the outset, I shall conform to the common terminology.

From earliest times men and women have blamed external events for the birth of monsters or deformed children. Whether it was witchcraft, the ire of the deity, or maternal impressions that were blamed for the abnormalities of a child, it was always an external cause acting during or after conception that was held responsible for the disastrous outcome of a pregnancy. Even when rational explanations were introduced, the source of maldevelopment usually was sought outside of the embryo. However, it should be emphasized that from the times of Morgagni[14] to modern days no sharp distinction was usually made between teratogenic diseases of the fetus, of the fetal membranes, or of the mother; but during the 19th century, the pathology of the amnion assumed a dominant role in explanations of embryonic maldevelopment. It was held to be "the chief cause, direct or indirect, of all those malformations or monstrosities that are characterized by defective development."[2] Disease, pressure and arrested development of the amnion were considered as the main factors in teratogenesis. There exist indeed monstrous specimens which show amniotic sheets or bands attached to malformed parts of the head, the face, the abdomen or the extremities. Such observations led Etienne Geoffroy-Saint-Hilaire[6] early in the 19th century to the conclusion that amniotic bands were the leading cause of all monstrosities. The role of the amnion as a teratogenic factor was supported by experimental work in chicks, when the eminent teratologist Dareste[4] found that abnormal environmental conditions of the egg resulted in abnormal development of the amnion, defective secretion of amniotic fluid, and in abnormal amniotic pressure, while the malformations produced were rather unspecific. However, now it appears that in these experiments the changes of the amnion and of the embryo were parallel phenomena rather than cause-and-effect. As early as 1829, Rudolph[17] recognized that amniotic adhesions were not necessarily the cause, but rather the effects of the fetal malformations. This anticipated the findings of Streeter[18] who many years later emphasized that amniotic strands found with abnormal embryos do not produce the abnormalities but that they are due to the same abnormal process which affects both the amnion and the closely related germ disk.

Maternal diseases or injuries have been blamed for deformities of the child since early times. Ancient medicine, ignorant of

99

the pathogenic factors known to modern science, advanced mechanical theories along these lines. Hippocrates[10] spoke of crippling of the child by a fall or a contusion of the mother, thus blaming the external environment for the anomalies of the child. Also, he considered narrowness of the womb as an impediment to normal development of the infant. Therefore, one can trace the distinction between extramaternal and intramaternal teratogenic environments to about 400 B.C. With only slight modifications, accusing abnormal maternal posture, abdominal constriction, increased pressure upon the embryo by a twin or faulty moulding, the ideas of Hippocrates[10] were transmitted through the centuries to modern times.

In the 19th century, inflammation was recognized as a pathogenic process, and it was natural to consider inflammation of fetal parts or membranes a satisfactory environmental explanation for congenital malformations. Kreysig,[12] for instance, attributed many forms of congenital heart disease to fetal endocarditis.

With the discovery of bacteria and other micro-organisms as pathogenic factors, the causes of teratogenic inflammation seemed to be found. Since syphilis and other infectious diseases can bring about fetal death and abortion, it was thought that they also could cause malformations in less severely injured fetuses. Because of the prevalence of syphilis during the past centuries there were, of course, thousands of children who had congenital malformations and also syphilis or positive serologic tests. In addition, it was well established that syphilis could cause congenital deafness and mental retardation. Thus, syphilis was considered by many physicians as a frequent cause of malformations, including cleft lip and palate, anencephaly, spina bifida and many others. Febrile diseases of pregnant women occasionally preceded the birth of deformed children, and it was not surprising that they too were considered as teratogenic. But, these beliefs of some physicians usually were counterbalanced by the skepticism of others who regarded the association of such maternal diseases and fetal malformations as accidental. However, lacking good statistical methods and studies, the question still would be undecided if time had not resolved it. The answer was obtained when prevention and treatment reduced congenital syphilis to a medical rarity while congenital malformations continued to flourish. At about the same time, faith was lost in fetal endocarditis as a cause of congenital heart disease, a theory which had been accepted since the beginning of the 19th century. Thus, the belief in infection as a cause of congenital malformations was at an all-time low when in 1941 Gregg[8] discovered that German measles affecting the mother in the 1st trimester of pregnancy can cause congenital malformations in the child. The story has been told so many times that it is not necessary to repeat it here at length. Cataract, microphthalmus, congenital heart disease of many types, microcephaly, mental retardation, deafness and possibly other congenital defects can be induced by a maternal infection with rubella. The facts are well established and generally accepted; but the discovery has left us with more questions than answers. At first it was thought that all embryos whose mothers had had German measles during the 1st trimester of pregnancy were rendered abnormal. This belief was found to be incorrect and present estimates of teratologic effects vary between 12 and 40 per cent. Why does the virus deform some embryos severely while it spares others? How does the virus deflect the development of the affected tissues from their normal pathways? To my knowledge, the virus never has been observed in action. We know its devastating results as they appear in infants or fetuses, but in all patients or specimens described so far the acute stage of the disease was over when clinical or histologic studies were made. The effects on the embryo do not parallel the intensity of the maternal disease. In mild and even in subclinical cases of rubella the embryo may be affected as seriously as in florid cases. The questions concerned with prophylaxis are complex. By exposure of young girls to rubella and by administration of convalescent rubella gamma globulin, congenital defects may be preventable in some instances. However, there remain the agonizing situations where a mother develops rubella or a rash resembling it in early pregnancy, and a decision has to be made concerning the continuation or the interruption of the pregnancy. Our present inadequate knowledge of the problems surrounding rubella in pregnancy often constitutes a calamity rather than a blessing.

Are there other viral diseases with comparable teratologic effects? Many observers have reported congenital anomalies in children whose mothers had had measles, mumps, chickenpox, hepatitis or other viral diseases during pregnancy. One cannot draw any conclusions from such isolated observations, since they cannot be distinguished from coincidental associations. No typical syndromes have been established for other virus diseases. However, one could err in dogmatic negative statements also. As long as it was believed that all children whose mothers had rubella in early pregnancy were born with malformations, the many normal children born after maternal mumps or chickenpox seemed to rule out that these infections were teratogenic. Now, since we know that even rubella affects only some of the embryos exposed to it, we cannot rule out the possibility that in rare cases the association of other maternal viral diseases with malformations in the child may be more than a coincidence.

Many questions in these areas probably could be answered if congenital malformations could be produced experimentally in the young of mammals infected with viruses. Although malformations have been induced in chick embryos by viruses injected into the egg, comparable experiments in mammals have not been conclusive. Reports of con-genital malformations in fetal pigs treated with hog cholera virus[11] require repetition and extension.

The discovery of prenatal toxoplasmosis[22] as a cause of hydrocephalus, microcephalus, microphthalmus or chorioretinitis was of great theoretic interest. These malformations originate not in the embryonic period but during late fetal life when originally normal organs suffer secondary destruction by these protozoa. Toxoplasma apparently are more destructive to fetal than to adult tissues. Therefore, toxoplasmosis in the mother may take a mild or subclinical course, while the infection transmitted to the fetus results in severe structural changes. More recently cytomegalic inclusion disease has been shown to cause similar malformations such as hydrocephalus, microcephalus and chorioretinitis. This disease also can be transmitted through an apparently healthy mother.[16]

A remark about terminology may be in order here. It has been suggested that the anomalies produced by prenatal rubella are not "congenital malformations" but "embryopathies." Similarly, some have recommended that the defects produced by toxoplasmosis should not be considered as "congenital malformations" because they are due to secondary destruction of originally normal organs. There is little justification for such hair- or term-splitting. The term "congenital malformations" should be applied to gross, structural anomalies present at birth, irrespective of their etiology or morphogenesis. It would lead to needless confusion if we were to call a septal defect due to rubella an "embryopathy," and a septal defect of unknown origin a "congenital malformation." Similarly, a hydrocephalus present at birth should be considered a congenital malformation whether it is of genetic, toxoplasmic or unknown origin.

Before I turn to man-made teratogenic factors, something should be said about nutritional deficiencies. That a lack in the maternal diet of specific nutritional elements such as vitamins can induce severe congenital malformations has been shown in numerous animal experiments. Fortunately, the conditions under which such malformations are induced in animals are not imitated by human circumstances. However, there existed and still exists a congenital anomaly in man which is closely related to maternal nutritional factors, namely, endemic cretinism. Endemic cretinism occurs in areas in which goiter is endemic. These anomalies are on the wane, but they should not be forgotten as examples of physical and mental degeneration which can be inflicted upon man by his geographic environment. The only congenital malformation visible in an endemic cretin is an enlarged thyroid, but his serious handicaps result from deafness and mental retardation. A few generations ago, there were probably ten thousands of endemic cretins in Europe, and there were and still are many in other continents. Endemic goiter and cretinism usually are attributed to dietary iodine deficiency, but their etiology may be more complex. Whatever these etiologic factors may be, both conditions can be wiped out within 2 generations by removal of a family from the endemic area, by change of the diet, importation of food, or by administration of iodized salt.

The teratogenic effects of antimetabolites can be mentioned as examples of nutritional or of toxic factors. Such substances have been widely used in teratologic animal experiments, and they are effective also in man. Fortunately, only few human examples can be cited. Aminopterin (4-amino-pteroylglutamic acid) used as an abortive[19,20] or Myleran (busulfan[5]) used for therapeutic purposes have induced congenital malformations in human embryos. Harelip and cleft palate, hydrocephalus, encephalocele, anencephaly and other defects have been observed in affected embryos or infants. To these examples of toxic teratogenic factors, one could add a few cases of brain injury following intra-uterine carbon monoxide poisoning. Micro-cephalus, hydrocephalus and malacia of the basal ganglia have been observed in children of mothers poisoned by illuminating gas during pregnancy.[3,9,13,15]

During the decades following the discovery of x-rays, a number of human embryos were inadvertently or for abortive purposes exposed in utero to large (therapeutic) doses. Some of the children born after such procedures showed microcephaly, microphthalmus, spasticity or mental retardation and sometimes also malformations in the genital and the skeletal systems.[1,7,24] As soon as the danger of intra-uterine x-irradiation became known, the number of children made defective in this way decreased rapidly, and today malformations attributable to large doses of x-rays have become rare. Following the explosion of the atomic bomb in Nagasaki,[23] microcephaly was found in 4 children whose mothers were exposed to the resulting radiation during pregnancy.

Malformations attributable to maternal endocrine disturbances have been looked for, but the evidence for such causation is meager. Recently, it has been shown that some female fetuses whose mothers received synthetic progestins in the treatment of threatened abortion are born with masculinized genitalia.[21] It is not clear why this effect occurs in some of the children exposed to such treatment while most remain normal.

The few examples of proved environmental teratogenic factors which I cited account for only a negligible fraction of the congenital malformations seen in children's hospitals or outpatient clinics. It is a rare case in pediatric experience that can be clearly related to one of the environmental agents enumerated. Yet, the examples cited are of great theoretic importance because they demonstrate the possibility of deformation of a normal ovum or embryo in utero after conception. Knowledge of this possibility keeps the clinician and the laboratory on the alert, so that any leads which may appear on the horizon seem to be worth following and investigating. Also, it should serve as a constant warning that clinical entities which clearly are determined genetically in some cases are not *always* due to genetic factors. Clinical entities such as microcephalus, hydrocephalus, cataract, congenital heart disease and many others may be of mixed etiology, and it often takes time and special methods to differentiate between cases of genetic and environmental origin.

Beyond the few known facts, one can only speculate about undiscovered environmental teratogenic processes. That we have learned to induce congenital malformations in mammals by a host of environmental procedures does not prove anything about human congenital malformations. Yet, even in mammals the scales are easily tipped from the side of normal to the side of abnormal development so that one may be permitted to believe that many more environmental teratogenic mechanisms which are still undiscovered may be at work in man.

Another fact that points in the same direction is the occurrence of identical (monozygotic) twins who differ in regard to congenital malformations (discordance). That identical twins often are both affected by similar malformations is not surprising. They have the same genetic endowment and develop in the same uterus at the same time. But when 2 genetically identical organisms *differ* in regard to a congenital malformation, their difference must be due to nongenetic factors, to environmental circumstances which must be of a special kind. At first glance this does not seem to be possible, since identical twins develop in the same mother and the same uterus, often enclosed in one chorion and nourished by one placenta. The intra-uterine world of such twins may seem to be to us homogeneous, but actually they inhabit different amniotic cavities, and they are connected with the placenta by different umbilical cords inserted into different loci of the placenta. The twins' position and their movements differ. Thus, identical twins who seem to develop in

identical environments actually grow up each in his own microcosmos with its individual protective properties and its individual weaknesses. Many processes of growth and development can go wrong in one microcosmos without affecting the other, and this could lead to malformations in one twin and leave his partner normal. Although we have little knowledge of such internal environmental factors, we know that they exist because monozygotic discordant twins exist. Of course, internal environmental factors which decide between normality and abnormality need not be limited to twins but probably exert their influence also in single embryos; they may be teratogenic in few or in many cases; they may be teratogenic for some but not for other malformations.

If we think of internal environmental factors we must not confine our thoughts to such gross and late structures as the placenta or the umbilical cord. Throughout embryonic development the genetic and the nongenetic elements of the cells are interdependent, and disturbances in either department can lead to maldevelopment. So far, we recognize only those disturbances which either originate in the external environment or are reflected in it by external manifestations. But there are probably many disturbances of the internal environment which are not detectable by us because their only manifestations appear belatedly in the form of congenital defects. Some of these disturbances may be accessible to experimental investigation. I am thinking of the variable effects of certain teratogenic methods on the offspring of inbred strains of mice, a subject which probably will be discussed tomorrow. Other micro-environmental factors may be detectable by methods of modern microscopy, electron microscopy or biochemical cytology. In every cell, the genetic material is surrounded by substances and structures which may be called the intimate environment. The intimate environment of many cells has been investigated intensively in recent years, but the findings of these investigations have not yet been applied to teratology. We must think only of the phenomena in nongenetic structures which can be observed during fertilization and the first cell divisions to perceive some of the possible disturbances which may lead to faulty development. Chromosomal aberrations or somatic mutations could be due to such micro-environmental changes.

At this point the inadequacy of the antithesis of exogenous versus endogenous teratogenic factors should be emphasized. Forces acting within the internal or the intimate environment can hardly be called "exogenous," a word used as a rule for the outside of an organism.

One cannot leave the subject of environmental teratogenic factors without mentioning that some genetic mutations which lead to congenital malformations probably are caused by environmental forces such as ionizing and nonionizing radiations or chemical and thermal factors. Seen from this point of view, environmental forces become paramount in teratogenesis, while genetic mechanisms are reduced to the role of transmitters of such external forces. That this point of view is not purely theoretic and speculative is demonstrated by the present-day concern over man-made radiation effects, which implies that scientists have arrived at a point where environmental forces acting through genetic mechanisms are considered as actual teratogenic factors which are accessible to regulation by man.

In conclusion, it can be stated that although our knowledge of environmental teratogenic factors is very limited, a host of such factors may exist and be responsible for many congenital malformations. Our ignorance of such factors need not be a measure of their insignificance. There is room and need for ecologic investigations in teratology which must include changes of the external, the internal and the intimate environment.

REFERENCES

1. Aschenheim, E.: Schädigung einer menschlichen Frucht durch Röntgenstrahlen, Arch. f. Kinderh. **68**:131, 1920.
2. Ballantyne, J. W.: Manual of Antenatal Pathology and Hygiene, The Embryo, Edinburgh, W. Green & Sons, 1904.
3. Brander, T.: Microcephalus und Tetraplegie bei einem Kinde Nach Kohlenmonoxydvergiftung der Mutter während der Schwangerschaft, Acta paediat. **28**(suppl. 1):123, 1940.
4. Dareste, C.: Recherches sur la Production Artificielle des Monstruosités ou Essais de Tetratogénie Expérimentale, ed. 2, Paris, C. Reinwald et Cie, 1891.
5. Diamond, I., Anderson, M. M., and McCreadie, S. R.: Transplacental transmission of busulfan (Myleran®) in a mother with leukemia; production of fetal malformation and cytomegaly, Pediatrics **25**:85, 1960.
6. Geoffroy-Saint-Hilaire, E.: Philosophie Anatomique, Des monstruosités humaines, vol. 3, Paris, 1822.
7. Goldstein, L., and Murphy, D. P.: Etiology of ill-health in children born after maternal pelvic irradiation; defective children born after post-conception pelvic irradiation, Am. J. Roentgenol. **22**:322, 1929.
8. Gregg, N. M.: Congenital cataract following German measles in mother, Tr. Ophth. Soc. Australia **3**:35, 1942.
9. Hallervorden, J.: Ueber eine Kohlenoxydvergiftung im Fetalleben mit Entwicklungsstörungen der Hirnrinde, Allg. Z. Psychiat. **124**:289, 1949.
10. Hippocrates: De Genitura, cited by Ballantyne.[2] This work is attributed by some historians not to Hippocrates but to his school (Major, R. H.: A History of Medicine, Springfield, Ill., Thomas, 1954).
11. Kitchell, R. L., Sautter, J. H., and Young, G. A.: The experimental production of malformations and other abnormalities in fetal pigs by means of attenuated hog cholera virus (American Association of Anatomist, abstracts), Anat. Rec. **115**:334, 1953.
12. Kreysig, F. L.: Krankheiten des Herzens systematisch bearbeitet, Berlin 1814/17.
13. Maresch, R.: Ueber einen Fall von Kohlenoxydgasschädigung des Kindes in der Gebärmutter, Wien. med. Wchnschr. **79**:454, 1929.
14. Morgagni, J. B.: De sedibus et causis morborum per anatomen indagatis libri quinque, 1761.

15. Neuburger, F.: Fall einer intrauterinen Hirnschädigung nach einer Leuchtgasvergiftung der Mutter, Beitr. gerichtl. Med. 13:85, 1935.

16. Potter, E. L.: Placental transmission of viruses, with special reference to the intrauterine origin of cytomegalic inclusion body disease, Am. J. Obst. & Gynec. 74: 505, 1957.

17. Rudolph, C. E.: Monstrorum trium praeter naturam cum secundinis coalitorum disquisitio, Berolini, typ. A. Petschii, 1829.

18. Streeter, G. L.: Focal deficiencies in fetal tissues and their relation to intrauterine amputation, Carnegie Inst. Washington (Pub. 414), Contrib. Embryol. 22:1, 1930.

19. Thiersch, J. B.: The control of reproduction in rats with aid of antimetabolites and early experiences with antimetabolites as abortifacient agents in man, Acta endocrinol. 23(suppl. 28):37, 1956.

20. Warkany, J., Beaudry, P. H., and Hornstein, S.: Attempted abortion with aminopterin (4-amino-pteroylglutamic acid); malformations of the child, A.M.A. Am. J. Dis. Child. 97:274, 1959.

21. Wilkins, L., Jones, H. W., Jr., Holman, G. H., and Stempfel, R. S., Jr.: Masculinization of the female fetus associated with administration of oral and intramuscular progestins during gestation: non-adrenal female pseudohermaphrodism, J. Clin. Endocrinol. 18:559, 1958.

22. Wolf, A., Cowen, D., and Paige, B. H.: Toxoplasmic encephalomyelitis; new case of granulomatous encephalomyelitis due to a protozoon, Am. J. Path. 15:657, 1939.

23. Yamazaki, J. N., Wright, S. W., and Wright, P. M.: Outcome of pregnancy in women exposed to the atomic bomb in Nagasaki, A.M.A. Am. J. Dis. Child. 87:448, 1954.

24. Zappert, J.: Hat eine Strahlenbehandlung der graviden Mutter einen schädlichen Einfluss auf das Kind, Wien. klin. Wchnschr. 38:669, 1925.

Virus Infections and Congenital Malformations

A. J. RHODES, M.D., F.R.C.P. (EDIN.), F.R.S.C.

INTRODUCTION

Nearly 20 years have passed since the Australian ophthalmic surgeon, Gregg, drew attention to a hitherto unsuspected complication of a virus infection—the production of deformities in the offspring of women who suffered from rubella in the 1st trimester.[38] These defects were chiefly cataracts, deafness, patency of the ductus arteriosus and interventricular septum.

Gregg's observations have been amply confirmed. However, it has not proved possible to devise a model for laboratory study, because the virus is not pathogenic for small animals, chick embryos, or tissue cultures. To complicate investigation even more, there is no simple laboratory diagnostic test for the presence of rubella virus or its specific antibody.

I shall review, as a virologist, the relationship of rubella and certain other viruses to fetal malformations of men and other animals. The mode of action of rubella virus has not yet been explained satisfactorily and remains a challenge to those trained in the disciplines of virology, epidemiology and genetics.

THE ROLE OF RUBELLA IN THE PRODUCTION OF FETAL MALFORMATIONS

THE ORIGINAL OBSERVATIONS IN AUSTRALIA

In 1941, Gregg saw an unusual number of cases of congenital cataracts in newborn babies in Sydney;[38] many also had heart disease. The 78 cases then reported constituted a minor "epidemic." Gregg elicted a history of rubella in the 1st trimester in all except 10 of the mothers.

Soon these observations were extended, notably by Swan in South Australia, and by 1946 over 400 cases were collected.[39,108-114]

The Australian findings were soon confirmed in the United States, the United Kingdom, Scandinavia, Switzerland, France and Turkey.[3,7,8,13,26,30,35,40,54,55,74,75,89,109,117,121,123,124]

The rubella infection occurred in the first 4 months of pregnancy in 870 of 939 cases (92.7%) reviewed by Swan.[111]

There has been much speculation as to whether the association of rubella with malformations occurred before 1941. It seems that it did, for a number of reports refer to isolated instances of fetal malformations, e.g., in the later years of the 19th century,[71,72] and in the 1930's.[13,71]

SPECIAL FEATURES OF RUBELLA IN ADULTS

Young adults have been infected in considerable numbers in rubella epidemics in the last 20 years, and it has been said that 10 per cent of all reported cases are in women in the child-bearing age groups.[7]

Rubella in adults has certain special features: rheumatic-like involvement of joints and muscles; follicular tonsillitis with severe sore throat; soreness of gums; generalized and persistent lymphadenopathy; conjunctivitis; severe rash and peeling of the skin and severe constitutional disturbance.[8,38,48,66,75]

PROPERTIES OF RUBELLA VIRUS

Rubella can be transmitted to susceptible children and adults by the intramuscular or the subcutaneous inoculation of blood or by the administration of a spray into the nasopharynx.[5,49,66-68]

The experimental disease resembles the natural and is transmissible to contacts. The incubation is 11 to 20 days. Lymphadenopathy begins 7 days after inoculation. Some persons become infected without showing a rash. Resistance to reinfection develops in convalescence.

Rhesus monkeys were infected with blood and nasal washings by Habel.[41] After an incubation of about 8 days, the animals developed fever and a macular rash; an early leukopenia was followed by lymphocytosis.

Suckling mice do not appear to be susceptible, and tissue cultivation—that richly rewarding technic of modern virology—has proved to be negative.[94]

In my laboratory, we have failed to grow the virus in tissue cultures of human amnion. Throat washings, whole blood and stool from several patients have not induced any specific cytologic evidence of infection.

Despite the failure to propagate the virus, the general biologic characteristics of the disease strongly suggest a virus etiology. Infection has been secured by the inoculation of filtrates. Furthermore, the causal agent remains infectious on storage in the dry ice chest for at least 2 years, and infectivity is neutralized by specific antibody in convalescent serum.[67]

Further evidence for a rubella virus-neutralizing antibody is the demonstration that contacts can be protected from clinical infection by the administration of convalescent serum or gamma globulin.[6,65,67,85,119]

THE RUBELLA SYNDROME

General Features. The relative frequency of the various defects is shown in a summary prepared by Swan: eye defects were present in 435 babies; heart disease was found in 403, deafness in 400, microcephaly in 164; and mental retardation was present in 126 babies. Many showed 2 or more defects.[111]

Other defects include harelip, cleft palate, pyloric stenosis, spina bifida and mongolism.

The precise nature of the defects is determined by the stage in pregnancy at which the infection takes place.[8,54,84,108,109]

For example, cataracts are attributable to rubella in the 6th week of pregnancy; deafness results from infection in the 9th week; cardiac defects follow infection in the 5th to the 10th weeks; and dental deformities result from rubella between the 6th and the 9th weeks.

These periods are said to correspond to the stages of active differentiation and multiplication of the embryonic cells concerned. Nevertheless, the severity of the maternal infection does not seem to determine the extent of the malformations.

Almost all malformations have been in babies born to mothers who had not suffered from clinical rubella previously. However, there are a few cases where an apparently immune woman, exposed to rubella, failed to develop a rash yet gave birth to a baby with malformations.[12,75,112,113] Schick suggests that the immunity of the skin is due to cellular mechanisms, and that if humoral immunity is of low degree, virus will circulate in the blood and reach the fetus.[100]

The pathologic changes are in the eye, the ear, or the heart, but sclerosis of the renal glomeruli has been demonstrated, suggesting an action of the causal agent on blood vessels.[53,110,115]

There are a few cases on record where malformations have been caused by rubella occurring from 1 to 3 weeks before conception.[8,34,46,111,112]

Eye Defects. Cataracts are the most common eye defects:[24,38,39,84,108-111,115]

1. They are usually bilateral (75% bilateral; 25% unilateral).

2. They are evident at birth.

3. The opacities are central and involve all but the outermost layers of the lens.

4. Microphthalmos also may be present.

5. Heart defects frequently coexist, and the babies are usually underweight.

6. Histologically, the central nuclear portion of the lens has undergone massive necrosis; also, there is degeneration of fibers

in the cortical zone.[25,84,108-110,115] The pathologic process involves both primary and secondary lens fibers. This indicates that the effects of the pathologic process must continue after the 7th to the 8th week. Vascular thrombosis and infiltration of eosinophils has been attributed to sensitization to lens protein released in the embryonic period.[115]

Other eye defects include glaucoma, uveitis, dacryostenosis, retinal pigmentation and strabismus.

Deafness is attributed to defective development of the organ of Corti:[44,57,58,71,73,86,108-113]

1. Deafness seldom is complete.

2. Two thirds of cases have bilateral involvement, but one ear may be more affected than the other.

3. Heart defects occur in about one third of cases, but cataracts are rare.

4. Deafness may not be detected until about 4 years of age, when detailed hearing tests can be conducted.

Cardiac Defects. Cardiac defects were present in the original cases of Gregg and Swan and have been reported by many others.[4,7,32,33,61,84,97,108-114]

Patent ductus arteriosus is the commonest defect; patent interventricular septum and foramen ovale are quite frequent. Cataracts or deafness may be present as well.

The etiologic importance of rubella in the total picture of congenital heart disease is not great. Less than 1 per cent of all cases of congenital heart disease can be attributed to maternal rubella,[7,33,61] but in 100 cases of patent ductus arteriosus investigated at the Hospital for Sick Children, Toronto, Keith *et al.* found the incidence of maternal rubella to be 8 per cent.[61]

Other Defects. Dental defects include retarded eruption and hypoplasia of enamel and usually are associated with more serious malformations. Physical retardation is common, many babies being below normal weight. Microcephaly and mental deficiency also have been attributed to rubella.[62]

Abortions and Stillbirths. Rubella in the 1st trimester may lead to abortion or to stillbirth, although the precise risk is not known.[7,37,46,70,75,89,90,109,111,123]

Abortion may be more frequent than hitherto believed, for Siegel and Greenberg[107] in New York City reported no less than 26 fetal deaths in 51 cases of rubella (50%) occurring in the first 8 weeks of pregnancy; there were 11 deaths in 53 cases where the rubella occurred in the 3rd month (20%). There were few fetal deaths after the 1st trimester.

Aborted fetuses examined pathologically have shown cataracts and heart defects.

ESTIMATES OF RISK OF FETUS DEVELOPING MALFORMATIONS ATTRIBUTABLE TO MATERNAL RUBELLA

Introduction. There may be some merit in listing some of the difficulties peculiar to an estimation of the risk to the fetus from rubella.[7,16,35,36,74,75,81,120]

1. The disease usually is mild, and a physician may not be consulted. A history of "German measles" from a patient, without medical confirmation, is open to serious question.

2. The disease in adults may be severe, with unusual clinical features (see above) and may not be diagnosed even by a physician.

3. Some of the characteristic defects can be assessed only by a specialist physician and sometimes not until 2 to 4 years of age.

4. Rashes caused by several other viruses, notably ECHO and Coxsackie, may be attributed wrongly to rubella.[19,23,51,59,69,88,95,98]

5. The virus has not been isolated, and there is no laboratory diagnostic test.

6. In some countries, therapeutic abortions are performed quite commonly for rubella in early pregnancy.

7. Rubella is incompletely reported to official health agencies.

8. Children seriously incapacitated are cared for by many different agencies—institutes for the blind, schools for the deaf,

homes for the mentally defective and clinics for heart disease. No single agency sees the total picture.

Retrospective Studies. Gregg[38,39] originally discovered the teratogenic action of rubella virus by a retrospective study, and there have been many similar studies.[3,7,8,10, 13,40,56,67,89,108,109,123] These inquiries generally tend to exaggerate the risk to the fetus, because normal infants are excluded from consideration.

Prospective Studies. A more precise estimate of the probability that rubella will produce malformations can be obtained by a prospective study.[7,22,35,37,46,47,70,74,75,76,79,106]

The study of Hill, Doll and colleagues[46,47] is of particular interest and was made from health insurance records of women who suffered from rubella (medically certified) and later claimed maternity benefit. The data were combined with those from 3 other prospective studies.[15,16,92] These 4 studies satisfied the following criteria: (1) The occurrence of rubella was recorded before the child was born; (2) Babies born to nearly all of the affected mothers were examined; and, (3) A separate estimate of the risk for each month of pregnancy could be made.

The results of these studies are shown in Table 1.

Note the apparent decrease in the risk of fetal malformations from 50 per cent when rubella occurred in the 1st month, to 25 per cent for the 2nd month, 17 per cent for the

3rd month, 11 per cent for the 4th month, and 6 per cent for the 5th month. Essentially similar risks were reported subsequently by Coffey and Jessop[21] from Dublin.

In contrast, the study of Lamy and Seror[70] in France estimated the risk of malformations attributable to rubella in the first 2 months to be over 80 per cent. The risk may vary from place to place and from time to time—perhaps due to some peculiar virulence of the causal agent.

THE ROLE OF OTHER VIRUSES IN THE PRODUCTION OF FETAL MALFORMATIONS

HUMAN VIRUS INFECTIONS

The evidence for the teratogenic role of rubella virus is so striking that it is no surprise to learn that many investigators have studied other virus infections from this point of view.

Of course, it has been known for generations that virus infections early in pregnancy often lead to abortion. Infections late in pregnancy may result in the birth of a baby showing clinical evidence of infection with the maternal virus: smallpox, vaccinia, measles, varicella, poliomyelitis, Coxsackie B and herpes simplex. However, I am not concerned here with this evidence that a virus can infect fetal tissues. Rather, I propose to consider the possibility that a maternal infection early in pregnancy may lead to malformations.

This relationship has been studied in sev-

TABLE 1. Risk of Defect in Infant Following Maternal Rubella in Pregnancy*

	Stage of Pregnancy at Which Rubella Commenced	Number of Infants	Infants With Major Defects	
			Number	Per Cent
Weeks of Pregnancy	1st to 4th	12	6†	50
	5th to 8th	20	5†	25
	9th to 12th	18	3‡	17
	13th to 16th	18	2§	11
	17th to 24th	17	1§	6
	25th or later	19	0	0

*Hill *et al.* (1958) Brit. J. Prev. Soc. Med., 12, 1–7.
†All 11 infants had cataract, deafness, or heart disease.
‡Two infants had heart disease, and one a harelip and cleft palate.
§One infant was deaf, and the other two were a mongol and an anencephalic.

eral ways: retrospective studies;[7,31,40,60,93,109,111,112] prospective studies;[46,79] and, examination of vital statistics.[17]

It seems worthwhile to recommend the compulsory notification by physicians of all congenital malformations. Examination of such data from the Canadian Provinces of British Columbia and Ontario discloses as much as a 3-fold variation in monthly rates, and a lesser variation by year.[28,103] These fluctuations merit the attention of epidemiologists.

It may be said at once that only very rarely has a virus infection early in pregnancy been associated with the characteristic rubella defects—cataract, deafness and heart disease.

I agree that there are many reports in the literature of isolated cases of malformation attributable to virus infections in early pregnancy. These defects have included genu valgum, talipes equinovarus, pyloric stenosis, harelip and cleft palate, mongolism, nevi, myelocele, spina bifida and urogenital malformations. The following viruses have been incriminated.

1. Enteric viruses, especially poliomyelitis[7,40,60,105,111,116] and Coxsackie A4 virus;[83]
2. Varicella and herpes zoster;[7,40,60,111,112]
3. Infectious hepatitis;[40,96,111]
4. Measles;[31,40,42,60,111,112]
5. Virus pneumonia;[60]
6. Infectious mononucleosis;[60]
7. Salivary gland virus.[87]

Three additional common infections merit comment.

Vaccinia has been administered to hundreds of thousands of women in the early months of pregnancy. The virus circulates in the blood yet it rarely affects the fetus.[77] The general belief, more recently expressed by Bellows et al.[11] and Abramowitz[1] on the basis of experiences in New York and Cape Town, is that vaccination early in pregnancy does not affect the fetus adversely. In contrast, MacArthur,[78] in Scotland, found a high incidence of abortions and stillbirths in those vaccinated between the 4th and the 12th weeks.

Influenza has been epidemic on many occasions since the original report of Gregg directed attention to the teratogenic action of a virus, and a few cases of malformations have been reported.[7,20,60,111]

The recent 1957 pandemic of influenza caused by Asian virus provided an unusual opportunity for investigation. Observers in the United States report no increase in the incidence of malformations.[118,127]

On the other hand, from Dublin, Coffey and Jessop[21,22] report a substantial increase in malformations (see Table 2). The risks apportioned to the various trimesters of pregnancy were as follows: first, 7.4 per cent; second, 4.3 per cent; and third, 2.0 per cent. The malformations in both influenza-infected and control groups included spina bifida, meningocele, hydrocephalus and mongolism.

TABLE 2. Incidence of Malformations in Offspring of Mothers Who Had Influenza and in Offspring of Controls*

	Mother's History	
	Influenza	No influenza
Normal infants.......	639	653
Malformed infants....	24	10
Total infants.........	663	663
Malformed births as per cent of total....	3.6 per cent†	1.5 per cent

*Coffey and Jessop, 1959, Lancet 2:935–938.
†Risk for various trimesters: first, 7.4 per cent, second, 4.3 per cent, third, 2.0 per cent.

Mumps virus perhaps has been incriminated as the cause of malformations more frequently than any virus except rubella.[31,36,40,50,60,91,102,111,112,114]

The results of a review of 91 instances of maternal mumps reported by two Finnish authors are shown in Table 3.[128]

Note that 22.6 per cent of babies born to mothers who contracted mumps in the 1st trimester showed malformations — a rate double that when the disease occurred in the 2nd and the 3rd trimesters.

TABLE 3. Cases of Parotitis in Pregnancy*

Mumps in Pregnancy	Mothers with Mumps	Outcome of Pregnancy				
		Normal Infant	Abortion	Premature Infant	Stillbirth	Malformation
First trimester.....	31	19	5	0	0	7 (22.6%)
Second and third trimester.......	60	50	2	1	1	6 (10%)
Total........	91	69	7	1	1	13

*Ylinen and Järvinen: Acta. Obst. Gynec. Scand. 32: 121-132, 1953.

VIRUS INFECTIONS IN ANIMALS

In domestic animals, many natural virus infections lead to abortion and virus invades the fetus. These infections often occur in epizootics. Malformations seldom have been described, either in aborted fetuses or in those surviving to term, although the latter sometimes have presented certain abnormal clinical signs. It seems that exploration of this aspect of the pathogenic role of viruses in veterinary medicine has been meager.[9,64]

A list of infections in which abortion is frequent includes:[9] *in sheep,* enzootic abortion of ewes,[80] Rift Valley fever,[29] and Wesselsbron infection;[122] *in swine,* Japanese B encephalitis;[18,104] *in horses,* enzootic abortion of mares, equine rhinopneumonitis and infectious anemia.

Of much greater interest are reports of fetal malformations after the administration early in pregnancy of live attenuated virus vaccines. Hog cholera strains, rabbit-adapted, given to sows in the early weeks of pregnancy, invade the fetus and cause abortion, stillbirth and malformations.[99,129-131] Deformities of nose, leg, kidney, testes, and gallbladder have been described.

Blue tongue virus of sheep, attenuated in the chick embryo,[82] has been shown to produce hypoplasia of the brain and loss of Purkinje cells.[101]

Experimental inoculation of viruses in animals, early in pregnancy, also may lead to abortion or stillbirth. The virus can be isolated from aborted fetuses, but surviving offspring appear normal. Viruses studied in this way include: swine influenza virus in mice;[52] equine influenza virus in mares;[27] Columbia SK virus in mice;[63] and herpes simplex virus in rabbits.[14]

MALFORMATIONS INDUCED IN CHICK EMBRYOS

Several viruses, after inoculation in the vicinity of 48-hour-old chick embryos produce microcephaly, twisting and folding of the main axis, microplasia of the lens and the otocyst, and defective growth of the amnion. This effect has been shown for influenza A virus, Newcastle disease virus, vaccinia and herpes simplex.[2,43,45,125,126] Although the specificity of this action is doubtful, it may be noted that influenza virus rendered noninfectious by heat, ultraviolet light, or antiserum did not produce defects. Furthermore, neither mumps nor distemper viruses caused malformations.

CONCLUSIONS

I have attempted to summarize the present state of knowledge of the role of viruses in the causation of fetal malformations. The original Australian observations on the teratogenic role of rubella in the 1st trimester have been widely confirmed, and efforts have been made to discover if other viruses have the same effect.

The results of such investigations have been slender. Influenza and mumps occurring early in pregnancy seem to increase the incidence of "run of the mill" malformations. They seldom cause the cataracts, deafness, and patency of the ductus arteriosus and the interventricular septum so characteristic of the rubella syndrome. In the veterinary field, hog cholera and blue tongue live virus vaccines seem also to exert a teratogenic effect.

It would appear that rubella virus is a specific teratogenic agent. It is difficult to explain why no other human virus seems to have the same action. Perhaps we require another Gregg to discover some such effect.

Of course, specificity of pathologic lesions is a common finding with viruses, and the virologist would explain the teratogenic action of rubella virus in terms of localization of virus in developing embryonic cells, with intracellular multiplication and consequent cell destruction.

At least two other explanations of the teratogenic effect have been advanced. Thus, Hurst[53] suggested that the virus might act on blood vessels, presumably in some way restricting blood flow, e.g., to the lens (see also Tedeschi *et al.*[115]). Gillman[34] postulated that the virus might initiate a metabolic disorder— thus making the teratogenic action of the virus similar to that of other noxious agents.

Until such time as the virus that causes rubella is isolated, cultivated and analyzed biochemically the problem about which I have been speaking will remain a challenge to virologists, epidemiologists, and geneticists alike. There is room for much further study of the role of viruses in the etiology of congenital malformations.

ACKNOWLEDGEMENTS

The personal research work of the author and his colleagues at the School of Hygiene, University of Toronto, has been supported for many years by funds allocated by the Province of Ontario under the National Health Grants Program of the Government of Canada, and more recently also by the Connaught Medical Research Laboratories, University of Toronto.

The author is much indebted, in the preparation of this paper, to the following colleagues for providing information on subjects in which they are specially interested: Professors W. Harding le Riche and L. W. Macpherson, School of Hygiene, University of Toronto; Dr. A. H. Sellers, Department of Health for Ontario, Toronto, Ontario; Mr. J. H. Doughty, Department of Health and Welfare for British Columbia, Victoria, B. C.; Professor D. L. T. Smith, Ontario Veterinary College, Guelph, Ontario; Dr. Victor Cabasso, Lederle Laboratories, Pearl River, N. Y.; and Dr. John D. Keith, The Hospital for Sick Children, Toronto, Ontario.

REFERENCES

1. Abramowitz, L. J.: Vaccination and virus diseases during pregnancy, South African M. J. **31**:1-3, 1957.
2. Adams, J. M., Heath, H. D., Imagawa, D. T., Jones, M. H., and Shear, H. H.: Viral infections in the embryo, A.M.A. Am. J. Dis. Child. **92**:109-114, 1956.
3. Albaugh, C. H.: Congenital anomalies following maternal rubella in early weeks of pregnancy, J.A.M.A. **129**:719-723, 1945.
4. Anderson, R. C.: Causative factors underlying congenital heart malformations, Pediatrics **14**:143-152, 1954.
5. Anderson, S. G.: Epidemiological aspects of rubella, M. J. Australia **2**:389-390, 1950.
6. Anderson, S. G., and McLorinan, H.: Convalescent rubella gamma globulin as a possible prophylactic against rubella, M. J. Australia **1**:182-185, 1953.
7. Aycock, W. L., and Ingalls, T. H.: Maternal disease as a principle in the epidemiology of congenital anomalies. With a review of rubella, Am. J. M. Sc. **212**:366-379, 1946.
8. Bass, M. H.: Diseases of the pregnant woman affecting the offspring, Advances Int. Med. **5**:15-58, 1952.
9. Beer, J.: *In* Zuchtygiene, Fortpflanzungs Storungen und Besamung der Haustiere, Bd. 2, pp. 164-178, Hanover, 1958.
10. Bell, J.: On rubella in pregnancy, Brit. M. J. **1**:686-688, 1959.
11. Bellows, M. T., Hyman, M. E., and Merritt, K. K.: Effect of smallpox vaccination on the outcome of pregnancy, Pub. Health Rep. **64**:319-323, 1949.
12. Berliner, B.: Personal communication to J. Warkany, 1947.
13. Beswick, R. C., Warner, R., and Warkany, J.: Congenital anomalies following maternal rubella, Am. J. Dis. Child. **78**:334-348, 1949.
14. Biegeleisen, J. Z., and Scott, L. V.: Transplacental infection of fetuses of rabbits with herpes simplex virus, Proc. Soc. Exper. Biol. & Med. **97**:411-412, 1958.
15. Brawner, D. L.: Maternal rubella; results

following epidemic, J. M. A. Georgia **44**: 451-454, 1955.

16. Brown, C. M., and Nathan, B. J.: Maternal rubella and congenital defects, Lancet **1**:975-976, 1954.

17. Buck, C.: Exposure to virus diseases in early pregnancy and congenital malformations, Canad. M. A. J. **72**:744-746, 1955.

18. Burns, K. F.: Congenital Japanese B encephalitis infection of swine, Proc. Soc. Exper. Biol. & Med. **75**:621-625, 1950.

19. Clarke, M.: Aseptic meningitis with rash, Canad. M. A. J. **77**:41-42, 1957.

20. Clayton-Jones, E.: Maternal influenza and congenital deformities, Lancet **2**:1086, 1959.

21. Coffey, V. P., and Jessop, W. J. E.: Maternal influenza and congenital deformities, Lancet **2**:935-938, 1959.

22. ———: Rubella and incidence of congenital abnormalities, Irish J. M. Sc. (Sixth Series) No. 397:1-11, 1959.

23. Committee on the Enteroviruses, National Foundation for Infantile Paralysis: The enteroviruses, Am. J. Pub. Health **47**: 1556-1566, 1957.

24. Cordes, F. C.: Cataract formation in the human embryo after rubella, Arch. Ophth. **42**:596-605, 1949.

25. Cordes, F. C., and Barber, A.: Changes in lens of embryo after rubella. Microscopic examination of eight week old embryo, Arch. Ophth. **36**:135-140, 1946.

26. Dogramaci, I.: Rubella or German measles, Ann. paediat. **173**:85, 1949.

27. Doll, E. R., Richards, M. G., and Wallace, M. E.: Cultivation of the equine influenza virus in suckling Syrian hamsters. Its similarity to the equine abortion virus, Cornell Vet. **44**:133-138, 1954.

28. Doughty, J. H.: Personal communication, 1960.

29. Findlay, G. M.: Rift Valley Fever or enzootic hepatitis, Tr. Roy. Soc. Trop. Med. & Hyg. **25**:229-265, 1931-32.

30. Fox, M. J., and Bortin, M. M.: Rubella in pregnancy causing malformations in newborn, J.A.M.A. **130**:568-569, 1946.

31. Fox, M. J., Krumbiegel, E. R., and Teresi, J. L.: Maternal measles, mumps, and chickenpox as a cause of congenital anomalies, Lancet **1**:746-749, 1948.

32. Gibson, S.: Discussion on paper by Kaye *et al.*, Am. J. Obst. & Gynec. **65**:109-118, 1953.

33. Gibson, S., and Lewis, K. C.: Congenital

heart disease following maternal rubella during pregnancy, A.M.A. Am. J. Dis. Child. **83**:317-319, 1952.

34. Gillman, J., Gilbert, C., and Gilman, T.: A preliminary report on hydrocephalus, spina bifida and other congenital anomalies in the rat produced by trypan blue, South African J. M. Sc. **13**:47-90, 1948.

35. Gordon, J. E., and Ingalls, T. H.: Death, defect and disability in prenatal life, Am. J. Pub. Health **38**:66-74, 1948.

36. Greenberg, M. W., and Beilly, J. S.: Congenital defects in the infant following mumps during pregnancy, Am. J. Obst. & Gynec. **57**:805-806, 1949.

37. Greenberg, M., Pellitteri, O., and Barton, J.: Frequency of defects in infants whose mothers had rubella during pregnancy, J.A.M.A. **165**:675-678, 1957.

38. Gregg, N. McA.: Congenital cataract following German measles in the mother, Tr. Ophth. Soc. Australia **3**:35-46, 1942.

39. ———: Further observations on congenital defects in infants following maternal rubella, Tr. Ophth. Soc. Australia **4**:119-131, 1944.

40. Grönvall, H., and Selander, P.: Some virus diseases during pregnancy and their effect on the fetus, Nord. med. **37**:409-415, 1948.

41. Habel, K.: Transmission of rubella to Macacus monkeys, Pub. Health Rep. **57**: 1126-1139, 1942.

42. Hagstromer, A.: Two cases of congenital malformations after exposure to measles in early pregnancy, Acta paediat. **35**:242-246, 1948.

43. Hamburger, V., and Habel, K.: Teratogenic and lethal effects of influenza A and mumps viruses on early chick embryos, Proc. Soc. Exper. Biol. & Med. **66**:608-617, 1947.

44. Hay, D. R.: Maternal rubella and congenital deafness in New Zealand, New Zealand M. J. **52**:16-19, 1953.

45. Heath, H. D., Shear, H. H., Imagawa, D. T., Jones, M. H., and Adams, J. M.: Teratogenic effects of herpes simplex, vaccinia, influenza-A (NWS), and distemper virus infections on early chick embryos, Proc. Soc. Exper. Biol. & Med. **92**:675-682, 1956.

46. Hill, A. B., Doll, R., Galloway, T. McL., and Hughes, J. P. W.: Virus diseases in pregnancy and congenital defects, Brit. J. Prev. & Social Med. **12**:1-7, 1958.

47. Hill, A. B., and Galloway, T. McL.: Ma-

ternal rubella and congenital defects; data from National Health Insurance records, Lancet **1**:299-301, 1949.

48. Hillenbrand, F. K. M.: Rubella in a remote community, Lancet **2**:64-66, 1956.

49. Hiro, Y., and Tasaka, S.: Die Roteln sind eine viruskrankheit, Monatsschr. Kinderh. **76**:328-332, 1938.

50. Holowach, J., Thurston, D. L., and Becker, B.: Congenital defects in infants following mumps during pregnancy, J. Pediat. **50**:689-694, 1957.

51. Horstmann, D.: The new Echo viruses and their role in human disease, A.M.A. Arch. Int. Med. **102**:155-162, 1958.

52. Howell, W. E., Winters, L. M., and Young, G. A.: Prenatal and early postnatal survival in the mouse as affected by infection of the mother with swine influenza virus during gestation, J. Immunol. **71**:280-283, 1953.

53. Hurst, E. W.: Personal communication, 1943. Cited by Swan, 1944.

54. Ingalls, T. H.: The study of congenital anomalies by the epidemiologic method, New England J. Med. **243**:67-74, 1950.

55. Ingalls, T. H., and Gordon, J. E.: Epidemiologic implications of developmental arrests, Am. J. M. Sc. **214**:322-328, 1947.

56. Ingalls, T. H., and Purshottam, N.: Fetal risks from rubella during pregnancy, New England J. Med. **249**:454, 1953.

57. Ivstam, B.: Deafness and deaf mutism in children, with special reference to rubella, Nord. med. **49**:208-211, 1953.

58. Jackson, A. D. M., and Fisch, L.: Deafness following maternal rubella. Results of a prospective investigation, Lancet **2**: 1241-1244, 1958.

59. Johnston, T., Bottiger, M., and Lofdahl, A.: An outbreak of aseptic meningitis with a rubella-like rash probably caused by Echo virus Type 4, Arch. ges. Virusforsch. **8**:306-317, 1958.

60. Kaye, B. M., Rosner, D. C., and Stein, I. F.: Viral diseases in pregnancy and their effect upon the embryo and fetus, Am. J. Obst. & Gynec. **65**:109-118, 1953.

61. Keith, J. D., Rowe, R. D., and Vlad, P.: Heart Disease in Infancy and Childhood, New York, Macmillan, 1958.

62. Kirman, B. H.: Rubella as a cause of mental defect, Lancet **2**:1113-1115, 1955.

63. Knox, A. W.: Infection and immunity in offspring of mice inoculated during gestation with murine poliomyelitis virus, Proc. Soc. Exper. Biol. & Med. **74**:792-796, 1950.

64. Koprowski, H.: Counterparts of human viral disease in animals, Ann. New York Acad. Sc. **70**:369-382, 1958.

65. Korns, R. F.: Prophylaxis of German measles with immune serum globulin, J. Infect. Dis. **90**:183-189, 1952.

66. Krugman, S., and Ward, R.: The rubella problem. Clinical aspects, risks of fetal abnormality, and methods of prevention, J. Pediat. **44**:489-498, 1954.

67. ———: Rubella. Demonstration of neutralizing antibody in gamma globulin and re-evaluation of the rubella problem, New England J. Med. **259**:16-19, 1958.

68. Krugman, S., Ward, R., Jacobs, K. G., and Lazar M.: Studies on rubella immunization. I. Demonstration of rubella without rash, J.A.M.A. **151**:285-288, 1953.

69. Laforest, R. A., McNaughton, G. A., Beale, A. J., Clarke, M., Davis, N., Sultanian, I., and Rhodes, A. J.: Outbreak of aseptic meningitis (meningoencephalitis) with rubelliform rash: Toronto, 1956, Canad. M. A. J. **77**:1-4, 1957.

70. Lamy, M., and Seror, M. E.: Resultats d'une enquete sur les embryopathies d'origine rubeolique, Bull. Acad. nat. méd. **140**:196-203, 1956.

71. Lancester, H. O., and Pickering, H.: The incidence of births of the deaf in New Zealand, New Zealand M. J. **51**:184-189, 1952.

72. L'Etang, H.: Rubella and congenital deafness, Lancet **1**:849, 1947.

73. Lindsay, J., and Harrison, R. S.: The pathology of rubella deafness, J. Laryng. & Otol. **68**:461-464, 1954.

74. Logan, W. P. D.: Incidence of congenital malformations and their relation to virus infections during pregnancy, Brit. M. J. **2**:641-645, 1951.

75. Lundstrom, R.: Rubella during pregnancy. Its effects upon perinatal mortality, the incidence of congenital abnormalities and immaturity. A preliminary report, Acta paediat. **41**:583-594, 1952.

76. ———: Rubella during pregnancy. A patho-anatomic study of foetuses 1, Acta path. et microbiol. scandinav. **41**:449-461, 1957.

77. Lynch, F. W.: Dermatologic conditions of the fetus with particular reference to variola and vaccinia, Arch. Dermat. & Syph. **26**:997-1019, 1932.

78. MacArthur, P.: Congenital vaccinia and

vaccinia gravidarum, Lancet **2**:1104-1106, 1952.

79. McDonald, A. D.: Maternal health and congenital defect, New England J. Med. **258**:767-773, 1958.

80. McEwen, A. D., Littlejohn, A. I., and Foggie, A.: Enzootic abortion in ewes. Some aspects of infection and resistance, Vet. Rec. **63**:489-492, 1951.

81. McIntosh, R., Merritt, K. K., Richards, M. R., Samuels, M. H., and Bellows, M. T.: The incidence of congenital malformations: A study of 5,964 pregnancies, Pediatrics **14**:505-522, 1954.

82. McKercher, D. G., McGowan, B., Jr., Cabasso, V. J., Roberts, G. I., and Saito, J. K.: Studies on bluetongue. III. The development of a modified live virus vaccine employing American strains of bluetongue virus, Am. J. Vet. Res. **18**:310-316, 1957.

83. Makower, H., Skurska, Z., and Halazinska, L.: On transplacental infection with Coxsackie virus, Texas Rep. Biol. & Med. **3**:346-354, 1958.

84. Mann, I.: Tr. Ophth. Soc. Australia **4**:115-118, 1944.

85. Morgan, F. G., Burnet, F. M., McLorinan, H., and Bryce, L. M.: The preparation, distribution and use of anti-rubella gamma globulin, M. J. Australia **2**:490-491, 1950.

86. Murray, N. E.: Deafness following maternal rubella, M. J. Australia **1**:126-130, 1949.

87. Nelson, J. S., and Wyatt, J. P.: Salivary gland virus disease, Medicine **38**:223-241, 1959.

88. Neva, F. A.: A second outbreak of Boston exanthem disease in Pittsburgh during 1954, New England J. Med. **254**:838-843, 1956.

89. Ober, R. E., Horton, R. J. M., and Feemster, R. F.: Congenital defects in a year of epidemic rubella, Am. J. Pub. Health **37**:1328-1333, 1947.

90. Oxorn, H.: Rubella and pregnancy. A study of 47 cases, Am. J. Obst. & Gynec. **77**:628-631, 1959.

91. Philip, R. N., Reinhard, K. R., and Lackman, D. B.: Observations on a mumps epidemic in a "virgin" population, Am. J. Hyg. **69**:91-111, 1959.

92. Pitt, D. B.: Congenital malformations and maternal rubella, M. J. Australia **1**:233-239, 1957.

93. Pleydell, M. J.: Anencephaly and other congenital abnormalities. An epidemiological study in Northamptonshire, Brit. M. J. **1**:309-315, 1960.

94. Rhodes, A. J.: Personal communication, 1960.

95. Robinson, C. R., Doane, F. W., and Rhodes, A. J.: Report of an outbreak of febrile illness with pharyngeal lesions and exanthem: Toronto, summer 1957—Isolation of group A Coxsackie virus, Canad. M. A. J. **79**:615-621, 1958.

96. Roth, L. G.: Infectious hepatitis in pregnancy, Am. J. M. Sc. **225**:139-146, 1953.

97. Rutstein, D. R., Nickerson, R. J., and Heald, F. P.: Seasonal incidence of patent ductus arteriosus and maternal rubella, A.M.A. Am. J. Dis. Child. **84**:199-213, 1952.

98. Sabin, A. B., Krumbiegel, E. R., and Wigand, R.: Echo Type 9 virus disease, A.M.A. Am. J. Dis. Child. **96**:197-219, 1958.

99. Sautter, J. H., Young, G. A., Luedke, A. J., and Kitchell, R. L.: The experimental production of malformations and other abnormalities in fetal pigs by means of attenuated hog cholera virus, Proc. Am. Vet. M. A. pp. 147-150, 1953.

100. Schick, B.: Displacental infection of the foetus with the virus of German measles despite immunity of the mother. Analogous observations in smallpox, Acta paediat. **38**:563-570, 1949.

101. Schultz, G., and DeLay, P. D.: Losses in newborn lambs associated with bluetongue vaccination of pregnant ewes, J. Am. Vet. M. A. **127**:224-226, 1955.

102. Schwartz, H. A.: Mumps in pregnancy, Am. J. Obst. & Gynec. **60**:875-876, 1950.

103. Sellers, A. H.: Personal communication, 1960.

104. Shimizu, T., Kawakami, Y., Fukuhara, S., and Matumoto, M.: Experimental stillbirth in pregnant swine infected with Japanese encephalitis virus, Jap. J. Exper. Med. **24**:363-375, 1954.

105. Siegel, M., and Greenberg, M.: Poliomyelitis in pregnancy: effect on fetus and newborn infant, J. Pediat. **49**:280-288, 1956.

106. ———:Virus diseases in pregancy and their effects on fetus: preliminary report of controlled prospective study, Am. J. Obst. & Gynec. **77**:620-627, 1959.

107. ———: Fetal death, malformation, and prematurity after maternal rubella, New England J. Med. **262**:389-393, 1960.

108. Swan, C.: Congenital malformations in

infants following maternal rubella during pregnancy: a review of investigations carried out in South Australia, Tr. Ophth. Soc. Australia **4:**132-141, 1944.

109. ———: Rubella in pregnancy as an aetiological factor in congenital malformation, stillbirth, miscarriage and abortion, J. Obst. & Gynaec. Brit. Emp. **56:**341-363; 591-605, 1949.

110. ———: A study of three infants dying from congenital defects following maternal rubella in the early stages of pregnancy, J. Path. & Bact. **56:**289-295, 1944.

111. ———: *In* Banks, H. S.: Modern Practice in Infectious Fevers, vol. 2, p. 528, London, Butterworth, 1951.

112. Swan, C., and Tostevin, A. L.: Congenital abnormalities in infants following infectious diseases during pregnancy, with special reference to rubella: a third series of cases, M. J. Australia **33:**645-659, 1946.

113. Swan, C., Tostevin, A. L., Mayo, H., and Black, G. H.: Further observations on congenital defects in infants following infectious diseases during pregnancy, with special reference to rubella, M. J. Australia **31:**409-413, 1944.

114. Swan, C., Tostevin, A. L., Moore, B., Mayo, H., and Black, G. H.: Congenital defects in infants following infectious disease during pregnancy, M. J. Australia **30:**201-210, 1943.

115. Tedeschi, C. G., Helpern, M. M., and Ingalls, T. H.: Pathological manifestations in an infant after maternal rubella in the sixteenth week of gestation, New England J. Med. **249:**439-442, 1953.

116. Tondury, G.: Erkrankt der fetus bei poliomyelitis in graviditate, Schweiz. med. Wchnschr. **87:**809-812, 1957.

117. van Rooyen, C. E., and Rhodes, A. J.: Virus Diseases of Man, ed. 2, New York, Thomas Nelson, 1948.

118. Walker, W. M., and McKeen, A. P.: Asian influenza in pregnancy. Relationship to fetal anomalies, Obst. & Gynec. **13:**394-398, 1959.

119. Ward, H., and Parker, G.: Passive protection against rubella, M. J. Australia **1:**81-83, 1956.

120. Warkany, J.: Congenital malformations and pediatrics, Pediatrics **19:**725-733, 1957.

121. ———: Etiology of congenital malformations *in* Advances in Pediatrics, vol. 2, pp. 1-63, New York, Interscience, 1947.

122. Weiss, K. E., Haig, D. A., and Alexander, R. A.: Wesselsbron virus—a virus not previously described, associated with abortion in domestic animals, Onderstepoort J. Vet. Res. **27:**183-195, 1956.

123. Wesselhoeft, C.: Rubella (German measles) and congenital deformities, New England J. Med. **240:**258-261, 1949.

124. Willemin-Clocq, L., and Chardonnet, S.: De la fatalite de l'embryopathie rubeoleuse, Bull. et mém. Soc. méd. hôp. Paris **69:**954-958, 1953.

125. Williamson, A. P., Blattner, R. J., and Robertson, G. G.: Factors influencing the production of developmental defects in the chick embryo following infection with Newcastle disease virus, J. Immunol. **71:**207-213, 1953.

126. Williamson, A. P., Simonsen, L., and Blattner, R. J.: Specific organ defects in early chick embryos following inoculation with influenza A virus, Proc. Soc. Exper. Biol. & Med. **92:**334-337, 1956.

127. Wilson, M. G., Heins, H. L., Imagawa, D. T., and Adams, J. M.: Teratogenic effects of Asian influenza, J.A.M.A. **171:**638-641, 1959.

128. Ylinen, O., and Jarvinen, P. A.: Parotitis during pregnancy, Acta obst. et gynec. scandinav. **32:**121-132, 1953.

129. Young, G. A.: Influence of virus infection, vaccination, or both on embryonic and fetal development, Proc. Book Am. Vet. M. A. **126:**377-381, 1955.

130. ———: A preliminary report on the etiology of edema of newborn pigs, J. Am. Vet. M. A. **121:**394-396, 1952.

131. Young, G. A., Kitchell, R. L., Luedke, A. J., and Sautter, J. H.: The effect of viral and other infections of the dam on fetal development in swine. 1. Modified live hog cholera virus—immunological, virological, and gross pathological studies, J. Am. Vet. M. A. **126:**165-171, 1955.

The Interplay of Intrinsic and Extrinsic Factors in the Origin of Congenital Malformations

WALTER LANDAUER, Dr. phil. nat.

The long and patient labors of embryologists have given us detailed descriptive accounts for many organisms of the sequences of events intervening between fertilization and the completion of normal development. Such information also is available for a considerable variety of teratologic conditions, both hereditary and experimentally induced. Analytic inquiries into the events which are responsible for particular steps of normal embryogenesis have brought to light many important causal mechanisms, such as inductor and evocator relationships or differential metabolic properties, but we appear still to be far from possessing unifying principles which can be applied to an interpretation of morphogenesis and differentiation in more general terms—if, indeed, such principles can be formulated.

Every organism represents a clearing house of complex interactions between external forces and the metabolic functions derived from hereditary endowment. The developmental dislocations which lead to the occurrence of congenital defects may take their origin from without or from within the organism; they are always the reflection of a failure in adaptability to novel conditions.

The kinds of malformations which may arise during development of any particular type of organism—and we shall only refer to vertebrates—obviously will vary with its own prospective design. It is also clear that during vertebrate evolution and parallel with the transition from the extramaternal development of lower vertebrates to the more sheltered surroundings of the mammalian uterus the dangers posed by variations in the external environment were reduced. Of course, this heightened security was acquired at the expense of such hazards as were inherent in the new surroundings.

The development of many organisms is easily disturbed by forces of the environment. In chicken embryos, for instance, all of the readily identifiable chemical or physical components of the atmospheric surroundings under appropriate conditions may play a role in chains of teratogenic events.[20] Again, in all organisms which have been sufficiently studied, numerous mutations have been found which are responsible for the origin of congenital malformations. In the present discussion, we shall not be concerned with cataloguing the kinds of such extrinsic and intrinsic agencies with teratogenic effects (though this field should offer fascinating problems to comparative teratologists) but shall examine evidence relating to the interaction between the two sources of variation and disturbance.

Studies on Drosophila have brought to light numerous instances in which the phenotypic expression of mutant genes is influenced by, or indeed dependent upon, conditions of the environment. Very little evidence of this kind has as yet become available in work with vertebrates, but such information should contribute much to an understanding of the causes of congenital malformations and perhaps something even to their prevention.

It is well recognized that penetrance and expressivity of mutant genes often vary with the residual genotype, and that multiple, ubiquitously occurring genes with minor individual effects, the so-called modifying genes, play a prominent role in this respect. Do such genes have a function in the causation of congenital malformations by extrinsic agencies? Is the role of environmental factors in teratogenesis mediated or circumscribed by remote effects of the maternal heredity (supply of nutrient reserves to the egg, the uterine conditions) as well as by the zygotic genotype (cellular metabolism, peculiarities of growth and differentiation, etc.)? These and related questions I propose to discuss for a number of concrete examples.

To start with, we may recall that the initial rate of segmentation of the fertilized egg is determined by the maternal heredity in many different types of animals. Presumably, this is an expression of the fact that the genes contributed to the zygote by the sperm nucleus require a considerable lapse of time before they begin to assert themselves in metabolic terms. The maternally controlled early developmental rate of embryos varies with the mother's genotype and to some extent can be shifted by selection. We have demonstrated, in experiments with insulin, that the degree of teratogenic response of chicken embryos may be affected by such variations in early developmental rate.[23]

Sex determination is likely to exert effects *ab initio* on cellular metabolism. Presumably, this is responsible for the occurrence, unrelated to sex linkage, of significant and often striking differences between the sexes in the incidence of congenital malformations. As a convenient example, we refer to the fact that in birds as well as in mammals, and in spite of the differing sex determining mechanisms in the two groups, otocephaly occurs much more commonly in females than in males.[12,30] It is likely that these differences arise as a consequence of dissimilarities in growth rates which, however slight, are sufficient to bring about differential results in the operation of a threshold mechanism. In the case of otocephaly of guinea pigs, extrinsic factors play an additional role. This will be discussed later.

Unequal and asymmetrical embryonic growth rates, the causes of which unquestionably are anchored in the genotype, probably contribute frequently to the occurrence and the phenotypic expression of hereditary as well as induced malformations. There is strong reason to believe that the tendency, in guinea pigs and fowl, for unilateral expression of hereditary polydactylism to occur on the left rather than on the right side of the body is predicated by corresponding asymmetries of growth rates. The asymmetrical manifestations of the mutation to polydactylism are, at least in fowl, susceptible to plus or minus selection, it being easier to reinforce than to counteract the existing trend. They are also readily influenced by forces of the environment. The experimental modification, by the use of insulin, of the polydactyl phenotype is channeled by the same inherent peculiarities of embryonic growth.[13] A similar dependence of teratogenic manifestation on local growth conditions is found in the effects of selenium on developing chicken embryos and is another demonstration of the importance of hereditary growth factors of the skeleton. It was found that the incidence and the severity of selenium-induced malformations is raised in the presence of the micromelia of Creeper fowl.[11] Asymmetries in the phenotype of hereditary and ethyl-carbamate induced crossbeak of chicken embryos are an expression of similar conditions.[17] Gruenwald[9] reported the occurrence of transient size differences of the eyes in normal development of the chicken embryo, differences that presumably are related to the differential growth rates which bring about the turning of the head and to attendant inequalities in tissue oxygenation; but circulatory asymmetries and concomitant differentials in the amount of nutrition reaching the primordia also may play a role.[28] The point of interest for our present discussion is that these events, normally corrected with the establishment of an efficient circulation, provide background against which unilateral anophthalmia or microphthalmia or unequal expression of eye defects with the same lateral preference occur in chicken embryos as sporadic or hereditary malformations and also after experimental intervention.

Certain instances of maternal inheritance, on account of peculiarities of the uterine environment, also are likely to find their explanation in circulatory peculiarities with resulting variations in the adequacy with which supplies of nutrients or oxygen reach the embryo. Hereditary microphthalmia of rats[1] is probably a case in point. Another instance of this sort may be seen in the influence which the uterine environment has on variation in the number of lumbar vertebrae of mice (McLaren and Mitchie,[26] with references to earlier work of Russell and Green). The specific reactions of certain parts or organs to the uterine environment undoubtedly are brought about by the operation of genetically set threshold mechanisms or of quasicontinuous variations in the sense of Grüneberg.[7,8]

It is well recognized that processes of cellular degeneration which play a morphogenetic role in normal development may proceed as a consequence of mutation far beyond their ordinary course, thereby contributing to the origin of congenital malformations, and that under the influence of modifying genes normal development may be re-established by small steps. Such processes may involve the degeneration of presumptive tissues, as in dominant rumplessness of fowl,[31] or they may accomplish their ends by the regression and the resorption of already formed parts, as in the recessive mutation to rumplessness.[32] Phenocopies may arise by homologous events, as Moseley[27] has demonstrated for insulin-induced rumplessness of chicken embryos. In the case of recessive and insulin-induced rumplessness, it could be shown that the similarities in the mechanisms of their development

are not fortuitous, since both are affected in similar ways by distinctive residual genotypes.[14,16] Such common ground even exists between rumplessness of fowl as a phenodeviant in Lerner's[24] sense and as produced by mechanical shaking.[22] Another instance in which the developmental events leading to malformation involve an exaggeration of normally occurring tissue degeneration was found in the chondrogenic tissue of the long bones of insulin-treated chicken embryos,[33] and this presumably is, in fact, an important mechanism in the genesis of other malformations, both hereditary and experimentally induced.

The complex interactions of extrinsic and intrinsic factors in the origin of malformations are particularly well illustrated by the situation found in otocephaly of guinea pigs[30] and in perocephaly of fowl.[18,19] In both instances we are dealing with hereditary malformations with highly variable incidence and morphologic expression. The frequency of occurrence of these malformations and their degree of severity in any particular strain are determined by the interaction of a varying constellation of minor and major genes and of extrinsic agencies, an interaction which decides success or (more or less complete) failure in surmounting a threshold mechanism, the detailed nature of which remains to be unravelled. It is evident that in both instances factors of the external or the internal environment, often of an apparently unimportant nature, decide among genetically identical embryos whether their development shall be normal or abnormal. Sex has been mentioned already as one of the factors influencing the incidence of otocephaly. In chicken embryos of the stock carrying perocephalic tendencies a brief exposure early in incubation to reduced oxygen tension, to an extent harmless to genetically normal embryos often will shift the course of development into the perocephalic direction when, without that intervention, the embryos would have become entirely normal chicks. Such threshold-dependent events in traits determined polygenically probably are common mechanisms in the origin of congenital malformations. The interesting observations of Coffey and Jessop[3,4] suggest that anencephaly provides an example of this type from human teratology. The incidence of anencephaly seems to vary greatly in different population groups (additional evidence on this by Stevenson and Warnock[29]), and a number of factors of external and internal environment (sex, maternal age, blood-group relationships, nutrition) seem to take part in pushing the balance of events into the direction of anencephalic development.

Our present knowledge might be taken to suggest that, in situations such as the ones that have just been discussed, unspecific agencies produce "stress" which in turn by weakening the embryo is responsible for abnormal development. However, the impression of the existence of such "unspecific" reactions may merely be the product of our ignorance. An example from our own experience may illustrate this.[15] When we found, in experiments concerning the teratogenic effect of boric acid on chicken embryos, that the frequency and the extent of malformations was greater in embryos with pigmented than in those with unpigmented down, we assumed that the phenomenon was related to the reduced viability reported for embryos with extended black plumage pigmentation and slow feathering.[6,10] This argument was weakened by our observation that, in treated progenies of parents heterozygous for plumage color, pigmentation of the mother was a greater handicap than pigmentation of the embryo itself. Further studies revealed (1) that boric acid interfered with riboflavin metabolism and that supplementary riboflavin reduced its teratogenicity, and (2) that pigmented breeds of fowl need increased riboflavin supplies for efficient reproduction. Therefore, a direct metabolic link involving reproductive functions of laying hens was found between down pigmentation and the incidence and the severity of malformations. Such specific metabolic links with more or less widespread implications in cellular requirements presumably are at the bottom of all teratologic events.

Experimental work relating to the production of phenocopies, i.e. of nonhereditary variations which closely resemble known mutant traits, has brought additional information on the intertwined relationships between environment and genotype. To start with, there is the role which heterozygosity for recessive mutant genes may play in promoting the occurrence of malformations. This can be illustrated best by an example from our work with chickens.[21] In a recessive mutation of fowl, known as "crooked-neck dwarf," the principal feature of the lethal phenotype is an abnormality of the cervical spine, resembling the Klippel-Feil syndrome of man, with poor differentiation and irregular fusion of the vertebrae. Heterozygous animals appear to be perfectly normal in every respect. A condition which mimics not only the cervical defects but also all of the other components of the syndrome can be produced by injecting nicotine into eggs during early stages of development. Embryos which are heterozygous for the crooked-neck dwarf gene responded much more readily to treatment with nicotine than did their sibs which did not carry the mutant gene. A similar situation was found in a stock of fowl in which homologous malformations of the cervical vertebrae are inherited polygenically. Comparable conditions may play a significant role in the etiology of congenital malformations of man. It is important to note that heterozygosity for the crooked-neck dwarf lethal gene did *not* promote expressivity of a teratogen with *nonhomologous* phenotypic effects. This was shown in recent experiments with insulin to which embryos from two groups of sisters reacted without significant differences. It must be concluded, therefore, that specific relations exist between the mutant gene for crooked-neck dwarf and its phenocopy. More generally, it remains to be investigated to what extent the increased response to extrinsic factors, found in organisms which are heterozygous for certain recessive mutant genes, opposes the heightened capacity of equilibration so often associated with heterozygosity.

At any rate, it is clear that developing organisms will reveal under stress the resources as well as the limits of their adaptability. Numerous experiments have shown that many teratogenic agents have quite selective, and frequently stage-dependent, effects on particular parts and organs. However, it was also found that certain parts (e.g., tail, long bones and eyes of chicken embryos) are much more vulnerable than others, and that those parts which respond most readily to extrinsic agents are also the ones which are most often affected by mutant genes. These observations and the further fact that the activity of gene substitutions and the consequences of environmental agents with homologous phenotypic results frequently can be influenced by identical sets of modifying genes, point to the conclusion that the developmental processes of the organs and parts in question are poorly canalized or equilibrated.

In many experiments with chicken embryos the response to particular teratogenic agents followed a highly significant temporal trend, the incidence of malformations after certain treatments increasing with advancing season but decreasing during the same period with other treatments. These gradients are the result of interplay with other factors of the environment which act either on the embryos directly or via the maternal organism (e.g., by limiting reserve materials supplied to eggs). In view of the many rhythmic events in nature which in one way or another are imprinted upon organisms (see Brown[2]), it may be expected that future studies will establish fluctuations in the occurrence of congenital malformations tracing to environmental sources of this kind.

The important findings of Gentry, Parkhurst and Bulin[5] supplemented by the statistical evaluation by McDonald[25] on a positive correlation between the incidence of congenital malformations in man and the level of natural radioactivity of the ground or of the water supply in the particular area of residence, may, in addition to an increased rate of mutation, well be an expression of the heightened response of embryos, heterozygous for certain mutant genes, to extrinsic teratogenic agents of a relatively mild nature. These problems call for confirmation and much further study. Of course, such extrinsic sources of variation serve to reveal some of the many mistakes of the evolutionary past which are buried in the genotype of organisms.*

The kinds of interrelations between genotype and environment, affecting the origin of congenital malformations, as here discussed, may seem trivial to some. Yet, in the extremely complex and highly integrated process of vertebrate embryology, it is the trivial dislocations that end in congenital malformation, since more serious disturbances are likely, in early development, to interfere with viability.

REFERENCES

1. Browman, L. G.: Microphthalmia and maternal effect in the white rat, Genetics 39:261-265, 1954.
2. Brown, F. A., Jr.: The rhythmic nature of animals and plants, Am. Scientist 47:147-168, 1959.
3. Coffey, V. P., and Jessop, W. J. E.: A study

* Since these comments were written, several reports have come to the author's attention which greatly strengthen the suspicion that the natural background radiation is a factor in the origin of malformations, whether by mutation or, probably more often, by disruption of normal developmental events. See: Kratchman, J., and Grahn, D.: Relationships between the geologic environment and mortality from congenital malformation, U.S. Atomic Energy Commission, TID-8204, Office of Technical Services, U.S. Department of Commerce 1959; Solon, L. R., *et al.*: External environmental radiation measurements in the United States, U.S. Atomic Energy Commission Health and Safety Laboratory (HASL-25, Office of Technical Services, U.S. Department of Commerce) 1958 with important comments upon it by I. H. Herskowitz: Birth defects and chromosome changes, Nuclear Information, St. Louis, Missouri, U.S.A., vol. 3, no. 2, 1960.

of 137 cases of anencephaly, Brit. J. Prev. & Social Med. **11**:174-180, 1957.

4. ———: A three years study of anenceph- aly in Dublin: a report on 181 cases, Irish J. M. Sc. 391-413, 1958.

5. Gentry, J. T., Parkhurst, E., and Bulin, G. V., Jr.: An epidemiological study of con- genital malformations in New York State, Am. J. Pub. Health **49**:497-513, 1959.

6. Gredina, T. V.: Quoted from Landauer, 1960.

7. Grüneberg, H.: The genetics of a tooth defect in the mouse, Proc. Roy. Soc., London. ser. B **138**:437-451, 1951.

8. ———: Genetical studies on the skeleton of the mouse. IV. Quasicontinuous varia- tions, J. Genet. **51**:95-114, 1952.

9. Gruenwald, P.: Studies on developmental pathology. II. Sporadic unilateral microph- thalmia and associated malformations in chick embryos, Am. J. Anat. **74**:217-252, 1944.

10. Hutt, F. B.: Quoted from Landauer, 1960.

11. Landauer, W.: Studies on the Creeper fowl. XIII. The effect of selenium and the asym- metry of selenium-induced malformations, J. Exper. Zool. **83**:431-443, 1940.

12. ———: Sex and season in relation to mal- formations of chicken embryos, Anat. Rec. **86**:365-372, 1943.

13. ———: The phenotypic modification of hereditary polydactylism of fowl by selec- tion and by insulin, Genetics **33**:137-157, 1948.

14. ———: Hereditary abnormalities and their chemically-induced phenocopies, Growth Symposium **12**:171-200, 1948.

15. ———: Malformations of chicken em- bryos produced by boric acid and the prob- able role of riboflavin in their origin, J. Exper. Zool. **120**:469-508, 1952.

16. ———: Recessive and sporadic rumpless- ness of fowl: effects on penetrance and expressivity, Am. Nat. **89**:35-38, 1955.

17. ———: Hereditary and induced cross- beak of fowl, J. Exper. Zool. **132**:25-38, 1956.

18. ———: Cyclopia and related defects as a lethal mutation of fowl, J. Genetics **54**:219- 235, 1956.

19. ———: Oxidative metabolism and sea- sonal variations in the incidence of pero- cephaly of chicken embryos, J. Exper. Zool. **136**:171-183, 1957.

20. ———: The hatchability of chicken eggs as influenced by environment and heredity,

Storrs Agricultural Experiment Station Monograph 1, 1960.

21. ———: Nicotine-induced malformation of chicken embryos and their role as pheno- copies, J. Exper. Zool. **143**:107-122, 1960.

22. Landauer, W., and Baumann, L.: Rump- lessness of chicken embryos produced by mechanical shaking of eggs prior to incuba- tion, J. Exper. Zool. **93**:51-74, 1943.

23. Landauer, W., and Bliss, C. I.: Insulin- induced rumplessness of chickens. III. The relationship of dosage and of develop- mental stage at time of injection to re- sponse, J. Exper. Zool. **102**:1-22, 1946.

24. Lerner, I. M.: Genetic Homeostasis, New York, Wiley, 1954.

25. McDonald, J. E.: A study in genetic dam- age. Hearings before the Special Subcom- mittee on Radiation of the Joint Committee on Atomic Energy, Congress of the United States, 86th Congress, First Session on Fall- out from Nuclear Weapons Tests, May 5-8, 1959, **3**:2402-2422, 1959.

26. McLaren, A., and Michie, D.: Factors affecting vertebral variation in mice. 4. Experimental proof of the uterine basis of a maternal effect, J. Embryol. & Exper. Morphol. **6**:645-659, 1958.

27. Moseley, H. R.: Insulin-induced rumpless- ness of chickens. IV. Early embryology, J. Exper. Zool. **105**:279-316, 1947.

28. Orts Llorca, F., Genis-Gálvez, J. M., and Ruano-Gil, D.: Malformations encéphali- ques et microphthalmie gauche aprés sec- tion des vaisseaux vitelline gauches chez l'embryon de poulet, Acta anatomica **38**: 1-34, 1959.

29. Stevenson, A. C., and Warnock, H. A.: Observations on the results of pregnancies in women resident in Belfast. I. Data relat- ing to all pregnancies ending in 1957, Ann. Human Genet. **23**:382-391, 1959.

30. Wright, S.: On the genetics of subnormal development of the head (otocephaly) in the guinea pig, Genetics **19**:471-505, 1934.

31. Zwilling, E.: The development of dominant rumplessness in chick embryos, Genetics **27**:641-656, 1942.

32. ———: The embryogeny of a recessive rumpless condition of chickens, J. Exper. Zool. **99**:79-91, 1945.

33. ———: Micromelia as a direct effect of insulin—evidence from in vitro and in vivo experiments, J. Exper. Zool. **104**:159-174, 1959.

SESSION III

Discussion

Moderator

SIR DUGALD BAIRD, MD., F.R.C.O.G.

*Professor of Midwifery and Gynaecology, University of Aberdeen,
Aberdeen, Scotland, United Kingdom*

Panel Members

FRANK L. HORSFALL, JR., M.D.

*President and Director, Sloan-Kettering Institute for Cancer Research,
410 East 68th Street, New York 21, New York, U.S.A.*

PROFESSOR JAMES WALKER, M.D., F.R.C.O.G.

*Department of Midwifery and Gynaecology, St. Andrew's University,
St. Andrew's Fife, Scotland, United Kingdom*

PROFESSOR GIAN TÖNDURY

Department of Anatomy, University of Zurich, Zurich, Switzerland

PROFESSOR W. R. S. DOLL, O.B.E., M.D., F.R.C.P.

*Statistical Research Unit, Medical Research Council, London School of Hygiene
and Tropical Medicine, Keppell Street, London, W.C. 1, United Kingdom*

DR. DOLL: I offer a personal assessment of two factors which have been referred to in papers by Dr. Rhodes and Dr. Landauer. First, does Asian influenza produce congenital abnormalities? The data are conflicting, and some people hesitate to accept that Asian influenza can produce abnormalities because viremia has not been recognized. This objection need not weigh heavily, for undoubtedly there is toxemia which may produce the effect. The effect certainly is not large. Coffey and Jessop found that 7.4 per cent of a series of women affected in the 1st trimester of pregnancy produced babies with malformations, usually of the central nervous system. I shall assume that if the effect exists, it is specifically in the production of anencephaly. Results in the United States have been negative.

My colleagues and I have interrogated women who attended an antenatal clinic. We inquired whether they had had Asian influenza and attempted to check the diagnosis from their general practitioners. Our results show that of 63 women thought to have been attacked in the 1st trimester, 1 gave rise to a stillbirth, and 2 had children with abnormalities: hypospadias in one case and a heart lesion in the other case. Of the 66 women attacked late in pregnancy or before their last menstrual period, 1 had a stillbirth, and 2 had children with defects. This result can be compared with a group of 60 women who had attacks of mumps, varicella or morbilli: 3 had stillbirths, and 2 had defects. Not, I think, very impressive evidence of a positive effect. Taken in conjunction with the American reports, our results raise the question whether the Dublin results were due to chance fluctuation, or whether there were local influences in Dublin which produced a high incidence of anencephaly following Asian influenza. In Dublin there is a high risk of anencephaly. The effect may have been too slight to be noticed in other parts of the world where anencephaly is rarer.

I have examined the data published by the Registrar General for Scotland, who publishes the cause of stillbirths. In 1958, we should have expected an increase in the frequency of stillbirths attributed to anencephaly. The results show that there were 330 stillborn anencephalics, the highest level for 5 years, 19 per cent above the average. In the first 4 months there were 95 deaths, the lowest figure but one of the 5-year-period—7 per cent below the average. These children would have gone through the period of organogenesis before their mothers could have been affected. In the second 4 months there were 116 deaths, the highest level of the 5 years, 45 per cent above the average. In the third 4 months there were 119 deaths. This period normally has a high incidence of anencephaly, as Professor McKeown pointed out. It is again highest, but only 26 per cent above average.

Our conclusions are that Asian influenza approximately doubles the risk of anencephaly, but that this risk has been too slight to be detected in the studies in the United States and in England. It was detected in Dublin where anencephaly is common.

I refer now to the possibility that background radiation produces an observable increase in the frequency of congenital malformations. Dr. Neel, like Dr. Landauer, mentioned the publication of the Atomic Energy Commission and said that in his opinion the present data were not utilizable to test this hypothesis. I agree and believe that they are irrelevant. The data of Gentry, Parkhurst and Bulin are of much greater significance. However, there are some difficulties about accepting them. First, we must remember that the association was with specific geologic backgrounds and not with high doses of irradiation, and it has to be shown that there was the close association with radiation that was anticipated. Second, sporadic measurements of radiation suggest that the maximum difference between the areas was not more than 50 per cent. The difference in congenital malformations was 36 per cent, too large to fit in with any of our present theoretic concepts.

The third point—and I think an important one—is that malformations were by no means fully recorded in Gentry's study. Less than one half of the deaths attributed to malformation under the age of 1 year had been recognized at birth. For example, the incidence of mongolism was recorded as 0.3 per 1,000. It is reasonable to conclude that at least one half of the significant malformations were missed. Therefore differences in recording may account for the results.

In a recent survey, we made fairly accurate estimates of the radiation dose received by residents in 4 parts of Scotland. Aberdeen, built almost entirely of granite, had 40 per cent more external gamma radiation than Edinburgh and Dundee. However, in terms of gonad dose, the difference was only 20 per cent. The data provided by the Registrar General for the last 5 years gives the incidence of stillbirths and infant deaths (per 1,000 total births) due to malformations as follows: Scotland, 10.4; Glasgow, 11.3; Dundee, 10.5; Edinburgh, 9.7; and Aberdeen, 5.4. This result is not surprising. One would expect background effects to be obscured by other causes. These data suggest that we should hesitate to accept Gentry's data as evidence of the quantitative effect of background radiation on congenital malformations.

DR. HORSFALL: A large amount of thought and much work has been expended on so-called extrinsic factors that may contribute to the occurrence of congenital malformations, and numerous hypotheses have been subjected to such tests as have been feasible. Unfortunately, the yield so far has been slender in relation to the dimensions of the problem.

As Dr. Warkany has pointed out, extrinsic factors known to be causally related— iron deficiency, German measles, possibly radiation—account for only a negligible fraction of malformations. Many as yet unknown factors may contribute to the occur-

rence of malformations. We should consider carefully the suggestion of Dr. Landauer that seemingly trivial interrelationships between so-called intrinsic and extrinsic factors may produce dislocations that result in malformations. More serious dislocations may interfere with viability.

In the absence of an acceptable unifying principle, separation between extrinsic and intrinsic factors may be artificial. Genes and viruses are similar chemically: both appear to be manifestations of specialized nucleic acid structure; both seem to affect enzyme character and, therefore, metabolic activity; indeed, some viruses seem to induce what has been referred to as infective heredity. In the light of this, any differentiation between intrinsic and extrinsic factors seems to be tenuous at best.

As Dr. Rhodes has emphasized, rubella seems to stand apart in being unequivocally related to malformations. Yet, suggestive data have been accumulated in respect of other virus diseases; for example, influenza and mumps. Also, important results have been obtained with attenuated virus vaccines in animals; for example, hog cholera and blue tongue. They lead one to suspect strongly that rubella is not unique in its relation to malformations. Of course, mumps is viremic. Some may question whether influenza can be related to the occurrence of congenital malformations, since there is no evidence that it leads to viremia and much that it does not. But noninfective influenza virus particles are toxic, and far more noninfective particles are produced than infective. If these reach the embryo and there exert toxic effects on the central nervous system, the induction of congenital malformations could be understood readily. Since smallpox virus, the largest of the true viruses that is known, can penetrate the placenta, there is no reason to suspect that any smaller virus can not do the same.

Some thought should be given to the more than 100 viral agents that are seen so commonly in normal persons, both in the respiratory tract and in the intestine. The important distinction between viral infection and viral disease should be emphasized. Most studies have been directed toward discovering a relation between recognizable viral diseases of the mother which, of course, are defined in clinical terms. Is it not possible that viral infection of the mother, which is so extremely common, may result in overt viral disease of the embryo? Viral infection would not be recognized in clinical signs, but viral disease of the embryo could well result in malformations, as in the case of rubella.

Extensive prospective serologic studies might provide information on this hypothesis. Individual, premarital serum specimens might be stored frozen and additional serum specimens obtained at the first visit for suspected pregnancy, as well as at intervals of 3 months thereafter. The first visit is only rarely earlier than 2 months and is generally at 3 months. Later comparison of antibody levels in sera from each individual, against numerous human viruses, would reveal viral infections of the mother before, during and after the 1st trimester of pregnancy. Then such data could be correlated with the occurrence of congenital malformations discovered after pregnancy was completed. This procedure would provide information on each of the numerous viruses that could be employed in such serologic tests and would have the further advantage of a high degree of specificity, which, in most viral diseases, is not provided by clinical evaluation alone.

In conclusion, although it is evident that only a few of the factors that contribute to the occurrence of congenital malformations have been identified positively so far, it will be surprising if current broadening interest in them does not soon lead to the discovery and the identification of many more. With precise knowledge of cause at hand, can we not look forward to effective prevention?

PROFESSOR TÖNDURY: Many fetuses die if their mothers have had rubella in the 1st trimester of pregnancy. Mortality is highest when the mother is infected in the 2nd month. The rate decreases with infections that occur later in pregnancy. This is readily understood when we remember that the fetus is extraordinarily sensitive to various noxae during the 2nd month.

I wish to discuss two questions. First: Why and of what do the fetuses die? Fifty per cent of the fetuses of mothers infected during the 2nd month die. I have examined 47 fetuses of various ages and wish to draw attention to the changes found in the heart. The heart of a fetus 15 days after the appearance of the disease in his mother showed that parts of the myocardium were abnormal. Sections from the wall of the heart with normal myocardial tissue had adjoining necrotic muscle. The cellular nuclei were pyknotic, and the muscle fibers and the cytoplasm were markedly eosinophilic. Parts of the necrotic muscular tissue were seen expelled into the circulation. In another section, normal fibers and necrotic muscle fibers were seen with a reaction of the endocardium. The endocardium is transformed into a syncytium and expelled into the blood vessels. This process results in a denudation of the interior surface of the myocardium which enables the infusion of necrotic parts into the circulation. This process was clearly visible in another section. The expelled endocardium formed giant cells, and the myocardium was denuded. Myocardial substance was expelled into the circulation, and the arteries of the fetus were obstructed. This kind of myocardial necrosis was encountered in 15 human fetuses, and in all of them we observed expulsion of the endocardium with formation of giant cells and arterial emboli, causing obstructions in the vessels. In the same way, a septum, which was formed normally, again may be destroyed. Evidently, therefore, the histologic investigation of the fetuses must not be neglected, for it elucidates the action of the virus.

I refer now to the effect of poliomyelitis in pregnancy. Some authors presume the fetus to become infected; others do not.

However, the statistics of Siegel and Greenberg (1956), show that 21.6 per cent of the fetuses die. I have investigated microscopically 10 human fetuses whose mothers had been infected during the 2nd and the 3rd months. Externally, the fetuses were completely normal.

I showed a section representing the brain of a fetus of the 3rd month, fixed 30 days after the outbreak of the disease in the mother. This showed a section through one hemisphere. This was the anuclear lamina zonalis. Beneath it was the primitive cortex, and there were 2 large cysts in the zona intermedia. The walls of the cysts were loosely constructed, their surroundings being completely nonreactive. The cerebral tissue clearly had reacted to the noxious agent.

Another section showed the cause of the development of the cysts. One saw again the primitive cortex and a blood vessel surrounded by erythrocytes, where a hemorrhage had occurred; the cerebral tissue into which it had bled had been dissolved subsequently. The nonreactivity of the surroundings was striking. The question is now: Is this abnormality caused by the action of the poliovirus?

Another section also showed a large cyst. One could still recognize the blood vessel in its interior. The surrounding tissue into which blood had penetrated had been dissolved. The brains of such fetuses are interspersed with innumerable cysts.

We now have found the solution of the enigma in connection with the investigation of the spinal cord. The spinal cord already functioned in fetuses of this age. In the ventral horn were cells which were almost completely mature.

In the next section one saw normal cells of the ventral horn taken from the spinal cord of a human fetus with a length of 12 cm. It showed the big cystiform cellular nuclei with the nucleolus and, in the cell plasm, the typical diffusely spread large granular Nissl bodies.

The last section showed the spinal cord of the fetus whose brain I referred to earlier. Changes of the cellular nuclei were recognizable. The cellular nuclei were inflated and pressed to the cellular walls. These were the so-called "fish-eye nuclei." All the Nissl substance lay close to their walls. Moreover, the Nissl bodies had agglutinated, forming a conglomerate. This is the picture described in children who have had poliomyelitis. The only difference is the complete absence of any reaction. However, the motor neurons are about to dissolve, and a similar destructive process occurs throughout the ventral horn of the spinal cord, as other preparations have demonstrated.

In the light of these observations, based on 6 human fetuses, we may assume that the polio virus is able to penetrate into the fetal blood circulation, causing serious injuries in the brain and the spinal cord. The fetuses die and probably are expelled. This is why symptoms have not been observed in surviving fetuses whose mothers have had poliomyelitis in the 2nd or the 3rd month.

Finally, I wish to refer to the significance of Asian influenza. Asian influenza appeared in epidemic form in Switzerland in the autumn of 1957, and we corroborated the observations of Hamburger and Habel on the effect of influenza A virus on the chicken fetus. In young human fetuses of the 2nd month, a general injury resulted, usually affecting the brain. From the 7th month, however, we demonstrated the existence of a typical pneumonia with alveolar hemorrhages. Therefore, we must assume that maternal influenza is related to the injuries encountered in the fetuses.

PROFESSOR WALKER: In time, no doubt, elucidation of the interaction of genetic and external agents will lead to control of many major malformations of human populations. At present, however, the clinician is often helpless when confronted by the problem of malformation. Although the majority of malformations do not recur, some do; for example, anencephaly and hydrocephaly.

Clinical experience suggests that social

class is significant in the etiology of many malformations but particularly in anencephaly. Social class reflects the influence of many variables, such as housing, overcrowding, risk of infection, diet, rest, noise and exposure to toxic agents. The marriage pattern is also important. In social class V, those who are poorly endowed tend to remain in the same class, whereas those who are well-endowed tend to marry into a higher class. Less well-endowed people in higher classes tend to marry into lower classes. This means that there are genetic as well as environmental differences between classes.

The ethnic observations on anencephaly are somewhat inconsistent with the class variation, since in colored populations of America and Africa, anencephaly is comparatively rare. Moreover, even among women from the poorest circumstances, malformed offspring are uncommon. Of course, we cannot exclude the possibility that many malformations are lost as abortions.

From a clinical point of view, it seems most important that we should begin to consider the significance of the subclinical states which Dr. Horsfall outlined. Moreover, many viral infections which are recognizable clinically are never reported. For example, many cases of mumps undoubtedly are missed.

Another question of considerable interest is the possibility that folic acid deficiency in early pregnancy may be teratogenic. This has been demonstrated in experimental animals. In some parts of Great Britain, approximately 5 per cent of patients have a manifest folic acid defiiciency in late pregnancy.

MODERATOR BAIRD: I would like to ask Dr. Warkany about the significance of nutrition. During the war in Britain and other countries, the death rate from all causes fell quite considerably. However, this was not true for malformations. Yet, in the city of Aberdeen, we find big differences in the incidence of central nervous system malforma-

tions by social class. Professor Walker has referred to the poor nutrition of mothers in Class V whose growth is inhibited. They have an excess of malformations of the central nervous system but not of malformations of soft tissues. Can Dr. Warkany explain these observations? Also, it is reported that in the slums in Hong Kong and Singapore central nervous malformations are very uncommon, whereas cleft palate and some other abnormalities are common. Why should there be this difference? Is it related to nutrition?

DR. WARKANY: In animal experiments in which we have well-controlled observations, there is a definite difference between results of specific nutritional deficiency and of general starvation. Unspecific, nutritional deficiency may not be capable of producing malformations but may kill the embryo. However, there is at least one exception: Dr. Runner has shown that in a certain strain of mice, starvation of the mother does cause exencephaly—a condition which would end as anencephaly if development continued.

MODERATOR BAIRD: Dr. Milne of the United Kingdom asks: Why does Dr. Rhodes feel that malformations due to other viruses should conform to the syndrome which is associated with rubella?

DR. RHODES: I did not intend to imply that malformations due to other viruses need necessarily be the same as those produced by rubella, although I think they are likely to be so. There is a remarkable similarity in the biochemical structure of viruses, although they can be divided into a DNA group and an RNA group. Therefore, one would expect that pathologic changes induced by these viruses growing inside cells also would be similar.

MODERATOR BAIRD: What would the advice of the panel be in relation to poliomyelitis immunization of pregnant women in view of Dr. Rhodes's comment?

DR. RHODES: My remarks related specifically to the live, attenuated polimyelitis vaccines which are living viruses and some strains of which at least are known to cause viremia. There is no evidence of which I am aware that formalinized Salk-type poliomyelitis immunization has any adverse effect on pregnant women.

MODERATOR BAIRD: Mr. Denis Brown asks: Will the panel comment on the suggestion that the mechanical conditions of pregnancy may affect the child?

PROFESSOR WALKER: It is doubtful whether oligohydramnios and position of the baby have any effect except in rare instances. Among pregnancies which continue for much longer than normal, the incidence of oligohydramnios is 10 to 20 per cent, but there is no measurable increase in the frequency of fetal malformation. One would like to investigate this problem by prospective methods, if it were possible to measure the amniotic fluid during pregnancy.

MODERATOR BAIRD: Dr. Beck of the United Kingdom, asks: Is there any evidence that excessive intake of vitamin A is a cause of congenital malformation in man?

DR. WARKANY: Dr. Cohlan described congenital malformations due to hypervitaminosis A in rats and mice. In our laboratory we have used the same method with success, and hypervitaminosis A undoubtedly causes congenital malformations in rodents. However, the doses given are enormous: in the case of a rat between 50,000 and 150,000 international units. Comparable doses are never likely to be given in man, and a slight increase in vitamin A intake does not produce malformations in experimental animals.

MODERATOR BAIRD: Dr. de Rom of Belgium, asks: Is it not possible that hyperthermia by itself causes some disturbances in organogenesis and that this factor must be taken into account when studying the possible influence of viral disease during pregnancy?

DR. HORSFALL: I cannot speak of the effects of hyperthemia on organogenesis from my own experience, but many viral diseases cause exceedingly high fevers—measles, for example—without causing congenital malformation. Moreover, rubella does not usually produce a high temperature.

SESSION IV

General Developmental Mechanisms

Moderator

PROFESSOR CONRAD H. WADDINGTON, C.B.E., F.R.S.
Institute of Animal Genetics, University of Edinburgh,
West Mains Road, Edinburgh, Scotland, United Kingdom

INDUCTIVE MECHANISMS
EDGAR ZWILLING, Ph.D.
Department of Biology, Brandeis University, Waltham, Massachusetts, U.S.A.

NERVE GROWTH CONTROLLING FACTORS
RITA LEVI-MONTALCINI, Ph.D.
Department of Zoology, Washington University, St. Louis, Missouri, U.S.A.

NUCLEOCYTOPLASMIC INTERACTIONS DURING DEVELOPMENT
C. L. MARKERT, Ph.D.
Professor of Biology, Johns Hopkins University, Baltimore 18, Maryland, U.S.A.

Inductive Mechanisms

EDGAR ZWILLING, Ph.D.

During the course of their development, few, if any, structures in the body of vertebrate organisms are elaborated without the proper initial interaction of their constituent tissues. The evidence is clear that the formation of particular specialized tissues and organ components results from the transmission of some type of stimulus from a neighboring tissue to the responding tissue and, under most circumstances, that the particular development fails in the absence of the stimulus. Such phenomena have been called "inductions" or "inductive interactions." It may be well to cite the operationally convenient definition of Grobstein[14] which has the merit of indicating that both tissue components may be altered by their association. This states that

... inductive tissue interaction takes place whenever in development two or more tissues of different history and properties become intimately associated and alteration of the developmental course of the interactants results.

The best way to illustrate an inductive interaction is to indicate the consequences of its failure to occur. Probably the most dramatic example which can be cited is that of the amphibian exogastrula originally described by Holtfreter.[18] The pattern of invagination of the embryo of a salamander or a frog may be altered in such a way that all of the tissue which normally would migrate into the interior of the embryo moves outward from the blastopore. The result is a situation in which the tissue which would have formed the nervous system and related sensory structures does not make contact with the layer which normally should be in intimate association with it. As a consequence, the ectoderm differentiates into a rather simple epidermis and lacks all of the complex structures which should form from it under normal circumstances.

Information about inductive processes has been sought through a variety of experimental procedures which have involved transplantation, grafting, tissue and organ culture and a variety of combinations of these technics. The recent use of enzymes and chelating agents for separating tissue layers has enabled the experimenter to extend his range of manipulations. Careful studies of the effects of a variety of environmental and hereditary anomalies have made important contributions. While there have been many attempts to obtain an understanding of the molecular basis for inductive interactions, to date these have proved to be elusive, and most of our knowledge of these phenomena remains at a biologic level.

In this presentation, I should like to highlight some of the problems of tissue interaction with an account of the development of chicken limbs and then, as a basis for later discussion, to outline some of our knowledge about inductive mechanisms in general.

The developing chicken limb is a favorable object for studies of this sort. It is readily accessible to the experimenter; it may be removed from the embryo and then replaced in a variety of graft situations after subjection to manipulations of various sorts. In addition to this, there are a number of mutations which have proved to be of value in these analyses. When they first appear on the 3rd day of embryonic development, chick limb buds consist of two simple components. There is an inner core of rather uniform mesoderm and an outer covering of ectoderm. The latter is composed of two cell layers: a single cell thickness of low cuboidal epithelium which is covered by another single cell thickness of an epitrichial layer. Along the free edge of the bud, the epidermis is specialized and takes the form of a thickened crestlike structure known as the apical ectodermal ridge. The first experimental analysis which revealed an important developmental role for this ectodermal structure was performed by Saunders in 1948.[24] Surgical removal of the ridge from wing buds was followed by a cessation of limb outgrowth. The proximal regions of the limb developed as though they were still part of a normal limb, i.e., the size of the basal structures was normal even though distal parts were missing. The deficiencies were more extensive in a proximal direction when younger buds were subjected to this surgery than when older buds were used. Evidently, limb development involved a proximodistal sequence of establishment of limb parts in which the apical ectodermal ridge was intimately involved.

At that time, we were studying an amelic mutant, the so-called wingless mutation of Waters and Bywaters.[31] In this genetic condition, the homozygous recessives fail to form wings. The striking thing was that the gene-mediated anomalies were almost exactly like Saunders' surgically produced conditions in that the basal portions of the wings did form and were normal in size. An examination of the early embryos revealed that normal wing buds were present during the early part of the 3rd day but that the ectodermal ridge degenerated during the course of that day. Failure of wing elaboration was correlated with the gene-mediated elimination of the ridge and provided a striking corroboration of Saunders' conclusions about the importance of that structure for limb development.

Saunders[25,26] continued his analysis and was able to show that blocks of mesodermal tissue, ordinarily destined to become part of the thigh, would form digits when placed in contact with the ectodermal ridge in such a way that they came to lie in the distal regions of the limb. Limb type characteristics were retained by these tissues, since typical foot digits formed even when mesoderm from a leg bud was grafted beneath the ridge of a wing bud. The application of the technics of tissue layer separation and recombination (by means of trypsin and chelating agents) enabled us to extend the analysis of limb development. The inductive capacity of the ectodermal ridge was demonstrated in a positive way by experiments in which the mesoderm from a single limb bud was provided with more than one ridge and, as a consequence, developed two sets of distal structures: (1) those in which the ridge was rotated 90° to its original position; (2) induced limbs which were oriented in accordance with its new position.

Evidence that there was a reciprocal relationship between the two limb bud components was obtained from experiments in which genetically normal ectodermal ridges were combined with mesoderm from mutant limb buds. When such combinations were made with mesoderm from wingless buds, it was found that this mesoderm could respond to the outgrowth inducing influence of the normal ectoderm, since there was more elongation of such grafts than in control limbs, but that the integrity of the genetically normal ectodermal ridge was not maintained when it was associated with the mutant mesoderm. After a short interval, the ridge degenerated, and the limb outgrowth stopped. Our suspicions about the dependence of the ridge on some mesodermal factor were strengthened by the results of experiments with polydactylous buds (Po^d). Such limb buds cannot be distinguished from normal ones at the early stages which we employed. As they develop, it becomes evident that the formation of the accessory distal structures is preceded by the appearance of a more extensive apical ectodermal thickening than is found in normal buds. Mutant limb components were combined with genetically normal ones to determine which was responsible for the excess development. The results were clear. The genetically normal ridge, under the influence of the mutant mesoderm, was more extensive than normal, and the typical pattern of polydactyly was evinced in these combinations. On the other hand, the accessory limb components could be eliminated from a potentially polydactylous limb by merely removing an appropriate region of the ectodermal ridge (Hansborough, unpublished).

These results, along with others which I shall not relate, have been interpreted as follows: The sequential elaboration of limb parts depends on an inductive interaction between the ectoderm and the mesoderm. Outgrowth and continued formation of the more distal limb structures are due to an influence exerted on the mesoderm by the ectoderm, especially the ectodermal ridge. However, the ridge is not an independent structure but, in turn, requires some contribution from the mesoderm for its continued existence and activity. The mesodermal factor responsible for this function is distributed asymmetrically and produces resultant asymmetries in the ridge and the associated outgrowths which are typical for each limb type.[36]

Recently Saunders and his group[27] have performed an experiment which they have interpreted as confirming the above hypothesis. They have rotated the distal tips of wing buds and have replaced them, in reverse orientation, on the proximal stump in such a way that the anterior part of the tip is fused to the posterior end of the stump. A large proportion of such grafts develop duplicated distal structures, almost identical with those of mutant "duplicate" wings. Saunders interprets this to mean that the original region of high maintenance factor is maintained in the tip, while a second region of high ectodermal ridge maintenance factor is established as a result of the tip's contact with the region of high concentration in the stump. Amprino and Camosso[1] have per-

formed the same experiment independently and have obtained the same results but have interpreted them differently.

Reciprocal dependence between the interacting tissues of an inductive system is not unique to the developing limb. While the details may differ, similar relationships have been found during the development of the tail fin of salamanders[3] and the formation of feather germs in the chick.[29] Many other well-known examples may be cited. Another feature of inductive processes also should be mentioned; many structures form only after a series of inductions have taken place. To cite a well-known case: the formation of an eye involves first the induction of the brain by the underlying tissue, then the formation of the optic vesicle from the forebrain, induction of lens by optic vesicle and then the induction of the cornea by the lens and the optic cup. Reciprocal relationships are involved in the formation of the eye, too, since neither a normal eye cup or lens will develop without the continued normal association between the two structures.

While many attempts have been made to extend analyses of inductive mechanisms to the molecular level, to date, these have provided us with suggestive models but with no details for any particular case of inductive interaction. Most of the research has been concerned with the response of isolated bits of very early gastrula tissues, almost exclusively from amphibian embryos, and has involved the testing of various sorts of extracts from adult tissues[22,35] as well as the effects of substances released into a medium by embryonic tissues which have been cultured for long periods. In addition, indirect inferences have been made from experiments in which responsive tissues have been placed in contact with adult tissues which have been killed in various ways.[9,30] The first group of experiments, while not completely unequivocal, suggest the nucleoproteins or fractions thereof are important stimulators of differentiation. Niu favors the nucleic acid moiety, Yamada and his group a protein fraction, while Brachet[6] considers the nucleoprotein complex to be important in this regard. Brachet and his group have presented indirect evidence from studies of embryos under a variety of conditions which lend strong support to the involvement of nucleoproteins in the induction of the neural plate. There is some recent evidence that specific differentiations may be induced by particular nucleic acid or microsomal preparations. Niu[23] has claimed that liver and kidney may be induced by liver and kidney nucleic acids, and Ebert[10] has shown that heart microsomes may transform tissues of the chorioallantoic membrane of a chick embryo into cardiac tissue.

Since there has been so much uncertainty about the nature of the stimulus transmitted from the activating to the responding tissue in these systems, one important approach to the problem has been a study of the nature of the transmission mechanism. Are inducing substances freely diffusable or do they depend on some intimate tissue contact? Grobstein[13,15] and Grobstein and Dalton[17] have provided the most complete analysis of this question as it applies to the development of the submandibular (salivary) gland and the metanephric kidney-nerve cord inductive system of the mouse. By a combination of in-vitro technics—the use of Millipore filters with known porosity and thickness as well as electron microscopy—they have shown unequivocally that interaction in these secondary inductive systems may occur in the absence of cell contact between the interactants. However, the evidence does not support the notion that freely diffusable substances are involved, since these particular reactions did not occur across distances which exceeded 70 to 80 μ.[16] Preliminary findings indicated that a mucopolysaccharide may be involved. Grobstein's results are in contrast with those of others who have worked with other inductive systems and have shown that the interposition of a barrier between the interactants inhibits the induction. Some of these experiments have been crude

in that the porosity of the barriers has not been well controlled. Brachet has shown that induction between the neural plate and the roof of archenteron will not occur through an agar or thin cellophane barrier but may occur weakly through one with pores large enough (3.4 μ) to allow particles to pass.[4] Brahma[7] found no evidence of inductive transmission across Gradocol membranes with pore diameters of 4 mμ and 1.45 μ; but Saxén[28] has demonstrated the passage of neural inductive activity across a Millipore filter with .8 μ pores. It is interesting to note that McKeehan[20] has shown that lens induction does not occur through a thin cellophane barrier, but recently the same author[21] found that it may take place through a thin agar film. Lash, Holtzer and Holtzer[19] have shown that vertebral cartilage may be induced by spinal cord through a Millipore filter of .8 μ porosity.

We see from even this very brief glance at inductive mechanisms that no strong generalizations can be made at the present. Indeed, current information leads us to expect diverse mechanisms for different inductive systems despite the features which are common to many of them. The following are a number of suggested mechanisms which may be important; all of them should be evaluated carefully for each inductive system. These are essentially as outlined in Grobstein's analysis[14]:

1. Involvement of diffusible substances.
   A. Substrates for induced enzymes.
   B. Small molecules which may be involved, in one or the other interactant, in a specific synthesis.[33]
   C. Large soluble molecules which pass from one layer to the other.[34]
2. Contact interaction between tissues.
   A. Without transfer of material, but resulting in important molecular reorientation.[32]
   B. With transfer of particulates.[5,6]
3. Interaction between intercellular matrices.[13,14]

In the present context, a discussion of inductive mechanisms would be incomplete without some mention of how their malfunctioning may result in the production of congenital malformations. Whether mediated via environmental or hereditable factors, interference with inductive systems may have drastic consequences. Anomalies may result from: (1) distortion of the inductive pattern; (2) failure of the interactants to make proper contact; (3) loss of inductive capacity; or (4) loss of the ability to respond.

Examples of distortion of inductive patterns are numerous. Microcephaly and anterior duplications undoubtedly result from disturbances in the pattern of the head inducer. Polydactyly may result from an atypical distribution of ridge maintenance factor. Many other examples may be cited.

Two consequences of the second type of failure are anophthalmia and renal agenesis. Chase and Chase[8] have described the developmental events which precede the eyelessness or microphthalmia which are found in an anophthalmic strain of mice. In the extreme expression, the eye vesicle forms but does not make contact with the overlying epidermis from which the lens normally is induced. As a consequence, a lens does not form, and the vesicle remains quite rudimentary. In some cases, a reduced optic cup does make contact with the epidermis and induces a small lens. The presumption here is that growth of the optic vesicle is at fault, and that eye development fails because the two interacting tissues fail to make contact, but that the inducing and responding capacities of the two tissues are unimpaired.

A somewhat similar situation has been shown by Gluecksohn-Schoenheimer[11] to be responsible for the failure of metanephric kidney development of Sd mice. Normally, kidney tubules are induced by the ureteric duct which grows up from the posterior end of the mesonephric duct. In Sd mutants, the ureters frequently fail to branch and make contact with the bulk of the metanephrogenous tissue, and kidneys fail to develop or are represented by very rudimentary structures.

Preliminary results from an in-vitro analysis of the mutant tissues have revealed that both components interact reasonably normally when combined with a genetically normal partner.[12] These data support the notion that kidney agenesis in Sd mice results from a failure of proper branching of the ureter and not in its loss of inductive capacity.

The wingless mutant represents an example of loss of inductive capacity. As described above, the mutant mesodern fails to maintain the ectodermal ridge, and the consequence is amelia due to the loss of the ectoderm's capacity to induce limb outgrowth.

An in-vitro analysis of the somites of brachyuric mice[2] has provided us with an example of failure of a reacting system. Grossly abnormal somites are one feature of this lethal monozygous condition. The experiments showed that the mutant somites could not form cartilage when placed in contact with nerve cord, the normal inducer of vertebral cartilages. However, the mutant nerve cord could induce cartilage formation from genetically normal somites.

Numerous examples similar to the above exist in the literature, and many more remain to be clarified. In closing, it may be well to emphasize that there also is a strong reciprocal relation between studies of anomalies and efforts to understand normal development. Proper attention to both with modern methods will continue to be mutually rewarding.

REFERENCES

1. Amprino, R., and Camosso, M.: Experimental observations on influence exerted by the proximal over the distal territories of the extremities, Experientia 14:241-243, 1958.
2. Bennet, D.: In vitro studies of cartilage induction in T/T mice, Nature 181:1286, 1958.
3. Bodenstein, D.: Studies on the development of the dorsal fin in amphibians, J. Exper. Zool. 120:213-245, 1952.
4. Brachet, J., and de Scoeux, F. H.: Remarques sur le mode d'action de l'organisateur

chez les amphibiens, J. Cyto-embryo. Belg. Neerl. 3:56-60, 1949.

5. Brachet, J.: Chemical Embryology, New York, Interscience, 1950.

6. ————: Biochemical Cytology, New York, Academic Press, 1957.

7. Brahma, S. K.: Experiments on the diffusibility of the amphibian evocator, J. Embryol. & Exper. Morph. 6:418-423, 1958.

8. Chase, H. B., and Chase, E. B.: Studies on an anophthalmic strain of mice. I. Embryology of the eye region, J. Morph. 68:279-301, 1941.

9. Chuang, H.: Weitere Versuche Über die Veränderung der Induktions-leistungen von Gekochten Organteilen, Arch. f. Entwmech. Org. 140:25-38, 1940.

10. Ebert, J.: Viruses as tools in studying embryonic development, Carnegie Inst. of Washington, Year Book 58:406-410, 1959.

11. Gluecksohn-Schoenheimer, S.: The embryonic development of mutants of the Sd-strain in mice, Genetics 30:29-38, 1945.

12. Gluecksohn-Waelsch, S.: in discussion of Hadorn, E., "Role of Genes in Developmental Processes," in McElroy, W. D. and Glass, B. (eds.): Chemical Basis of Development, p. 793, Baltimore, Marylanu, Johns Hopkins Press, 1958.

13. Grobstein, C.: Tissue interaction in the morphogenesis of mouse embryonic rudiments in vitro in Rudnick, D. (ed.): Aspects of Synthesis and Order in Growth, pp. 233-256, Princeton, New Jersey, Princeton Univ. Press, 1954.

14. ————: Inductive tissue interaction in development, Advances Cancer Res. 4:187-236, 1956.

15. ————: Trans-filter induction of tubules in mouse metanephrogenic mesenchyme, Exper. Cell. Res. 10:424-440, 1956.

16. ————: Some transmission characteristics of the tubule-inducing influence on mouse metanephrogenic mesenchyme, Exper. Cell. Res. 13:575-587, 1957.

17. Grobstein, C., and Dalton, A. J.: Kidney tubule induction in mouse metanephrogenic mesenchyme without cytoplasmic contact, J. Exper. Zool. 135:57-73, 1957.

18. Holtfreter, J.: Die totale Exogastrulation, eine Selbstablösung des Ektoderms vom Entomesoderm, Arch. f. Entwmech. Org. 129:669-793, 1933.

19. Lass, J., Holtzer, S., and Holtzer, H.: An experimental analysis of the development of the spinal column. VI. Aspects of carti-

lage induction, Exper. Cell. Res. 13:292-303, 1957.

20. McKeehan, M. S.: Cytological aspects of embryonic lens induction in the chick, J. Exper. Zool., 117:31-64, 1951.

21. ————: Induction of portions of the chick lens without contact with the optic cup, Anat. Rec. 132:297-305, 1958.

22. Niu, M. C.: New approaches to the problem of embryonic induction in Rudnick, D. (ed.): Cellular Mechanisms in Differentiation and Growth, pp. 155-171, Princeton, New Jersey, Princeton Univ. Press, 1956.

23. ————: Current evidence concerning chemical inducers, in Evolution of Nervous Control, pp. 7-30, Washington, D.C., AAAS, 1959.

24. Saunders, J. W.: The proximo-distal sequence of origin of the parts of the chick wing and the role of the ectoderm, J. Exper. Zool. 108:363-403, 1948.

25. Saunders, J. W., Cairns, J. M., and Gasseling, M. T.: The role of the apical ridge of ectoderm in the differentiation of the morphological structure and inductive specificity of limb parts in the chick, J. Morph. 101:57-87, 1957.

26. Saunders, J. W., Gasseling, M. T., and Cairns, J. M.: Effect of implantation site on the development of an implant in the chick embryo, Nature 175:673-674, 1955.

27. Saunders, J. W., Gasseling, M. T., and Gfeller, M. D.: Interactions of ectoderm and mesoderm in the origin of axial relationships in the wing of the fowl, J. Exper. Zool. 137:39-74, 1958.

28. Saxén, L.: Transfilter neural induction of amphibian ectoderm, Dev. Biol. 3:140-152, 1961.

29. Sengel, P.: La différenciation de la peau et des germes plumaires de l'embryon de poulet en culture in vitro, Année biol. 34:29-52, 1958.

30. Toivonen, S.: Stoffliche Induktoren, Rev. Suisse Zool. 57(Suppl.):41-50, 1950.

31. Waters, N. P. and Bywaters, J. H.: A lethal embryonic wing mutation in the domestic fowl, J. Hered. 34:213-217, 1943.

32. Weiss, P.: The problem of specificity in growth and development, Yale J. Biol. & Med. 19:235-278, 1947.

33. Wilde, C. E.: Differentiation in response to the biochemical environment in Rudnick, D. (ed.): Cell Organism and Milieu, pp. 3-43, New York, Ronald Press, 1959.

34. Woerdemann, M. W.: Immunological ap-

proach to some problems of induction and differentiation *in* Butler, E. (ed.) : Biological Specificity and Growth, pp. 33-53, Princeton, New Jersey, Princeton Univ. Press, 1955.

35. Yamada, T.: Embryonic induction *in* McElroy, W. D., and Glass, B. (eds.) :

Chemical Basis of Development, pp. 217-238, Baltimore, Maryland, Johns Hopkins Press, 1958.

36. Zwilling, E.: Reciprocal dependence of ectoderm and mesoderm during chick embryo limb development, Am. Nat. 90:257-265, 1956.

Nerve-Growth Controlling Factors

RITA LEVI-MONTALCINI, Ph.D.

INTRODUCTION

Long before an embryologist thrust his glass needle into the brain vesicles of an amphibian embryo, it was known that the developing nervous system can be altered without substantial harm to the organism. Nature already had performed a countless number of such experiments, and legions of more or less severely brain-injured animals and men had survived long enough to witness the tolerance of all organisms for such mishaps. The survival and the further development of amphibian larvae after drastic brain operations were no exceptions to this rule.

It was not the investigation of this problem which suggested the experiment and directed the needle through the soft embryonic tissues but rather the hope to gain information about some more subtle aspect of neurogenesis which no spontaneous brain accident or gross malformation could elucidate. The experiments performed in the first two decades of the century were aimed at the analysis of the interrelations between the developing nervous system and the innervated organs. As the problem gained in precision and the surgical procedures improved, the glass or the steel needle performed more and more discrete operations, and the field of investigation narrowed down to a few well-delimited problems of neurogenesis. The progress achieved in recent years in this field is due to a large extent to the realization that the spinal cord and the spinal ganglia are more suitable objects for investigation than the complex brain centers. No less important was the more nearly correct timing of the postsurgical observations. In fact, it was realized that only by exploring the developmental processes at short time intervals after the operation, and by extending the observations to as many developmental stages as possible in operated and in control embryos, could one hope to gain an insight into the mechanisms of neurogenesis.

The achievements, the problems and the perspectives in this field were the object of monographs and extensive review articles in past as well as recent years.[10,13 17,19,35,36]

The present discussion will cover only a small sector of the field of developmental neurology and will reflect the main interest of the writer in this field. As indicated in the title, the discussion will center on the analysis of some nerve-growth controlling agents. The topic as well as the designation of these agents calls for some comment.

It was pointed out by P. Weiss that growth "is a word that covers like a blanket a multitude of various things and meanings."[37] The author warned against the use or rather the misuse of the term "growth." This criticism is well founded, and one can only agree in regretting the indiscriminate use of this word which came to indicate different and often dissimilar aspects of developmental processes. The student of neurogenesis, even more than students of other biologic systems, is confronted with the problem of the correct use of the term "growth," for in no cells does growth present itself in such a variety of aspects as in nerve cells. The structural complexity of nerve cells and nerve centers, already apparent since early embryonic life, is only one of the causes of perplexity in defining growth. Nerve cells, at variance with other cells also continue to increase in size even if at a much-reduced rate in the mature organism, and growth may be reactivated dramatically in adult nerve cells following transection of their neurite. Conversely, growth in the same cells may be interfered with and altogether blocked by simple experimental procedures which proved to be particularly successful when applied to embryos in early developmental stages. The simplicity of the technic was an open invitation to perform the experiments and to draw conclusions. The experiments consisted of either decreasing or respectively increasing the peripheral field of innervation of primary motor and sensory spinal neurons in amphibian larvae and in chick embryos by extirpating the limb buds or by transplanting additional limb buds in proximity to the limb of the host.

The operations invariably resulted in a parallel decrease or increase in the population of nerve cells innervating the experimentally depleted or enlarged field of innervation. The deceptive clarity of the results of these experiments suggested a simple and apparently satisfactory conclusion: growth in nerve cells is under control of the field of innervation, and the effect is mediated by nerve fibers which branch or are prevented from branching in the periphery. A linear relationship was indicated between the size of nerve centers and the extension of the innervated area.

We are not planning to discuss the results of these experiments and to comment on the complexity of these apparently simple phenomina, since they were analyzed and discussed extensively in some of the previous original papers and review articles.[10,12-19,35,36] Instead, we shall limit ourselves to the consideration of the response of nerve cells to two chemical agents. One belongs to the class of hormones, its chemical structure as well as its effects are known, and it seems to fit well into the more general field of endocrine effects. The other was discovered, only recently, and its biologic properties as well as its functional significance are still far from being well-known and understood. The comparison of the response of nerve cells to these two different agents will offer the opportunity of considering some aspects of growth processes and discussing some developmental mechanisms which may apply to all cells and not only to some nerve cells.

HORMONAL EFFECTS ON DEVELOPMENTAL NERVE CELLS

The dependence of amphibian metamorphosis upon thyroid hormone has been known ever since the early experiments by Gudernatsch in 1912.[11] In recent years the mechanism and the site of action of the hormone were the objects of a series of investigations. We shall consider in the following pages the hormonal effects on nerve cells.

The first demonstration of a direct effect of the thyroid hormone on the maturation of nerve cells was given by J. Kollross in 1943.[21] Previous observations by the same author had shown that one of the earliest metamorphic events in amphibian larvae is the appearance of the corneal reflex; it consists of the retraction of the eye bulb upon tactile stimulation of the cornea and surrounding skin. The reflex slightly precedes other metamorphic processes such as the emergence of the forelimbs.[20] The maturation of the reflex at the onset of the metamorphosis raised the question as to whether it is under direct hormonal control or whether the thyroid hormone acts primarily on non-nervous structures and only indirectly affects through the mediation of nerve fibers the nerve centers involved in the reflex. A simple operative procedure provided an answer to this question. Pellets of agar soaked in thyroxin solution were implanted in close proximity to the nerve centers which operate the reflex. Since both centers (trigeminal ganglion and abducens nerve) are located in the medulla, the pellet was inserted in the fourth ventricle. In such a position, the hormone reached the highest concentration in adjacent tissue. One would expect the corneal reflex to mature in advance of other metamorphic events only if the effect of the hormone is a direct effect on nerve cells. If, on the contrary, the thyroxin acts primarily on non-nervous structures, and if these in turn affect the maturation of the associated nerve centers, the proximity of the pellet to the nerve centers would make no difference in the onset of the reflex. The results favored the first alternative. Not only did the corneal reflex precede by many days the emergence of the forelimbs, but it also appeared earlier on the side near the implanted pellet than on the contralateral side. Subsequent experiments by Weiss and Rossetti gave evidence of a localized mitotic effect in the tadpole hindbrain following implantation of a thyroid pellet.[38] The direct response of nerve cells to the same hormone was investigated again by Kollross and Mc-Murray a few years later.[23] This investigation shed light on some new aspects of the hormonal action, and since these results are of particular interest for the discussion to follow, they will be presented here in more detail.

The experimental analysis began with study of the normal development of the mesencephalic nucleus in Anurans.[22] It was found that the cells of this nucleus undergo an abrupt increase in size and number immediately before and during metamorphosis, while other nerve cells in the same area do not show significant size changes. The effect of thyroxin was tested by immersions of larvae at different developmental stages in thyroxin solution and by local implantation of thyroxin-cholesterol pellets.

The first series of experiments showed that the mesencephalic nerve cells of the V nucleus are not receptive to the hormonal action until after they have reached a given stage of differentiation. At this stage, the cell size increases far above the size of cells of this nucleus in comparable metamorphic stages. Hence, it was concluded that thyroxin exerts a more powerful effect on these cells than on other metamorphic processes

such as reabsorption of the cloacal tailpiece and thinning of the skin window.

The second series of experiments showed that local implantation of thyroxin-cholesterol pellets calls forth a size increase in the same cells directly proportional to the concentration of the hormone: in fact, cells near the pellet were considerably larger than cells farther away.[23] Two additional groups of experiments revealed that the hormonal response of these nerve cells is not correlated with the response of other larval structures: (a) weak concentration of thyroxin evoked some metamorphic changes like forelimb emergence and did not affect the cell size and number of the V nucleus; (b) changes in size and number of the V nucleus cells are reversible. Upon discontinuation of the hormonal treatment, the cells revert to the size prior to the onset of the experiment. No such reversibility was observed in other metamorphic processes. The author concluded that

the size of the larval V nucleus appears to be continuously influenced by thyroxin and is modulated according to the amount of the hormone available to the cells.[23]

Similar results were obtained in subsequent investigations on the effects of the thyroid hormone on other nerve cells.[1,34] The question arises as to whether still other nerve cells, as well as the ones that have been investigated, are hormonal dependent, and if so, whether such dependence persists throughout all life.

Using the same technic of local implantation of thyroxin pellets as in the experiments mentioned above, F. H. Wilt observed the conversion of the visual pigment in the retina of larvae of *Rana catesbiana* from porphyropsin to rhodopsin.[39] The same process, which is known to take place during metamorphosis, involves a simple chemical reaction in the chromophore group of the pigment: vitamin A-2 aldehyde of porphyropsin is converted in vitamin A-1 aldehyde of rhodopsin possibly through "loss of

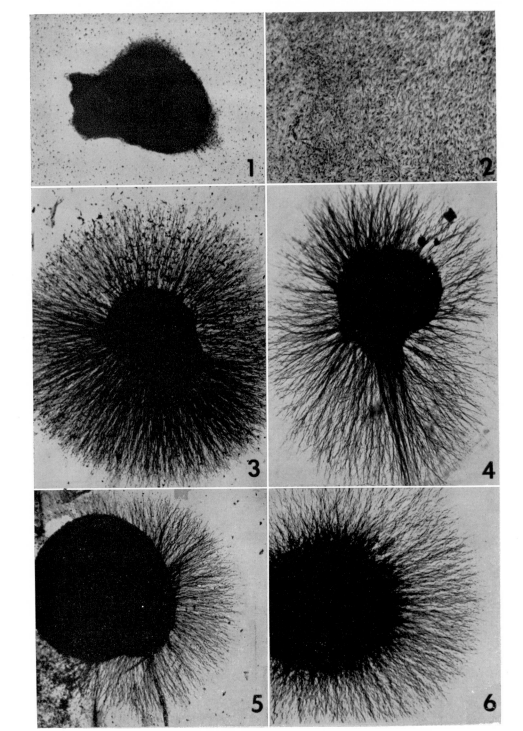

an enzyme or enzyme-forming system concerned with vitamin A-2 synthesis."[39]

These results which offer evidence of a differentiative rather than a growth process, will be considered again in the discussion.

In the following sections we shall present evidence for a growth effect restricted to nerve cells. This effect while differing in many important respects from the ones considered above, share with them some aspects. The similarities and the differences will be discussed after presentation of the results.

A SPECIFIC NERVE-GROWTH FACTOR

In the past 10 years, a nerve-growth agent was isolated from a variety of tissues and organic fluids from animals of different classes and species. The remarkable similarity in the chemical properties of the isolated agent, and the almost identical growth response elicited in all instances in two types of nerve cells, strongly suggest that we are dealing in all instances with the same stimulus-response system. The details of this work are given elsewhere.[2,5,7-9,24-33] Here we shall present only the sequence of experiments which led to the isolation of the agent and to the hypothesis that this agent may play a role in the developmental and growth processes of the receptive nerve cells.

Biochemical Aspects and Distribution of the Growth Factor

The Tumor Factor. The first evidence for the existence of a diffusible substance with striking nerve-growth promoting activity was reported in 1951.[24] Previous experiments had shown that mouse sarcoma 180 when transplanted in the body wall of 3-day-old chick embryos becomes heavily innervated by sensory fibers outgrowing from adjacent sensory ganglia.[2] The growth response observed in these ganglia was correlated with the size increase in the peripheral field of innervation resulting from the rapid growth of the tumor.

A more detailed analysis revealed new facets of the phenomenon and suggested an entirely different interpretation of the results. The sympathetic ganglia of the tumor-bearing embryos also were found to be enlarged; in fact, their growth response was much more impressive than the growth response of the sensory ganglia.[25,31] The effect of the tumor was not restricted to the adjacent sympathetic ganglia but extended to all sectors of the ganglionic system. The decisive evidence for a remote rather than a contact effect, came from experiments of transplantation of the tumor onto the allantoic membrane of chick embryos 4 to 5 days old. When transplanted there, the tumor shared only the circulation with the embryo. The massive enlargement of the sympathetic ganglia of the host indicated that the tumoral agent had reached the embryo through this channel.[24,25,32] The hyperplastic and hypertrophic ganglia produced nerve fibers far in advance and in excess of the ganglia of control embryos.

The striking result was an altered tem-

(Figs. 1 & 5 are from: Levi-Montalcini, R., and Angeletti, P. U.: Biological Properties of a Nerve-Growth Promoting Protein and its Antiserum, New York, Pergamon, 1960; Fig. 3 is from: Levi-Montalcini, R.: Chemical stimulation of nerve-growth *in* McElroy, W. D., and Glass, B. (eds.): The Chemical Basis of Development, pp. 645-664, Baltimore, Johns Hopkins, 1958. Fig. 4 is from: Levi-Montalcini, R.: Some trends of cellular differentiation and morphogenesis, 19:609, 1957; Figs. 14-16 are from: Levi-Montalcini, R., and Angeletti, P. U.: Growth control of the sympathetic system by a specific protein factor, Quart. Rev. Biol. 36:99-108, 1961.)

Figs. 1 to 6. Figures 1, 3, 4, 5, and 6 are microphotographs of sensory ganglia after 24 hours in vitro. Silver impregnation. Figure 1, ganglion of an 8-day chick embryo in control medium. Figure 2, rat granuloma tissue. Figures 3 and 4, 8-day sensory ganglia of chick embryo in a medium containing the purified salivary gland extract (Fig. 3) and the purified snake venom (Fig. 4). Figures 5 and 6, 8-day sensory ganglia of chick embryo combined in vitro with rat granuloma (Fig. 5) and with mouse sarcoma 180 (Fig. 6).

poral and spatial pattern of nerve distribution. Viscera which normally do not receive sympathetic innervation before the end of embryonic development were now found to be flooded with nerves already in the second week of incubation. Structures which normally are impermeable to the penetration of nerves such as blood vessels, now became permeable to the invasive and rapidly growing sympathetic nerve fibers.

The next step was the investigation of the nerve-growth agent. The method of tissue culture provided a rapid and simple bioassay and was used in this and in all subsequent investigations directed to detect the presence of the nerve-growth agent in different biologic sources.[33] Briefly, the method consisted of explanting a sensory or sympathetic ganglion from a chick embryo 7 to 9 days old in a drop of chicken plasma and synthetic medium. A fragment of the tissue to be assayed or of control tissues was explanted in proximity to the ganglion, and then the culture was incubated at 37°C. Next the culture was inspected 10 to 24 hours later. The observation that ganglia confronted with mouse sarcomas but not with other tissues produced a dense halo of nerve fibers within 10 to 14 hours (Figs. 1, 6) gave additional support to the hypothesis that the tested mouse sarcomas harbor a diffusible nerve-growth agent. Two other lines of evidence indicated that we were dealing with a specific agent acting on target cells: the sarcoma agent did not affect motor centers or parasympathetic ganglia; other tumors of epithelial origin such as mammary carcinomas and neuroblastomas had no effect on sensory and sympathetic nerve cells.

The next problem was the identification of the active agent in the tumor extract. At first, the whole tumor homogenate was assayed and found to possess the nerve-growth activity on sensory and sympathetic ganglia explanted in vitro. Then a differential centrifugation led to the isolation of a microsomal active particle. The chemical analysis

gave evidence for the nucleoprotein nature of this particle. The following steps of this investigation need not be recounted here since they are reported in other publications.[7,9] It is sufficient to mention that the further purification of the active particle indicated that the protein rather than the nucleic acid component of the isolated fraction yields the specific nerve-growth activity. Sheer luck rather than logic came then to the rescue of the investigation, which seemed to be stalled and to present no prospects of further advance.

In an attempt to purify the active fraction from still residual nucleic acid components, phosphodiesterase was added to the fraction to be tested. As a source of this enzyme, Dr. S. Cohen made use of a crude preparation of snake venom. The experiment gave a most unexpected result: the presence of a minute amount of the venom in the medium of culture containing the tumor-active fraction resulted in a tremendous increase of the growth effect. Control cultures where only the venom was added did not differ from cultures containing the tumor extract and the venom. In both groups of cultures, the ganglia produced within 12 hours a halo of nerve fibers far more dense and compact than ever had been observed in experiments dealing with the tumor extract (Fig. 4). The discovery that snake venom is itself a most potent source of the growth factor was the starting point for a new series of investigations and of an entirely new approach to the whole problem.

The Venom Factor. The experiments in vitro with snake venom compared in all but one aspect with previous experiments with mouse sarcomas. The potency of the partially purified venom fraction was about 1,000 times higher than the activity of the purified tumor fraction. Further purification of the venom still increased its activity, which was now about 3,000 times higher than the activity of the fraction isolated from tumor. The venom factor was identified as a protein with a molecular weight of the order of 20.000. The chemical properties of this factor are reported in detail elsewhere.[8,29] It suffices to mention here that it is heat labile, destroyed by proteolytic enzymes and by incubation with antiserum to snake venom. Then the effect of this factor was tested in the growing chick embryo by injecting microgram quantities of the purified fraction into the yolk sac of chick embryos 7 to 9 days old. The results compared with the results obtained with sarcomas 180 and 37. The sympathetic ganglia appeared to be hypertrophic and hyperplastic. Again we observed an overproduction of nerve fibers, hyperinnervation of viscera and penetration of sympathetic nerve fibers into the lumen of blood vessels.

The presence of a nerve-growth factor with almost identical properties in mouse sarcomas and snake venom suggested the possibility that other similar agents may be widespread and present in many other animal structures. This hypothesis received support also from a previous observation which had remained unexplained at the time it was made. While exploring the effect of mouse sarcomas in vitro, it was found that other mouse tissues like mouse embryonic heart also possess a mild but clear-cut nerve-growth effect. Ganglia confronted in vitro with fragments of this tissue produced many more nerve fibers than control cultures confronted with chick embryonic tissues. This "mouse effect" had raised the question as to whether the nerve factor also was present in these mouse tissues.[33]

However, the question remained unanswered until it occurred to Dr. Cohen to test the mouse salivary glands. The idea was suggested to him by the previous finding of the nerve factor in the snake venom. Since the venom is produced in modified salivary glands, other salivary glands might well harbor the agent. The hypothesis received full confirmation in the experiments which followed. The mouse salivary gland proved then to be a third and even more potent source of the growth agent than the two agents isolated before.

The Salivary Factor. The ready availability of this growth factor, its potency and, last but not least, the experience acquired in previous work, made possible a more extensive and rapid analysis of this agent on the stimulus-response than in the two previous instances. Three series of experiments were performed. The results were already the object of previous reports[5,26] and will be summarized here:

EXPERIMENTS IN VITRO. The growth effect of the purified mouse salivary extract on sensory and sympathetic ganglia of the chick embryo was so much similar and in fact indistinguishable from the effect of the two already considered agents (Figs. 3, 4, 6) as to make a description unnecessary. Equivalent growth stimulation effects were obtained by 15,000 micrograms of a sarcoma 180 homogenate, 6 micrograms of snake venom and 1.5 micrograms of submaxillary gland of mouse per ml. of tissue culture medium.[5] The purified extract was tested also on sensory and sympathetic ganglia of mammalian fetuses including human fetuses. In all instances, the effects were similar to the effects elicited in the ganglia of chick embryos.

EXPERIMENTS IN VIVO. The daily injection of microgram quantities of the purified salivary extract into the yolk of chick embryos 7 to 10 days old resulted in the overgrowth of sensory and sympathetic ganglia and in the massive invasion of the viscera by sympathetic nerve fibers. The size increase of the sensory ganglia, barely detectable in previous experiments of chorioallantoic transplants of mouse sarcomas and of snake venom injection, was now one of the striking features of the response elicited by the growth agent (Figs. 7, 8). The sensory ganglia were found to be three times larger than control ganglia. A parallel hyperneurotization of the exteroceptive fields was observed. Experiments now in progress are aimed at the analysis of the effect of the

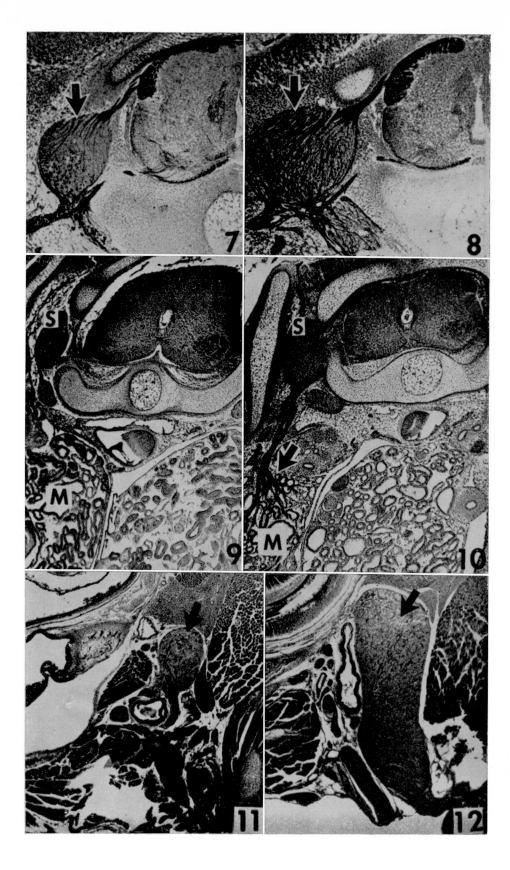

salivary factor on sensory cells deprived of their peripheral areas of innervation. It is well known from previous experiments that the extirpation of the limb bud in 3-day-old chick embryos results in the atrophy of nerve cells of the sensory ganglia which innervate the limb.[12,18] The extirpation of the limb bud was now combined with daily injections of the salivary factor in order to see if cells otherwise doomed to die would survive. The results of a preliminary series of experiments were not as we had expected. While in control embryos the nerves end abruptly at the region of the amputation, now they invaded the adjacent mesonephros and branched profusely among the epithelial tubules (Figs. 9, 10). This abnormal pattern of peripheral distribution and the rebound effect on the cells of origin is now under investigation.

EXPERIMENTS IN NEWBORN AND ADULT MICE. Daily injections of the purified salivary protein in newborn mice resulted in hyperplastic and hypertrophic effects in the sympathetic ganglia. The average volume increase, as determined by comparison of the superior cervical ganglia in experimental and control animals, between the 12th and the 19th days was 5:1.[28,30] Counts of mitotic figures showed that the agent calls forth a sharp increase of mitotic activity which results in a 2-fold increase in cell population. The hypertrophic effects are shown in Figs. 11 and 12. In adult mice, the same agent evokes size enlargement of individual neurons but no increase in their number. This is in line with the observation that mitotic activity, still very active at birth,

comes to an end toward the 9th postnatal day.

We also reported that a rabbit antiserum to the salivary protein elicits a diametrically opposite effect.[27,30] The antiserum was produced by S. Cohen, who injected the growth agent into the foot pads of rabbits, using the Freund's adjuvant technic.[6] Daily injections of the antiserum for a period of 8 days resulted in the near-total destruction of the sympathetic ganglia of newborn mice, rats, rabbits and kittens. Recently, we found that the same results can be obtained by reducing the number of injections to two; the total amount of antiserum injected is 0.1 ml./Gm. of body weight. This treatment, while having no adverse effects on other structures or organs, results in the destruction of 99 per cent of the population of sympathetic nerve cells. Such an effect is due to a sharp decrease in the mitotic activity, disintegration and disappearance of already differentiated neurons. The treated mice underwent normal development. Some of them were sacrificed 4 to 6 months later, and the superior and stellate ganglia were dissected out and compared with controls. A residual nerve cell population of about 1 per cent of the controls was still found to be present (Figs. 13, 15). These observations indicate that the damages inflicted by the treatment are permanent, and that the few cells which escaped death at the time of the injections are able to survive. Physiologic tests are planned to see if they are able to function.

Experiments with pregnant mice indicate that the antiserum does not affect the fetuses

---

FIGS. 7 to 12. Effects of the purified salivary gland extract in the chick embryo and in the newborn mouse. Silver impregnation. Figures 7 and 8, transverse sections through the thoracic level of 10-day chick embryos. Arrows point to spinal ganglia. Figure 7, control. Figure 8, embryo injected for 3 days with the purified salivary gland extract. Figures 9 and 10, transverse sections through lumbar level of 12-day chick embryos in which the right leg bud had been amputated at 3 days. Figure 9, control. Figure 10, embryo injected with the purified salivary gland extract. Notice larger size of ganglion (S) and penetration of sensory nerve into mesonephros (M). Arrow points to the nerve. Figures 11 and 12, transverse sections through the superior cervical ganglion in control (Fig. 11) and experimental mouse (Fig. 12) injected from the 1st day after birth to the 12th day with the purified salivary gland extract. Arrows point to ganglia.

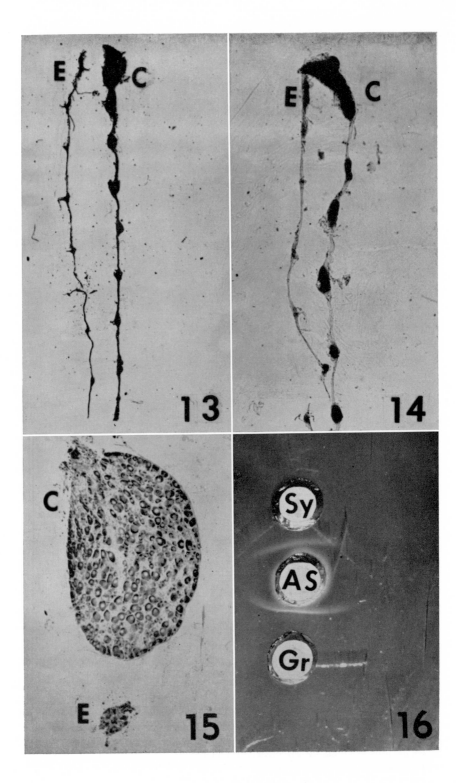

but, instead, is effective if injected in nursing mothers. Two females were injected soon after the delivery of the litters; in both instances, the injections resulted in the almost total destruction of the sympathetic ganglia of the babies (Fig. 14).

The effects of the antiserum were tested on only a few adult animals. The results show that sympathetic nerve cells remain vulnerable to this agent, but the atrophy is of a much less severe degree than in newborn animals. About 30 per cent of the nerve cells still were present after a 20-day injection period.

The effects of the growth agent as well as the effect of the antiserum on sensory ganglia in newborn animals were not investigated in detail. Volume measurements of ganglia in control and in treated mice indicate a slight increase in animals injected with the growth agent, and a slight decrease in animals injected with the antiserum. A more detailed analysis is in progress. This analysis is expected to answer the question as to whether all sensory cells are moderately affected by these agents, or if only a percentage of these cells are receptive to the growth and the antigrowth agent. The second alternative is suggested by results obtained in previous experiments in chick embryos.* Before referring to immunochemical experiments with the antiserum, it is of interest to consider still another aspect of the problem: the distribution of the growth agent in other tissues and body fluids.

---

* It was found that in the sensory ganglia only one of the two cell types which we described in a previous paper[31] is receptive to the nerve-growth factors isolated from mouse sarcomas, granuloma tissues (Table 1) and other mouse tissues.

TABLE 1. Specific Activities of the Nerve Growth Agent in Different Sources

Sources	Micrograms Protein Required to Show 3+ Response
Sarcoma	15,000
Granuloma	3,000
Sympathetic ganglia	~200
Snake venom	6
Salivary gland	1.5

Detection of the Growth Agent in Other Tissues and Body Fluids. The question was raised as to the bearing of the findings reported above on normal growth and developmental processes in the receptive nerve cells. Two alternatives were considered: either the "growth agent" is a by-product of other metabolic processes, and as such it is disposed of and is of no functional significance, or it is a controlling factor of growth and differentiative processes which take place in these cells. Observations reported in previous papers[28,30] favored the second alternative. They will be summarized here.

The growth agent was detected in the serum of both young and adult untreated mice. The experimental test was the same as in previous investigations: the growth of sensory and sympathetic ganglia of chick embryos explanted in a cultural medium containing the blood serum to be tested. We reported[28] that in a certain percentage of cases the addition of the serum evoked a growth effect similar to the effects elicited by other growth agents. In a few instances we also obtained a growth effect by the addition of saliva and urine to the cultural medium.

Fig. 13. Whole mounts of sympathetic chain ganglia of control (C) and experimental (E) mice, 4 months old. Experimental mouse was injected after birth with antiserum to the salivary gland factor. Figure 14, whole mounts of sympathetic chain ganglia of control (C) and experimental (E) 1-month-old mice. Experimental mouse was nursed by mother receiving 3 injections of the antiserum after delivery of the litter. Figure 14, at higher magnification than Figure 13. Figure 15, transverse sections of the superior cervical ganglia of the same mice as Figure 13. Control (C); experimental (E) mouse. Figure 16, agar diffusion reaction between antiserum (AS), salivary growth factor (GR) and extract of mouse sympathetic ganglia (Sy).

These results indicate that the agent under consideration is present in the blood and other body fluids. Its presence in tissues beside the mouse sarcomas was indicated by results reported in our first investigation of the in-vitro effects of mouse sarcomas.[32] Then, it was found that fetal mouse heart elicits a mild nerve-growth effect on the ganglia confronted with this tissue. These experiments were repeated and extended by another group of investigators. Bueker and co-workers, using the same in-vitro technic, found that a nucleoprotein fraction isolated from mouse kidney, muscle and thymus, elicits a nerve-growth effect.[3] More recently, they reported that a nucleoprotein fraction isolated from the chick embryo vertebral axis also elicits the same effect.[4] These last results are of particular interest, since they indicate that this same nerve growth agent is present in the embryonic tissues of a different species.

In turn, these observations raise other questions. Is the growth protein produced by any specific tissue or organ? Is it incorporated as such in the nerve cells or does it operate as a catalytic mechanism? We attempted to answer the first question by extending our search to other possible sources of the growth agent; the second question by an analysis of the receptive nerve cells and of some of the immunologic aspects of the phenomenon.

The Granuloma Factor. The finding of a factor with strikingly similar biochemical properties in different agents such as mouse sarcomas, snake venom and mouse salivary glands raised the question, whether all of them produce it or some of them (salivary and venom glands) only store it. Indirect evidence favored the second alternative and suggested that mesenchymal tissues might be the source or one of the sources of this factor.

In order to test this hypothesis, Dr. P. Angeletti and I injected a granuloma producing agent (carrageen[10]) into different mammals: mice, rats, guinea pigs, rabbits and monkeys. In most instances, this agent evoked a granuloma tissue in 5 to 7 days (Fig. 2). Fragments were explanted in vitro in proximity to sensory ganglia of 8-day-old chick embryos. In all instances, the ganglia produced exuberant nerve fibers within 8 to 10 hours on the side facing the granuloma. Extract of granuloma tissue added to the culture medium also stimulated the production of a dense halo of nerve fibers from sensory ganglia. These results compare in all respects with similar results obtained with mouse sarcoma (Figs. 5, 6). The granuloma agent is heat labile and is precipitated with alcohol like other nerve-growth agents. It is inactivated by the rabbit anti-serum against the purified salivary factor. This result indicates a similar antigenic structure of the salivary and granuloma nerve-growth agents.

Tests of the in-vivo potencies of the granuloma through transplantation of small fragments of rat or mouse granuloma into 3-day-old chick embryos indicated that this tissue possesses the capacity of stimulating the outgrowth of nerve fibers from the adjacent sympathetic ganglia of the host. Small nodules of the transplanted tissue projected into the abdominal cavity of the embryo and became invaded by nerve fibers outgrowing from the Remak intestinal ganglion. The results compare with previous results obtained with mouse sarcomas, although the much more limited growth capacities of the granuloma reflected in the much more restricted nerve-growth effects of this tissue which affected only adjacent but not remote ganglia. Similar results were obtained in some instances with mouse sarcomas.[25]

THE ROLE OF THE GROWTH PROTEIN IN THE METABOLISM OF SYMPATHETIC AND SENSORY CELLS

As mentioned above, our next problem was to attempt to elucidate the mechanism through which the sympathetic cells and apparently also a small percentage of sensory cells respond to the growth agent and to its antiserum.

At first, we investigated the possibility that the specific growth protein may be a normal constituent of the receptive cells. The results of the following experiments gave full support to this hypothesis.

Sympathetic ganglia were dissected out from adult mice. A total of 100 superior cervical ganglia were collected. The homogenate was diluted in physiologic solution in the proportion of plasma and one part of synthetic medium. Sensory and sympathetic ganglia of chick embryos cultured in this medium outgrew a dense halo of nerve fiber in 6 to 10 hours. The results were in all respects similar to the results obtained with previous assayed growth factors. A growth response also was obtained with extract of cat sympathetic ganglia and of mouse sensory ganglia. Table 1 gives the specific activity in the homogenate of nerve cells and other sources necessary to obtain a maximal growth response in tissue culture. The results indicate that the active agent is present in the highest concentration in snake venom and in mouse salivary glands.* These observations raised the question as to whether the same nerve cells may not be the source of the active agent in the organism. If this hypothesis would prove to be correct, the growth activity of sarcomas and of other tissues of mesenchymal origin should be explained in a different way. In fact, they could store but not produce the agent. The following experiments, while not denying a possible participation of sensory and sympathetic ganglia in the production of the growth agent, rule out the hypothesis that this is the only or the main source of the agent. The experiments consisted of testing the salivary gland and the serum of mice injected at birth with the antiserum. As already mentioned, these mice were almost entirely lacking the sympathetic ganglia. The

sensory ganglia were slightly reduced. The content of the specific protein in the salivary gland compared with the content of the gland of control mice. The growth agent also was detected in the blood serum. Hence, other sources beside the receptive nerve cells are responsible for the production of the growth agent.

Immunochemical Studies of the Antigenic Properties of the Growth Factor

The technical details of these experiments performed by Dr. P. Angeletti will be presented elsewhere. Here we shall consider briefly some results which have a bearing on the following aspects of the problem: (1) characterization of the growth agent detected in different biologic sources, and (2) site of action of the antiserum.

It was reported that the antiserum was produced by injection of the highly purified mouse salivary protein in rabbits. Then the antiserum was tested in vitro, at first against the salivary protein and then against the snake venom, the crude extract of mouse sympathetic and sensory ganglia and cat sympathetic ganglia. In all instances a precipitin reaction took place, thus indicating similar antigenic properties of this factor when located in body fluids, organs or in the receptive nerve cells. The precipitin test was not performed with sarcomas and granuloma extracts, since neither of them was available in a purified form. However, the in-vitro inactivation of the granuloma extract by the specific antiserum as reported above, indicates that this agent also has the same antigenic properties. The double diffusion technic according to Ouchterlony provided additional evidence for the antigenic similarity of the salivary protein and the protein extracted from mouse sympathetic ganglia. In both instances only one sharp band of precipitate was obtained (Fig. 16).

The site of action of the antiserum was investigated by labeling the antiserum with fluorescein and then confronting microsec-

---

* It is present in higher amount in the extract of nerve cells than in sarcomas, granuloma tissues (Table 1) and other mouse tissues.

tions of sympathetic mouse ganglia with the labeled antiserum. This treatment resulted in a fluorescence of the cytoplasm of sympathetic cells. These preliminary results, if confirmed by more extensive and detailed experiments now in progress, would give decisive support to the hypothesis that the antibodies present in the serum react with the antigen present in the nerve cells. Therefore, the hypothesis that the near-total destruction of the sympathetic cells of newborn animals injected with the antiserum is due to a direct cytotoxic effect receives a strong support from these results.

THE PROTEINIC NERVE GROWTH FACTOR

We are now confronted with the problem of evaluating the results and, indeed, the whole phenomenon which still awaits the right to be listed as a biologic phenomenon and not as a disturbing exception to well-known and accepted rules of growth and differentiation.

At first we shall summarize briefly the main findings. A protein with remarkably similar chemical and immunologic properties was isolated in the course of these last few years from a variety of biologic sources. A sequence of in-vivo and in-vitro experiments showed that it enhances, in a selective and specific way, the growth potentialities of two types of nerve cells: sympathetic and sensory cells. The former are highly receptive to the growth agent from early embryonic life up to maturity; the latter become less responsive as they mature. The suggestion is advanced that only a small percentage of sensory cells are affected by the growth agent. We have positive evidence in favor of this hypothesis for embryonic sensory cells, but only indirect evidence for mature sensory cells.

Injections of an antiserum produced from the purified protein isolated from mouse salivary glands resulted in the near-total destruction of sympathetic cells in newborn mammals and in a severe atrophy of the same cells in adult animals. The antiserum effects are still not investigated in detail in the sensory nerve cells. A size reduction of sensory ganglia in the injected newborn animals indicates that these ganglia also are affected adversely by the antiserum.

Three different kinds of structures were considered as the possible producers of the specific protein; the mouse salivary gland and its homologue the venom gland in reptiles, sympathetic and sensory cells, and mesenchymal derivatives. All the above structures share the property of harboring the specific protein. This is found in a very high concentration in the first group of structures, in a lower quantity in the second group of tissues and in an almost negligible amount in mouse sarcomas and mammalian granulomas.

Paradoxically, we reached the conclusion that the third group represents the most likely source of production of the specific protein in the organism. The evidence in favor of this hypothesis is shown on pages 152-153. At present, we offer the following tentative interpretation of the results: a proteinic nerve-growth factor is produced in the organism in a widespread array of tissues, possibly of mesenchymal nature. The protein is stored and disposed of by the salivary glands and its homologue the venom gland. Sympathetic and sensory nerve cells selectively incorporate this protein. In fact, immunologic and in-vitro experiments showed that this protein is a normal constituent of the receptive nerve cells.

HORMONAL GROWTH CONTROLLING AGENTS AND THE "NERVE GROWTH" FACTOR

Many times in the course of this investigation since the first discovery in 1951 of a diffusible nerve-growth factor in mouse sarcomas, it has been tempting to suggest that we are dealing with a nerve hormone. Two important aspects of this phenomenon are in fact suggestive of a hormonal effect: the target specificity of the effect coupled with lack of species specificity, and the requirement of a continuous supply of the agent to the realization of the growth response. However, we refrained from giving such a designation, which would satisfy the needs expressed above of "filing" the phenomenon in a well-known and highly respected category of biologic phenomena but would not add to our understanding of this perplexing stimulus-response effect. A comparison of this with hormonal effects briefly presented in the first part of this paper will bring the problem into focus.

Thyroid hormone administered in pellet form to amphibian larvae resulted in a selective growth response of some nerve cell populations. The effect was found to be in a direct relationship with the location of the pellet, the concentration of the hormone and the differentiative stage of the nerve cells. The characteristics of the response favored the hypothesis of a direct hormonal action on the cells which underwent precocious maturation and size increase. In commenting on these effects, P. Weiss stated that

the morphogenetic action of a hormone is not too unlike the action of the photographic developer in bringing out the latent picture on an exposed plate.[38]

In fact, the receptive fetal nerve cells attained the size characteristic of more mature nerve cells but did not trespass it.

One may wonder whether it is appropriate in this instance to speak of a "growth effect." The observation that the same cells reverted to their previous size upon discontinuation of the treatment is another interesting aspect of the phenomenon. Kollross ably avoids committing himself on the definition of the response by stating that "the changes in size and apparent cell number are examples of modulation in response to varying levels of thyroxin concentration."[23]

A local direct effect of thyroxin also was described on non-nervous cells. Using the same pellet technic as in the above experiments, Wilt gave evidence of the precocious conversion of visual pigment from porphyropsin to rhodopsin in eyes of amphibian larvae.[39] These results provide clear-cut evidence of a differentiative rather than a growth response.

The effects elicited by the nerve-growth factor differ in many significant respects from the above effects. The magnitude of the response far exceeds that of the thyroxin hormone and, indeed, of any other hormone. The effects apparently are restricted to two types of nerve cells: sympathetic and sensory cells. Both kinds of cells, the sympathetic cells in a much more impressive way, remain receptive to the agent throughout all their life. The hypertrophic effects are not merely a reflection of an accelerated maturation process: in fact, the cells attain a size much larger than in adult life. Adult cells, in turn, respond to this treatment by a further increase in size. Therefore, the term "growth factor" seems to be well justified in this instance. The factor is a protein, and it is a normal constituent of the receptive cells. This is perhaps one of the most puzzling features of the whole phenomenon; together with the other findings, it warns against the temptation of suggesting that we are dealing with a hormonal effect. The noncommitting term of "growth factor" seems to be more appropriate at the present time. Work now in progress is expected to elucidate other aspects of this phenomenon all the more challenging because apparently it does not fit into accepted schemes of growth and differentiation.

NOTES

1. The work described in this paper was supported in part by grants from the National Institute of Neurological Diseases and Blindness, Public Health Service, Bethesda, Md., and from the National Science Foundation, Washington, D.C., and by a contribution from the American Cancer Society to Washington University, St. Louis, Mo.

2. The carrageen was kindly supplied by the Marine Colloids, Inc., New Bedford, Mass.

REFERENCES

1. Beaudoin, A.: The development of lateral motor column cells in the lumbosacral cord in *Rana pipiens*. II. Development under the influence of thyroxin, Anat. Rec. **125**:247-259, 1956.
2. Beuker, E. D.: Implantation of tumors in the hindlimb field of the embryonic chick and the developmental response of the lumbo-sacral nervous system, Anat. Rec. **102**:369-390, 1948.
3. Beuker, E. D., Schenklein, I., and Bane, J.: Nucleoprotein fractions from organs of the mouse and their nerve growth stimulation effects on mouse ganglia in vitro, Anat. Rec. **133**:256, 1959.
4. ⸻: The problem of distribution of a nerve growth-factor specific for spinal and sympathetic ganglia, Cancer Res. **20**: 1220-1228, 1960.
5. Cohen, S.: A nerve growth-promoting protein, *in* McElroy, W. D., and Glass, B., (eds.): Chemical Basis of Development, pp. 665-677, Baltimore, Johns Hopkins Press, 1958.
6. ⸻: Purification of a nerve growth-promoting protein from the mouse salivary gland and its neurocytotoxic antiserum, Proc. Nat. Acad. Sc. **46**:302-311, 1960.
7. Cohen, S., Levi-Montalcini, R., and Hamburger, V.: A nerve growth-stimulating factor isolated from sarcomas 37 and 180, Proc. Nat. Acad. Sc. **40**:1014-1018, 1954.
8. ⸻: A nerve growth-stimulating factor isolated from snake venom, Proc. Nat. Acad. Sc. **42**:571-574, 1956.
9. ⸻: Purification of a nerve growth-promoting factor isolated from mouse sarcoma 180, Cancer Res. **17**:15-20, 1957.
10. Detwiler, S. R.: Neuroembryology: An Experimental Study, New York, Macmillan, 1936.
11. Gudernatsch, J. G.: Feeding experiments on tadpoles. I. The influence of specific organs given as food on growth and differentiation, Arch. Entwicklungsmech. Organ. **35**:457-483, 1912.
12. Hamburger, V., and Levi-Montalcini, R.: Proliferation, differentiation and degeneration on the spinal ganglia of the chick embryo under normal and experimental conditions, J. Exper. Zool. **111**:457-502, 1949.
13. ⸻: Some aspects of neuroembryology *in* Weiss, P. (ed.): Genetic Neurol-

ogy, pp. 128-160, Chicago, Univ. Chicago Press, 1950.
14. ⸻: Development of the nervous system *in* Miner, R. W. (ed.): The Chick Embryo in Biological Research, Ann. New York Acad. Sc. **55**:117-132, 1952.
15. ⸻: Trends in Neuroembryology *in* Waelsch, H. (ed.): Biochemistry of the Developing Nervous System, pp. 52-71, Princeton, New Jersey, Princeton Univ. Press, 1955.
16. ⸻: Developmental correlations in neurogenesis *in* Rudnick, D. (ed.): Cellular Mechanisms in Differentiation and Growth, pp. 191-212, Princeton, New Jersey, Princeton Univ. Press, 1956.
17. ⸻: The life cycle of the nerve cell, Am. Sci. **45**:263-277, 1957.
18. ⸻: Regression versus peripheral control of differentiation in motor hypoplasia, Am. J. Anat. **102**:365-410, 1958.
19. Harrison, R. G.: The Croonian lecture on the origin and development of the nervous system studied by the methods of experimental embryology, Proc. Roy. Soc. London, **118**:155-196, 1935.
20. Kollross, J. J.: Localized maturation of lid-closure reflex mechanism by thyroxin implants into tadpole hindbrain, Proc. Soc. Exper. Biol. & Med. **49**:204-206, 1942.
21. ⸻: Experimental studies on the development of the corneal reflex in amphibia. II. Localized maturation of the reflex mechanism effected by thyroxin-agar implants into the hindbrain, Physiol. Zool. **16**:269-279, 1943.
22. Kollross, J. J., and McMurray, V. M.: The mesencephalic V nucleus in anurans, J. Comp. Neurol. **102**:47-65, 1955.
23. ⸻: The mesencephalic V nucleus in anurans. II. The influence of thyroid hormones on cell size and number, J. Exper. Zool. **131**:1-26, 1956.
24. Levi-Montalcini, R.: Growth-stimulating effects of mouse sarcoma on the sensory and sympathetic nervous system of the chick embryo, Anat. Rec. **109**:59-60, 1951.
25. ⸻: Effect of mouse tumor transplantation on the nervous system, *in* Miner, R. W. (ed.): The Chick Embryo in Biological Research, Ann. New York Acad. Sc. **55**:330-343, 1952.
26. ⸻: Chemical stimulation of nerve growth *in* McElroy, W. D., and Glass, B., (eds.): Chemical Basis of Development,

pp. 646-664, Baltimore, Johns Hopkins Press, 1958.

27. Levi-Montalcini, R., and Booker, B.: Excessive growth of the sympathetic ganglia by a protein isolated from the salivary gland, Proc. Nat. Acad. Sc. **46:** 373-384, 1960.

28. ————: Destruction of the sympathetic ganglia in mammals by an antiserum to the nerve growth-promoting factor, Proc. Nat. Acad. Sc. **46:**384-391, 1960.

29. Levi-Montalcini, R., and Cohen, S.: In vitro and in vivo effects of a nerve growth-stimulating agent isolated from snake venom, Proc. Nat. Acad. Sc. **42:**695-699, 1956.

30. ————: Effects of the extract of mouse submaxillary salivary glands on the sympathetic system of mammals, Ann. New York Acad. Sc. **85:**324-341, 1960.

31. Levi-Montalcini, R., and Hamburger, V.: Selective growth stimulating effects of mouse sarcoma on the sensory and sympathetic nervous system of the chick embryo, J. Exper. Zool. **116:**321-363, 1951.

32. ————: A diffusible agent of mouse sarcoma, producing hyperplasia of sympathetic ganglia and hyperneurotization of viscera in the chick embryo, J. Exper. Zool. **123:**233-288, 1953.

33. Levi-Montalcini, R., Meyer, H., and Hamburger, V.: In vitro experiments on the effects of mouse sarcomas 180 and 37 on the spinal and sympathetic ganglia of the chick embryo, Cancer Res. **14:**49-57, 1954.

34. Pesetsky, I., and Kollross, J. J.: A comparison of the influence of locally applied thyroxin upon Mauthner's cell and adjacent neurons, Exper. Cell. Res. **11:**477-482, 1956.

35. Weiss, P.: An introduction to genetic neurology *in* Genetic Neurology, pp. 1-39, Chicago, Univ. Chicago Press, 1950.

36. ————: What is growth? *in* Hypophyseal Growth Hormone, Nature and Action, pp. 3-16, New York, McGraw-Hill, 1955.

37. ————: Nervous system (neurogenesis), Analysis of Development, Philadelphia, Saunders **7:**346-401, 1955.

38. Weiss, P., and Rossetti, F.: Growth responses of opposite sign among different neuron types exposed to thyroid hormone, Proc. Nat. Acad. Sc. **37:**540-556, 1951.

39. Wilt, F. H.: Differentiation of visual pigments in metamorphosing larvae of *Rana catesbeiana*, Devel. Biol. **1:**199-233, 1959.

Nucleocytoplasmic Interactions During Development

C. L. MARKERT, Ph.D.

In examining the mechanisms that underlie animal development, there is much to recommend the cell as the basic unit of development or differentiation. Certainly, the differentiation of cells is fundamental to all other expressions of development, such as histogenesis, organogenesis and the general anatomy and physiology of the organism. Likewise, aberrations of development commonly must owe their origin to the abnormal behavior of individual cells, and many extrinsic teratogens are effective primarily because they interfere with the normal course of cellular differentiation. Cell differentiation, whether proceeding normally or abnormally, basically involves the transformation of cells of identical potentialities into diverse types recognizably different in structure and function and frequently in their potentialities for further development. The source of these differences may lie either in the nucleus or the cytoplasm of the cell or in both. The behavior of nuclei and chromosomes at cell division implies that each cell of an organism is equipped with identical genetic endowments. Since an enormous variety of cell types can be identified in complex organisms like ourselves, it is obvious that the properties of a cell cannot reflect precisely its initial genotype. Many investigators previously concluded that the nuclei and the chromosomes were equivalent throughout the somatic cells of the body; the cytoplasm was believed to differentiate through epigenetic influences superimposed upon uniform genetic activity in all cells. In fact, the cytoplasm does express most noticeably the differentiated characteristics of the cell. But recent evidence and a more careful examination of older evidence show that the nucleus also is differentiated—if not so conspicuously as the cytoplasm, perhaps in a more profound way.

DIFFERENTIAL GENE ACTIVATION

Many investigators working in the area of developmental genetics have demonstrated repeatedly that genes control developmental events as well as the characteristics of the adult organism. Thus, both embryologists and geneticists are concerned closely with gene function as basic to an understanding of the phenomena they study. But embryologists have an additional concern. They must search for the mechanisms that, in effect, turn genes on and off in the right cells at the right time. Whatever these mechanisms may be, and they are still unknown, they are the very foundation of the processes of cellular differentiation and hence of all embryonic development. Furthermore, if genes do not function equally in all nuclei, then the nuclei must be differentiated with reference to gene function. Since we do not know the nature of primary gene function, it is difficult to know whether a gene is functioning or not. However, there is an ever-increasing number of examples in which we now can relate the presence of a particular gene to the synthesis of a specific macromolecule.[2,3] In these cases, generally it is quite clear that such molecules are synthesized in only a limited number of cell types which have reached a suitable stage of differentiation. The well-studied cases of hemoglobin synthesis[12] and of melanin synthesis provide good illustrations of the tissue and ontogenetic specificity[22] of gene action. In the case of melanin pigment, which is synthesized through the activity of the gene-controlled enzyme tyrosinase, only highly specialized cells—the melanocytes—synthesize this pigment and only relatively late in the ontogeny of the organism. The vast majority of cells never appear to synthesize the enzyme tyrosinase. Perhaps this failure may be attributed to the tyrosinase gene never having been "turned on" by the mechanisms of nuclear differentiation. Only cells exposed during embryonic development to that special sequence of environmental conditions that lead to the development of a melanocyte ever would normally contain activated genes for tyrosinase synthesis. These same general principles would apply with equal force to all cases in which gene-controlled synthesis of macromolecules has been demonstrated.

NUCLEOCYTOPLASMIC INTERACTIONS

Although the final events in differential gene activation must occur on the chromosome, the initial steps probably occur in the cytoplasm. The cell is a tightly integrated system of interacting components and ingenious and difficult technics commonly are required for the study of the different parts of the cell. Nevertheless, the relative roles of the nucleus and the cytoplasm and their interaction during development have been demonstrated by several lines of investigation. An old observation, but still meaningful, is that the eggs of certain animals normally become polyspermic at fertilization. However, only one sperm nucleus fuses with the egg nucleus, and this zygote nucleus then suppresses the remaining sperm in the cytoplasm.[13] In animals which have not evolved this type of nucleocytoplasmic interaction, polyspermy commonly leads to a polyploid zygote nucleus as in certain mammals.[4]

Another old observation demonstrates a remarkable influence of the cytoplasm on the nucleus. In a few animals there exists a peculiar phenomenon of chromatin diminution in which part of the chromosomes are lost from the nucleus during nuclear division. This phenomenon first occurs at the second nuclear division in one of the two nuclei of the developing Ascaris embryo. The nucleus which undergoes chromatin diminution does so because of the particular area of the cytoplasm in which it lies.[9] If the cytoplasm is redistributed by centrifugation, both nuclei will lose part of their chromosomes to the cytoplasm at the next division. Thus, in this example, the cytoplasm is primarily responsible for the behavior of the nucleus.

These old examples are still informative, but recently dramatic advances in the investigation of nucleocytoplasmic relationships have been made through the application of the technic of nuclear transplantation as worked out by Briggs and King.[10] These investigators surgically remove the nuclei from the unfertilized eggs of the frog, *Rana pipiens.* Then by means of a micropipette, a nucleus obained from an embryonic cell is injected into the enucleated egg. Such recipient eggs then divide, and the nature of their subsequent development measures the capacity of the donor nucleus to promote development. Nuclei taken from embryos in gastrula or earlier stages of development commonly support normal development in recipient eggs. When donor nuclei are taken from later stages of development the percentage of recipient eggs that develop normally declines until in late embryonic stages essentially none of the donor nuclei supports normal development. Furthermore, characteristic syndromes of abnormalities commonly appear. That is, endoderm nuclei from the neurula stage of development produce embryos deficient in ectodermal structures, but the endoderm develops normally. The persistence of developmental limitations in the transplanted nuclei was demonstrated dramatically by retransplanting nuclei from abnormal recipient embryos to freshly enucleated eggs. Again, the same syndrome of abnormalities appeared even when the re-transplanting procedure was repeated for several generations. Thus, under these conditions nuclei from advanced embryonic stages appeared to be differentiated irreversibly.[21]

The responsibility for this differentiation seems to fall most probably upon the chromosomes of the nucleus because they alone appear to replicate during nuclear division. All other nuclear components seem to be lost or at least would be diluted out through repeated nuclear divisions. About 12 to 14 cell divisions are required to produce a *Rana pipiens* gastrula.

CHROMOSOMAL CHANGES

The nature of chromosomal change during nuclear differentiation is of extreme importance to any understanding of embryonic development. The chromosomes contain several major constituents, DNA, RNA, phospholipids and protein, changes in any of which might affect the functional capacity of a chromosome. The great stability exhibited by differentiated cells has led several investigators to speculate that changes in DNA may occur during cell differentiation. Such changes would be akin to gene mutations and would be truly genetic. Changes in other constituents of the chromosome would be described more appropriately as epigenetic. Nuclear transplantation technics now make possible a direct test of the genetic characteristics of differentiated somatic nuclei. In fact, Blackler[8] already has begun such a test. The procedure involves the transplantation of differentiated somatic nuclei into the eggs of the amphibian, *Xenopus laevis*. The recipient eggs develop into abnormal embryos, but they nevertheless produce the tissue that contains the primordial germ cells. These cells lie among the endoderm cells on the floor of the blastocoele during the late blastula stage. The tissue containing these primordial germ cells — the nuclei of which are lineal descendants of differentiated somatic nuclei — may then be transplanted homotopically to a normal embryo. If such animals with transplanted primordial germ cells prove to be fertile and produce normal offspring, then changes in DNA during cell differentiation would seem to be improbable. From what we know about the precision with which DNA is replicated through many cell generations and from the prevailing hypotheses concerning mechanisms of replication, it seems highly unlikely that changes in primary DNA structure would be reversed readily.

Of course, these experiments have not been yet completed, and we must await the outcome before reaching firmer conclusions. Two other investigations that have been completed were designed to test the reversibility of the chromosomal changes that occur when chromosomes replicate in foreign cytoplasm. These investigations involve the transplantation of nuclei from one frog species into the eggs of a different species.[14,25] Such nuclei divide, and the recipient eggs develop into blastulae, but no further development occurs. Nuclei from such arrested blastulae may be transferred again to eggs of the foreign species. The same pattern of cell division and arrest of development at blastula will occur again. Since hybrid amphibian embryos commonly cease development as blastulae, this result is not surprising, but it does demonstrate a nucleocytoplasmic interdependence. Most suggestive however is the discovery that nuclei after a period of residence in foreign cytoplasm were not able immediately to support normal development even when retransplanted to their species-specific cytoplasm. The first such transplants produced only arrested blastulae as if the nuclei were still in foreign cytoplasm. Multiplication of the nuclei in foreign cytoplasm evidently had produced a persistent change, probably in the chromosomes. Gurdon[14] in extending this type of investigation with *Rana temporaria* and *Xenopus laevis* showed that the effect of foreign cytoplasm was cumulative but reversible after repeated transplantations into species-specific cytoplasm. The number of transfer generations required to restore the normal developmental capacities depended upon the number of nuclear divisions that had occurred in foreign cytoplasm. The effect of 12 to 14 nuclear divisions in foreign cytoplasm was reversed in about 50 nuclear divisions in species-specific cytoplasm.

Nuclear capacities also were correlated with the size of the nucleolus. While a nucleus was in foreign cytoplasm the nucleolus remained small, suggesting reduced RNA-protein synthesis. After transfer to species-specific cytoplasm, the nucleolus gradually returned to normal size, at which time the nucleus was capable of supporting normal development. A plausible interpretation of these observations is that replication of chromosomes in foreign cytoplasm leads to the attachment of foreign protein (or other non-DNA component of the chromosomes) to the chromosome, thus preventing its normal differentiation and inhibiting its heterosynthetic functions. It is important to realize that during nuclear division the entire chromosome replicates, not just the DNA. Therefore, many replications might be necessary in order for a chromosome to lose a component acquired during its residence in a foreign environment.

However, it should be noted that Moore[25] in his experimental analysis of development after nuclear transfers between *Rana sylvatica* and *Rana pipiens* obtained different results from those of Gurdon. Moore found that *Rana pipiens* nuclei that developed in *Rana sylvatica* cytoplasm were unable to promote normal development even after 5 back-transfers to the enucleated cytoplasm of their own species. In each generation, development ceased at the time of gastrulation. Thus, in this experiment, prolonged exposure to species-specific cytoplasm (about 60 nuclear divisions) did *not* reverse the effects of an initial nuclear multiplication in foreign cytoplasm. In interpreting these seemingly irreversible changes in chromo-

somes, Moore is inclined to place responsibility upon the DNA found in the foreign cytoplasm—a foreign DNA that might have been incorporated in the replicating *Rana pipiens* chromosomes in such a way as to make them permanently abnormal.

In addition to the biologic evidence suggesting chemical changes in chromosomes during nucleocytoplasmic interactions there is a growing body of evidence for such changes based on direct chemical measurements. The chemical composition and behavior of chromosomes is known to change during the course of development. During gametogenesis, the complex protein constituents of the chromosomes are simplified so that gamete chromosomes are composed largely of DNA and histonelike protein. During subsequent development, extensive additions and changes occur in the RNA and nonhistone protein associated with the chromosome. On the basis of staining reactions Alfert[1] has shown that when cells begin to function after cell-multiplication has ceased they exhibit a decline in DNA basophilia and histone acidophilia. Apparently, the DNA phosphate groups and the basic histone groups are no longer so accessible to staining, perhaps because of newly acquired components that regulate the functional activity of the chromosome. When nuclei degenerate and become pyknotic their DNA and histone stain heavily, presumably because of the loss of nonhistone protein from the no longer functional chromosomes.

EFFECT OF INJECTED NUCLEAR EXTRACTS

These observations on the changing chemical composition of chromosomes during development and on the failure of chromosomes to promote normal development after they had multiplied in foreign cytoplasm led us to the hypothesis that cellular differentiation involves the acquisition of specific substances by the chromosomes, probably protein or RNA. To examine this hypothesis, various cell fractions were prepared from adult frog (*Rana pipiens*) liver cells and injected into fertilized eggs of the same species and the effects on development recorded.[23] Those eggs injected with the globulin fraction from frog liver nuclei exhibited a consistent developmental arrest at the beginning of gastrulation. These arrested blastulae appeared normal except for the failure to gastrulate. Nuclei from these arrested blastulae were transplanted back into enucleated eggs and, again, the eggs developed into blastulae which arrested. Nuclei from such arrested blastulae were retransplanted for 7 generations without any change in the pattern of arrest at the beginning of gastrulation. The effects of the injected material thus appeared to be irreversible when tested in this manner. As little as 0.01 microgram of protein was present in effective globulin fractions. Heating for 5 minutes at 100° C. destroyed the activity. During cell division the chromosomes of injected eggs should have been freely accessible to the injected substances. The very small quantity of injected material suggests a highly specific effect and since this effect persisted through many nuclear divisions it seems reasonable to place the primary effect on the chromosomes. The behavior of these nuclei seems like that of the transplanted nuclei which multiplied in foreign cytoplasm; indeed, the chromosomes of the injected eggs were multiplying in "foreign" cytoplasm — a cytoplasm changed by virtue of the injected liver-specific proteins.

RNA SYNTHESIS

The evidence just discussed indicates an effect of cytoplasmic constituents on the nuclei and the chromosomes, but the molecular traffic certainly flows both ways. We know from numerous studies on gene-controlled specificity of macromolecules that, in some manner, the genes control the synthesis of cytoplasmic constituents. Ribonucleic acid is associated intimately with protein synthesis in the cytoplasm and is the leading contender for the role of intermediary between the chromosomes and protein synthesis. Recently, Goldstein and Micou,[16,17] using tritiated cytidine on human amnion cells grown in tissue culture, obtained evidence for a primary synthesis of RNA on the chromosomes. Labeled RNA first appeared on the chromosomes, then accumulated in the nucleolus and next moved into the cytoplasm. Additional evidence from enucleated cells of various types strongly supports the contention that RNA synthesis is an exclusive property of the nucleus, if not of the chromosomes themselves. It is equally probable that most protein synthesis occurs in the cytoplasm in association with RNA particulates or ribosomes. The synthetic activity of chromosomes and ribosomes is doubtless dependent upon their chemical composition. In important respects these two synthesizing organelles are compounded similarly—both contain nucleic acid, histonelike protein and nonhistone protein.[11]

ULTRASTRUCTURE OF DEVELOPING CELLS

Another source of evidence for nucleocytoplasmic exchange stems from an examination of the ultrastructure of developing cells by means of the electron microscope. Although a dynamic exchange cannot be reflected clearly in static pictures, the time course of the appearance of structure and suggestive details of morphology do imply an interaction between the nucleus and the cytoplasm.[7] The nuclear membrane, far from being a passive barrier to exchange, appears to be a complex organelle actively presiding over the passage of materials between the nuclear and the cytoplasmic parts of the cell. The nuclear envelope of many cell types exhibits a common structural plan. The envelope consists of 2 membranes each roughly 50 to 80 Å thick, separated by a perinuclear space of somewhat greater dimensions. Most important is the existence of discontinuities or "pores" through the envelope. These "pores" are larger than necessary to accommodate the passage of macromolecules or of ribosomes, but it is unlikely that passage would be by simple diffusion and the "pores" may be specialized organelles that exert a fine discrimination over what is permitted to pass. The nuclear envelope also has been incriminated in the production of mitochondria. Electron micrographs of a variety of tissues show the nuclear membrane cast into folds which have been interpreted as sites of mitochondrial formation.[18] It seems probable that the differentiated properties of the cell are, in part, a reflection of the diverse populations of mitochondria that it contains. Some relationship between the genome and the mitochondria of the cell seems to be essential, but this relationship is still obscure.

One conspicuous feature of the cytoplasm of many differentiated cells is an endoplasmic reticulum. This membranous system is attached to the outer nuclear envelope and to the cell membrane. Some evidence has been presented to show that the endoplasmic reticulum originates from the nuclear membrane,[15,20] which remains in close association with the chromosomes. The endoplasmic reticulum is extremely variable in different cell types, but generally is lacking or only slightly developed in embryonic cells.[26] As cell differentiation progresses, the reticulum commonly increases, and eventually most of the ribosomes become attached to it.[5]

In many embryonic cells, and in cancer cells too, the ribosomes are distributed largely unattached to any membranous system. However, recent studies on the eggs and the embryos of several tunicates, which show a mosaic type of embryonic development, reveal a rather extensive membranous system in the cytoplasm even in the earliest stages of development.[6] Whether or not these membranes compose a true endoplasmic reticulum remains doubtful.

Contrary to what the presence of these membranes might suggest, the cleaving eggs of tunicates do not possess extensive synthetic activities as compared with their later larval and adult stages. Tunicate eggs are surrounded by a tough membrane, the chorion. This membrane also encloses several hundred small cells (test cells) which thus are associated inescapably with the developing embryo until the time of hatching, when the chorion ruptures to release the swimming larva. The metabolic role, if any, of these test cells during development is unknown. However, they contain DNA in sufficient quantity to equip all the cells of the developing larva. In fact, about 1,000 times as much DNA is found within the chorion of *Ascidia nigra* eggs, including the test cells, as is found in a sperm. Whatever may be the source of DNA during tunicate development, there is good evidence to show that the ability to synthesize amino acids is slight during early embryonic life. At the time the embryo hatches and embarks upon a larval existence, an enormous expansion of synthetic activity occurs.[24] This enlargement of synthetic capability parallels the development of nucleoli, which are absent from the dividing cells of the early embryo but appear at a later stage in development. This evidence suggests that the nuclei (and the chromosomes) of these early embryos do not have much functional significance. Similar conclusions from a variety of evidence can be drawn about the nuclei of amphibian embryos up to the beginning of gastrulation. Only later do the nuclei begin to function and to play a crucial role in cellular differentiation.

The evidence submitted here, admittedly rather selected, enables us to sketch out a plan of nucleocytoplasmic interaction that is plausible and should provide a basis for further experimentation. The fertilized egg is equipped at the outset with a complete set of chromosomes, largely composed of nucleohistone. Many of the genes on these chromosomes are not functional in the zygote and, in fact, the nucleus itself plays only a minor role during the early cleavage stages of embryonic development. However, as the chromosomes are replicated, they acquire additional constituents (probably protein) from the surrounding cytoplasm. This increasing chemical complexity of the chromosomes activates many genes to function (and perhaps inhibits others). The synthetic activity of the genes then results in the formation of ribosomes that pass into the cytoplasm. The nuclear envelopes, which also owe many of their characteristics to the activity of chromosomes, may produce mitochondria and the endoplasmic reticulum on which many of the ribosomes become attached. The activity of these organelles in the cytoplasm, together with the ingress of materials from adjacent cells, results in a new chemically differentiated cytoplasm. New products arising in this cytoplasm then move back into the nucleus and by attaching to the chromosomes further differentiate them by activating new genes or by repressing previously active genes. The activated genes then release new products to the cytoplasm. Thus, an oscillating interaction between the nucleus and the cytoplasm is established that drives the undifferentiated cell toward its differentiated state where finally an equilibrium is achieved. The differentiated state is rather stable, particularly in the absence of nuclear division, but if mature cells are provoked to divide (as in tissue culture or after malignant transformation) then many of the specialized characteristics of the cell are lost, perhaps because of chromosomal changes brought about by chromosomal replication in a medium which no longer provides all of the materials needed to duplicate highly differentiated chromosomes. In fact, in both tissue culture and in cancer cells gross chromosome abnormalities are very common.[19]

Although current hypotheses of cellular differentiation must rest on fragile foundations, it seems safe to predict that nucleo-cytoplasmic interactions will prove to be involved fundamentally in the mechanisms of cellular differentiation, and hence of all embryonic development.

REFERENCES

1. Alfert, M.: Variations in cytochemical properties of cell nuclei, Exp. Cell Res. (Suppl.) **6**:227-235, 1958.
2. Allison, A. C.: Metabolic polymorphisms in mammals, Am. Nat. **93**:5-16, 1959.
3. Anfinsen, C. B.: The Molecular Basis of Evolution, New York, Wiley, 1959.
4. Austin, C. R.: Anomalies of fertilization leading to tripoidy, J. Cell. & Comp. Physiol. (symposium supplement) **56**:1-15, 1960.
5. Bellairs, R.: The development of the nervous system in chick embryos, studied by electron microscopy, J. Embryol. Exp. Morph. **7**:94-115, 1959.
6. Berg, W. E., and Humphreys, W. J.: Electron microscopy of 4-cell stages of the *Ascidians ciona* and *stycla*, Develop. Biol. **2**:42-60, 1960.
7. Bernhard, W.: Ultrastructural aspects of nucleo-cytoplasmic relationship, Exp. Cell Res. (Suppl.) **6**:17-60, 1958.
8. Blackler, A. W.: Transfer of germ-cells in *Xenopus laevis,* Nature **185**:859-860, 1960.
9. Boveri, T.: Über Differenzierung der Zellkerne während der Furchung des Eies von Ascaris megalocephala, Anat. Anz. **2**:688-693, 1887.
10. Briggs, R., and King, T. J.: Transplantation of living nuclei from blastula cells into enucleated frogs' eggs, Proc. Nat. Acad. Sc. **38**:455-463, 1952.
11. Butler, J. A. V., Cohn, P., and Simson, P.: The presence of basic proteins in microsomes, Biochem. Biophys. Acta **38**:386-388, 1960.
12. Conference on Hemoglobin, Publication No. 557, Washington, D. C., NAS-NRC, 1958.
13. Fankhauser, G.: The organization of the amphibian egg during fertilization and cleavage, Ann. New York Acad. Sc. **49**:684-708, 1948.
14. Fischberg, M., Gurdon, J. B., and Elsdale, T. R.: Nuclear transfer in amphibia and the problem of the potentialities of the nuclei of differentiating tissues, Exp. Cell Res. (Suppl.) **6**:161-178, 1958.
15. Gay, H.: Nucleocytoplasmic relations in Drosophila, Symposia Quant. Biol. **21**:257-269, 1956.
16. Goldstein, L., and Micou, J.: Nuclear cytoplasmic relationships in human cells in tissue culture. III. Autoradiographic study

of inter-relation of nuclear and cytoplasmic ribonucleic acid, J. Biophys. Biochem. Cytol. **6**:1-6, 1959.

17. ———: On the primary site of nuclear RNA synthesis, J. Biophys. Biochem. Cytol. **6**:301-303, 1959.

18. Hoffman, H., and Grigg, G. W.: An electron microscopic study of mitochondria formation, Exp. Cell Res. **15**:118-131, 1958.

19. Hsu, T. C., and Klatt, A.: Mammalian chromosomes in vitro. X. Heteroploid transformation in neoplastic cells, J. Nat. Cancer Inst. **22**:313-339, 1959.

20. Kaufmann, B. P., and Gay, H.: The nuclear membrane as an intermediary in gene controlled reactions, Nucleus **1**: 57-78, 1954.

21. King, T. J., and Briggs, R.: Serial transplantation of embryonic nuclei, Symposia Quant. Biol. **21**:271-290, 1956.

22. Markert, C. L., and Silvers, W. K.: The effects of genotype and cell environment on melanoblast differentiation in the house mouse, Genetics **41**:429-450, 1956.

23. Markert, C. L.: Biochemical embryology and genetics, pp. 3-18, Nat. Cancer Inst. Monogr. No. 2, 1960.

24. ———: Unpublished observations.

25. Moore, J. A.: Serial back-transfers of nuclei in experiments involving two species of frogs, Develop. Biol. **2**:535-550, 1960.

26. Palade, G. E.: Microsomes and ribonucleoprotein particles, pp. 36-61 *in* Roberts, R. B. (ed.): Microsomal Particles and Protein Synthesis, New York, Pergamon Press, 1958.

SESSION IV

Discussion

Moderator

PROFESSOR CONRAD H. WADDINGTON, C.B.E., F.R.S.

*Institute of Animal Genetics, University of Edinburgh, West Mains Road,
Edinburgh, Scotland, United Kingdom*

Panel Members

DR. H. B. FELL, F.R.S.

Director, Strangeways Research Laboratory, Werts Causeway, Cambridge, United Kingdom

VIKTOR HAMBURGER, Ph.D.

Department of Zoology, Washington University, St. Louis, Missouri, U.S.A.

MILAN HAŠEK, M.D.

*Ceskoslovenska Akademic Ved Biologicky, Ustav Praha-Dejvice, Na Criciste C.2,
Prague, Czechoslovakia*

JAMES D. EBERT, Ph.D.

Director, Carnegie Institution of Washington, Baltimore, Maryland, U.S.A.

DR. FELL: To give a biologically sound definition of induction is about as difficult as to give a biologically sound definition of cancer and for the same reason. Both terms include many different phenomena; these phenomena probably are related, but at present we are too ignorant of the fundamental processes involved to know exactly what the relationship is. If we take the different types of biologic interaction that have been presented in these three papers, we can arrange them in a series. At one end of the series are interactions that any embryologist would accept as inductions in the strict sense; at the other end are phenomena that he probably would refuse to regard as inductions. Yet, at no point in the series is there a sharp boundary line between the two categories. Dr. Zwilling's example of the interaction between the apical ridge of the chick limb-bud and the underlying mesoderm is clearly an induction of the conventional type. For example, this is indicated by the experiments in which Saunders and his collaborators showed that when presumptive thigh mesoderm is grafted beneath the apical ridge of the wing bud, it forms toes instead of a femur. Clearly, the thigh mesoderm has been deflected from its proper developmental pathway and under the influence of the apical ridge has differentiated into structures that it does not produce normally.

Grobstein's results are less easy to interpret. Grobstein showed that the epithelial component of the mouse salivary gland rudiment would develop only its normal branching structure if it were associated with its own mesoderm. When it is combined with kidney mesoderm, it was not induced to form kidney tubules and failed to differentiate. I have heard it argued that the salivary mesoderm does not really induce the formation of the glandular structure but merely provides certain essential environmental conditions that enable the epithelium to express its latent potentialities. The same remarks might apply to the elegant experiments of Lash, Holtzer and Holtzer on the influence of the spinal cord on the development of vertebral cartilage.

According to this argument, we should speak of an inductive influence only when one tissue acquires developmental potentialities from association with another. We ought not to apply the term to a situation in which a tissue already is endowed with its developmental potentialities but cannot manifest them unless the appropriate environmental conditions are provided by another tissue. Grobstein's results might be said to lie on the ill-defined area between what is and what is not true induction. If we regard Grobstein's results as true inductions, it is difficult to know where to stop. For example, there seems to be no logical distinction between the phenomena that he describes and certain hormonally induced changes. Dr. Levi-Montalcini quoted Wilt's experiments showing that the presence of thyroxine is an essential condition in the conversion of the visual pigment in the frog-tadpole retina from the porphyropsin of the larval retina to the rhodopsin of the adult frog. The retina is capable of making this change, but to do so requires the right environmental conditions, which are supplied by the thyroid gland.

An even more striking example of hormonal action on differentiation is in the effect of estrogens on the vaginal epithelium during the normal menstrual cycle. The epithelium possesses two sets of developmental potentialities, and the one expressed depends on the hormonal environment. In the presence of estrogen, the epithelium undergoes a complete metaplasia from a mucous to a squamous keratinizing structure. If the thyroxin-secreting and the estrogen-secreting tissues were in intimate contact with the retina and with the vaginal epithelium, respectively, we might refer to these responses as inductions; but, as the effects are produced by remote control, we do not.

DR. HAMBURGER: I agree completely with Dr. Fell's statements concerning embryonic induction. Dr. Zwilling has given a vivid picture of the complex interactions which are instrumental in the elaboration of structural differentiation. He certainly has not implied that induction is the only type of embryonic interaction. The embryonic nervous system provides a number of instructive examples of other types, and Dr. Levi-Montalcini already has referred to one of them.

In the case of the primary sensory and motor centers of the spinal cord, we have known since the early days of neural embryology that the peripheral structures to be innervated exercise a controlling influence on the growth, the proliferation and the differentiation of these centers. Starting from these primary reactions, we find transneuronal interactions which affect the more remote nerve centers. For instance, if we remove one of the sense organs' primordia, such as the optic cup, not only the primary optic centers, but eventually all other centers related to the optic system are affected. Conversely, primary defects in the primary nerve cells and nerve centers—motor centers—result in effects on the musculature which atrophies and eventually degenerates in the absence of motor nerves. In insects, an example is the early extirpation of nerve centers which prevents the primary differentiation of the musculature altogether.

In short, the nerve cell supplies trophic— I would not call them inductive — effects both for the maintenance of muscle cells and for the maintenance of other nerve cells through transneuronal interactions. If these noninductive correlations are viewed together with the inductive interactions, obviously a primary lesion at one focal tissue may have numerous manifestations in adjacent or in remote structures. Multiple defects—including those which are genetically controlled—may or may not be due to multiple local primary lesions.

Only the analytical experiment on the embryo can give evidence for causal relations. Polydactyly is correlated with an enlargement of the motor column. Only experiment can show in which direction the causal relationship lies.

First, I would stress the importance of the general concept of single focal lesions, resulting in a wide range of secondary effects. This concept is fundamental to an understanding of malformations.

Second: in the early days of teratology, the dictum so powerfully expounded by Stockard—that all abnormalities are due to arrested growth—was widely adopted. At that time, growth was poorly defined. It was implied that structures which are in a phase of particularly active growth at the time the disturbance occurs are differentially sensitive and that the pattern of malformations reflects the pattern of growth disturbance. Now this idea is discredited altogether. In all cases in which the mechanism of the origin of malformations is well elucidated, as for example, in the case of the teratogens carefully analyzed by Dr. Landauer, very specific metabolic events of specific enzymes are affected. This concept is now generally accepted for all malformations. Of course, some malformations, such as harelip and cleft palate, are the consequence of failure to complete a normal growth process. I suggest that these and all other malformations are not caused by a preceding general retardation of growth of the entire embryo, but that the pattern of manifest abnormalities reflects differential, highly specific, metabolic requirements for specific types of protein synthesis.

In this context, I would refer briefly to the specificity of virus infection. Although we know much about the results of rubella infection, the point of specificity is still obscure. I once infected the early chick embryo of 1½ to 2 days with influenza A virus and found that the ectodermal derivatives were affected. The same result was obtained by Blattner, using an infection by Newcastle disease virus. The effect was trivial in the sense that, since I poured the virus over the embryo, tissues which were infected showed the first manifestations. But whereas the early embryonic cells all seemed to be infected, 8 days later (as Burnet has shown) the virus was seen to have affected specifically the lung primordia. A study of embryos infected at different stages might make it possible to account for this specificity in terms of the metabolic changes in the embryonic cells.

Finally, the embryologist may be permitted to take exception to the conceptual validity of the term "congenital malformations." For the embryologist, birth is not a very important event. Of course, the embryo undergoes profound physiologic changes at birth, and certain malformations, such as the imperfect closure of the ductus arteriosus, may result. But for the manifestation of developmental mechanisms, resulting in normal or abnormal structure or function, birth has no significance, and the determination and the subsequent manifestations of malformations may occur continuously from the zygote to the adult.

DR. HASEK: Although epigenetic, as well as genetic, influences play an important role in differentiation, the genetic influence seems to be the primary mechanism. At the level of cell clones, effects mediated by genetic products of other cell clones play an active part. The series of experiments performed by Dr. Levi-Montalcini and her collaborators shows the existence of diffusible neurotropic substances and justifies the concept of the physiologic function of the substances.

The cytotoxic effect in vivo of the serum prepared against this protein is extraordinary. If I recall accurately the work of Dr. Levi-Montalcini published this year in the Proceedings of the National Academy of Science, the homologous cytotoxic sera were likewise effective in the rabbit. An exceptionally sensitive cytotoxic system must be involved. The question arises: Why cannot the sera attack other cells, in which this antigen is also present, for example, mesenchymal or salivary gland cells?

Dr. Markert has shown that nucleocytoplasmic interactions are of extreme importance to the differentiation processes. When the nucleic acid of the chromosomes replicates in foreign cytoplasm, foreign protein is incorporated in the chromosomes, thus preventing their normal differentiation and inhibiting their heterosynthetic functions. The differentiation of the nucleus may also be suggested by the changes in polytene chromosomes of some species at different stages of larval development, as shown by Beermann, Pavan and others. (Reviewed, Beermann.[2])

Probably, also, some phenomena of somatic cell heredity are important in differentiation. The determinants of somatic cell heredity may be cytoplasmic, as well as nuclear; but the role of somatic mutations in differentiation may be considerable, as shown by Burnet[4] and Lederberg[5] in 1959 when they discussed the differentiation of antibody-forming cells. The study of genetic changes in somatic cells was stimulated greatly by developments in bacterial and viral genetics, and several authors have attempted to demonstrate transformation in the cells of higher organisms. We have repeated the experiments of Benoit and his collaborators, and unlike them have obtained negative results (Benoit, LeRoy, Vendrely and Vendrely;[3] *see also* Beatty and Billet[1]).

In our laboratory, results obtained with antigenic transformation of heterozygous tumors in mice appear to be more promising. Transduction may also provide an important approach to the study of genetics of somatic cells. Cellular genetics of multicellular organisms may provide a connecting link between the embryologist and the geneticist.

REFERENCES

1. Beatty, R. A., and Billet, F. S.: Genetics of gametes. VI. Attempted genetic transformation in the rabbit, Proc. Roy. Soc. Edinburgh (B) 68:83-90, 1961.
2. Beermann, W.: Chromosomal differentiation in insects *in* Rudnick, D. (ed.): Developmental Cytology, pp. 83-104, New York, Ronald Press, 1959.
3. Benoit, J., LeRoy, P., Vendrely, R., and Vendrely, C.: Experiments on white Peking ducks injected with DNA from

khaki Campbell ducks, Trans. New York Acad. Sc. **22**:494-503, 1960.

4. Burnet, F. M.: The clonal selection theory of acquired immunity, Cambridge, Cambridge Univ. Press, 1959.

5. Lederberg, J.: Genes and antibodies, Science **129**:1649-1653, 1959.

DR. EBERT: I would recast the earlier considerations of embryonic induction in the light of Dr. Markert's discussion of nucleo-cytoplasmic interactions. He has presented a lucid picture of cellular architecture enabling one to pose at least a theoretic scheme whereby materials in the cellular milieu enter the cell and there exert their specific actions. How, then, may we consider embryonic induction, to use this term covering a multitude of different types of phenomena, in the light of Dr. Markert's scheme? We may regard it from two different points of view. First, returning to the point raised by Dr. Fell, let us consider induction by specific small molecules. Here we have the possibility, as envisioned by Markert, that a specific substrate might act either as a stimulus in the sense of inductive enzymogenesis or as a repressor in the light of the newer arguments of Pardee, Jacob and Monod,[4] in effecting a specific activation or deactivation of one or more genes, leading then to embryonic induction which would have essentially as its counterpart enzymic induction or repression. This is an attractive scheme; one which has been advanced from time to time over the past decade by Monod, by Spiegelman and others (for a recent discussion, see Ebert and Wilt[1]). Yet, it rests on very fragile evidence, and we must ask whether there is a single well-supported example of enzymic induction or repression in embryos which has developmental significance. By developmental significance, I mean not simply an example of physiologic enzymic induction in an embryo in which the quantity of a given enzyme is increased but one which is associated clearly with some major cellular differentiation. To my knowledge, there is no such example. The one most widely quoted (by Stearns and Kostellow[5]) is not well supported by other recent evidence (*see* Kato[2]).

Perhaps the difficulty is of experimental origin in that enzymic induction in microorganisms generally has been demonstrated using mutants or strains ideally suited for the particular purpose of the observer. Selection occurs at the outset of the experiment, and relatively few microorganisms or strains of organisms are favorable. The highly specific enzymic induction or repression may be difficult to demonstrate in the embryo.

Evidence of induction by large molecular stimuli, by the transfer of inductive agents by large molecules or by particulates, also is not as strong as might be wished. At most, there is inconclusive evidence of the passage of large molecular agents as revealed by radioactive and fluorescent labeling. A long series of experiments, notably those of Brachet already mentioned, indicate the involvement of RNA and/or RNA protein. We must keep open the possibility that both RNA and protein may be involved in these transformations.

Let us now consider the induction in the light of what I would like to call an epigenetic recombination, that is, an experiment like nuclear transplantation in which one simply implants into the cell a protein-synthesizing unit or a protein-synthesis directing unit from the donor. Here, one might visualize that the classic tool of the experimental embryologist, the recombination experiment involving recombination of tissues, may well be carried out, not only with nuclei as in the works of King, Briggs and others, but also with RNA or RNA protein particles. Perhaps what is needed is to afford the implanted agent a better foothold, or to give it a better opportunity to compete with the recipient system, by first destroying the homologous material of the recipient cell. A clue is given in experiments by Kramer and Straub[3] who were able to transfer the capacity for induction of the enzyme penicillinase in bacilli. They successfully transferred such enzyme induction by RNA only after the host's—the recipient's—RNA had been destroyed by RNAase.

In experiments with animal embryos the possibility exists, not only of using RNAase, but also of using as tools the viral agents to which Rhodes and Hamburger referred. The virus may be not simply a tool for the study of production of a syndrome of malformations but may assist in investigations of the development of specificity in the embryo, especially specificity of the cell surface. The virus also may be thought of as a tool which facilitates the transfer of inductive agents involving DNA, as suggested by the experiments of Lederberg, Zinder and others.

Finally, I would ask Dr. Levi-Montalcini a question which arises from Dr. Hasek's discussion of the effect of the antibody as a cytotoxic effect. To what extent does the evidence now justify the conclusion that the effect is cytoxic and not on the growth substance in the circulation? If this is a cytoxic effect, it would be the most striking one so far observed and might provide us with a first approach to the analysis of cytotoxicity, about which we know so little.

REFERENCES

1. Ebert, J. D., and Wilt, F. H.: Animal viruses and embryos, Quart. Rev. Biol. 35:261-312, 1960.
2. Kato, Y.: *in* Ebert, J. D.: Annual Report of the Director of the Department of Embryology, Carnegie Inst. Washington, Year Book 59:386-389, 1960.
3. Kramer, M., and Straub, F. B.: Role of specific nucleic acids in induced enzyme synthesis, Biochim. biophys. Acta 21:401-403, 1956.
4. Pardee, A., Jacob, F., and Monod, J.: The genetic control and cytoplasmic expression of inducibility in the synthesis of beta glactosidase by *E. coli,* J. Molec. Biol. 1:165-178, 1959.
5. Stearns, R. N., and Kostellow, A. B.: Enzyme induction in dissociated embryonic cells *in* McElroy, W. D., and Glass, B. (eds.): The Chemical Basis of Development, pp. 448-453, Baltimore, Johns Hopkins Press, 1958.

MODERATOR WADDINGTON: We might first ask Dr. Zwilling to comment on the reference to induction. Many people have emphasized, and I agree with them, that the word "induction" now has to be stretched to its limit to cover the types of phenomena with which we have become acquainted recently. It was introduced originally when few examples of tissue interaction in embryos were known and those were of a rather striking kind, such as the well-known induction of the neural tube in the amphibia. More recently, there have been many other examples of tissue interactions, from the purely potentiating interactions, such as Dr. Fell described, to inductions which seem to involve something more specific and positive than mere potentiation.

An aspect of this matter which has not been referred to is the nature of the cells that react to the stimulus. Many speakers have appeared to imply that these cells are waiting passively for some inducing substance—perhaps a protein-synthesizing particle—to affect them. I do not believe that this is the right way to think of the reacting cells. In the early stages of development, they usually seem to be undergoing a progressive series of changes. The inducing agent, or the tissue with which they interact, can be considered to deflect changes which already are in process. I suspect that the distinction between true induction and potentiating interactions should turn on whether processes are deflected which after the switch-point continue in one direction or another, or whether a single process is made to go a step further in its own direction. The switching of already existing processes of change is at any rate a consideration that needs to be accommodated in any acceptable formulation of ideas about induction.

DR. ZWILLING: It would be a serious mistake to waste much time over difficulties in terminology. As Dr. Ebert pointed out, we lack examples of specific mechanisms for tissue interactions of various sorts. There are certain objections to the term "induction," and tissue interaction may be more satisfactory.

Our concern should be with the particular mechanism at a given phase, and we may be led astray if we speak about true induction when we really are looking for mechanisms of various kinds of tissue interaction. The switching mechanism to which Professor Waddington referred may provide a clue. Indeed, I am surprised that Dr. Fell accepts limb development in the interaction between the ridge and the mesoderm as an example of true induction. There is no change in cell type during this interaction, but essentially a change in form in tissues which without the ectodermal ridge would go on to form cartilage, muscle, etc. But without this interaction the cartilages and muscles would not be in the form of a limb.

In another sense, the term "environmental requirement," as used by Dr. Fell may be a description of the objective in our quest for mechanisms of tissue interaction—the requirement of one tissue from another if a given morphogenetic event is to occur.

MODERATOR WADDINGTON: The first group of questions is concerned with the biochemical nature of the factors investigated by Dr. Levi-Montalcini and their source. For example: Can you give further information regarding the biochemical characterization of this specific protein? Is the protein the same in snake venom and in salivary gland? Is it a mucoprotein or a mucopolysaccharide? Is the factor present in other mammalian and, in particular, in human salivary gland?

DR. LEVI-MONTALCINI: The chemical nature of the agent was investigated by Dr. Stanley Cohen. He found that it had the characteristic of a protein: was destroyed by proteolytic enzyme; was not destroyed by an alkaline solution; and was destroyed by acid solution. The absorption spectrum had the characteristics of a protein. The molecular weight was about 20,000 in snake venom, and 44,000 in the salivary extract.

MODERATOR WADDINGTON: Is it a mucoprotein or a mucopolysaccharide?

DR. LEVI-MONTALCINI: There is no evidence that it is a mucoprotein.

MODERATOR WADDINGTON: And is it at present in other mammalian tissues?

DR. LEVI-MONTALCINI: Certainly not. We investigated this point in different mammals, including man. There was a small amount in the salivary gland of the rat. It is most significant that it is not present in the salivary gland of the mouse at birth. It increases as the animal grows and matures and reaches the maximum in the adult male. The level is about 10 times higher in the adult male than in the adult female.

MODERATOR WADDINGTON: The second group of questions is concerned with the mode of action of the substance. Is the effect due to a cytotoxic action, or to the inhibition of the growth substance in the blood plasma?

DR. LEVI-MONTALCINI: I have a little evidence in favor of the cytotoxic effect, based on preliminary experiments with fluorescent antibodies. A localization by fluorescent antibody of the substance in the sympathetic cells was observed. This evidence certainly is not conclusive but is suggestive.

Dr. Hasek asked about the effect of the antiserum on the salivary gland. When the antiserum is injected in the newborn mouse, it has no effect on the salivary gland, as the substance is not found there.

MODERATOR WADDINGTON: Has it any effect on human neuroblastoma?

DR. LEVI-MONTALCINI: This point is still under investigation.

MODERATOR WADDINGTON: Has is any effect on the parasympathetic system?

DR. LEVI-MONTALCINI: No.

MODERATOR WADDINGTON: Would Dr. Markert suggest that the basis of action of chemical teratogens must be a foreignizing of the cytoplasm of the cells involved to the chromosomes in their nucleus?

DR. MARKERT: The question touches upon perhaps the most difficult aspect of the relationship between the nucleus and the cytoplasm. Foreign substances made available to the cell would tend to alter the metabolic activities in the cytoplasm, so that the pattern of metabolism would be different. This change in the metabolism of the cytoplasm would be reflected subsequently in a change in the nucleus, but the mechanism by which changes in the cytoplasm affect the nucleus is unknown at present.

MODERATOR WADDINGTON: Dr. Markert has suggested that during differentiation, certain chromosomal potentialities are suppressed by chemical alterations in the chromosomal structure. Does he regard the remaining chromosomal potentialities as being accentuated at this or at later times? As I understand it, this question asks whether the whole of differentiation is to be explained by suppression of chromosomal potentialities, or whether it also involves accentuation of certain potentialities.

DR. MARKERT: I think that both are involved, but if one must be emphasized, I believe it is an accentuation of potentialities rather than a repression. The reason is that the nuclei of the cells of the early embryo can be shown to have very little activity; that is, the biochemical activities of early embryonic cells are minimal, and it is only later that the wide range of activities which we associate with the mature individual becomes apparent. These metabolic activities, in terms of enzyme synthesis and so forth, are to be related to the specific genes which control them. These genes appear not to be active in the early embryo but only to become active at later stages of development.

However, I think the question again touches another fundamental point that is difficult to answer: whether any acceleration of activity is connected intrinsically with an inhibition of activity. In embryonic development, as a cell is diverted down one path of differentiation to acquire certain specific characteristics, often it is precluded completely from acquiring alternative characteristics. Still difficult to explain is how the expression of a given capacity by a cell simultaneously inhibits the possibility of expressing alternative capacities. Whether a single event occurs which provides for one activity and inhibits an alternative one, or whether the two occurrences are completely unrelated, is difficult to say. But it does appear that when a cell can do a certain thing, it cannot do an alternative one.

DR. HAMBURGER: Dr. Markert has entered a convincing plea for considering the cell as the starting point and the essential element for the study of differentiation and development. The splendid progress that is being made in the study of cell differentiation certainly justifies this attitude. What the cell physiologist really studies is essentially the problem of how an embryonic undifferentiated cell acquires strain specificity, which means the production and the synthesis of specific proteins.

I would confirm this picture with reference to induction. Recently, I was able to see the remarkable work of Dr. Yamada at the University of Nagoya (reviewed, Yamada*). He obtained excellent inductions from amphibian ectoderm by pure proteins which are dissolved in the culture medium. This inductive agent, a pure protein completely deprived of any or of most nucleic acid components, resulted not in a strain specific differentiation of the pure muscle or cartilage tissue but in complex axial systems. Evidently, the purest inductive agents known produce complex patterns of differentiation, and the work of the cell physiologist has yet to be related to that of the inductionist. Our understanding of the situation is far from complete, since the inductions are highly complex.

MODERATOR WADDINGTON: Dr. Warkany asks: How should we distinguish between embryologic malformations and postnatal malformations: e.g., caused by rickets, pol-

---

* Yamada, T.: Embryonic induction *in* McElroy, W. D., and Glass, B. (eds.): The Chemical Basis of Development, pp. 217-238, Baltimore, Johns Hopkins Press, 1958.

iomyelitis, tuberculosis, etc., without using the word congenital?

DR. HAMBURGER: I have no objection to the use of the term "congenital." I agree with Dr. Zwilling that we should not be restricted by nomenclature and, in some rapidly developing fields, it is profitable to avoid precise definitions. But for practical purposes the term congenital malformation should be continued, provided that we are aware of the fraility of this concept.

MODERATOR WADDINGTON: Dr. Lash asks: Is there any evidence that the active portion of the large molecular inducers, such as nuclear protein, nucleic acid and so on, is in reality a smaller component, such as polynucleotide or even a single nucleotide or a single polypeptide? How large were the proteins that Yamada was using? Is there any evidence suggesting that there is a smaller active portion of these molecules?

DR. HAMBURGER: I do not know the molecular weight of the proteins that are being used.

MODERATOR WADDINGTON: Yamada reported that very short heat treatment of some of his native proteins apparently changed the type of pattern that it induces. A protein extract which induced the spinal cord and the posterior parts of the embryo was exposed to slight heat treatment which might be expected to give a slight denaturing effect. The part of the embryo induced shifted toward the anterior.

DR. HAMBURGER: Dr. Yamada considers this the change in the molecular structure of the single molecule.

MODERATOR WADDINGTON: Rather than of breaking down into polypeptides?

DR. HAMBURGER: I think he has quite good evidence, but I should stress again that these proteins are treated heavily with nucleases and agents which eliminate the nucleic acid, so that he is reasonably certain that pure proteins free from nucleic acids are active.

MODERATOR WADDINGTON: I have a further question addressed to Dr. Zwilling:

How can one reconcile Dr. Saunders' and Dr. Zwilling's results indicating the importance of the ectodermal ridge with the recent experiments by Bell,[1] in which chick limbs were found to develop normally after removal of the ectodermal ridge by ultrasonic treatment?

DR. ZWILLING: The evidence from Bell's laboratory represents a unique situation for the chick limb-bud in which limb development will take place in the absence of the ectoderm, including the ectodermal ridge. Dr. Bell and I have examined the differences between our observations. Our only conclusion is that following ultrasonation the surface of the mesoblast is different from that which follows any other treatments to which we have subjected it. We regard this difference as a hopeful clue to the mechanism of interaction. All of the other evidence supports the view that in normal morphogenesis, the ectoderm does play an active role and exerts a significant effect on the subsequent development of the mesoderm (*see* Bell, Saunders and Zwilling[1]).

MODERATOR WADDINGTON: This touches an important subject that we have not yet discussed adequately, namely, the way in which many of these tissue interactions take place. Our first impulse is to think of some specific chemical passing from one cell to another and eventually giving instructions to its chromosome. But there is much evidence that the tissue interaction does not take place at the level of a precisely defined chemical substance. In prewar investigations of the primary inducer in the amphibia, it was clear that the inductive interaction could be carried out by chemicals totally unrelated to those naturally present in the body. Here was an example of which it almost could be said that ultrasound treatment of the surface of the mesoderm had a similar effect to the inducing action of the apical ectodermal ridge. The whole question of the nature of these interactions—how far they involve specific chemical stimulants of gene action; how far they are simply changing the general metabolic set-up in the reacting cells—is one of the major problems for the future of experimental embryology. As Dr. Zwilling suggests, the example in the chick limb-bud may provide an interesting lead.

Dr. Zwilling: I would elaborate on the points to which Dr. Waddington has referred. Dr. Weiss and his collaborators, among others, (*see* Edds[2] for review) have shown that basement membranes and basement lamellae are composite structures produced by the co-operation of an epithelium and an underlying mesenchyme. The basement membrane in the chick limb-bud seems to be a favorable site for examination of the interaction between the two layers. The difference in the surface following ultrasound treatment is spectacular. PAS-positive material from the mesoblast seems to give it a surface, much like an exaggerated basement membrane.

REFERENCES

1. Bell, E., Saunders, J. W., and Zwilling, E.: Limb development in the absence of ectodermal ridge, Nature **184**:1736-1737, 1959.
2. Edds, M. V.: Origin and structure of intercellular matrix *in* McElroy, W. D., and Glass, B. (eds.): The Chemical Basis of Development, pp. 157-168, Baltimore, Johns Hopkins Press, 1958.

Moderator Waddington: The final question is in two parts: What are plasmogenes and how do they fit into your hypothesis? How does RNA act as a template in protein synthesis?

Dr. Markert: I seriously doubt whether a plasmogene exists in complex organisms. A plasmogene implies a self-reproducing particle in the cytoplasm, presumably containing nucleic acid. I know of no such particles in mammalian organisms or microorganisms.

Much investigation is now being directed toward the second part of the question, but the answer is not yet known. The most acceptable hypothesis is probably that the ribosome acts as a template for protein synthesis because of the specific linear sequence of the nucleotides in the ribonucleic acid components which, in some manner, organizes a correspondingly specific sequence of amino acids in the ribosome—the amino acids having been brought to the ribosome by soluble nucleic acid in the cytoplasm.

SESSION V

Abnormal Developmental Mechanisms

Moderator

PAUL A. WEISS, M.D.

Member and Professor, The Rockefeller Institute, Head, Laboratory of Developmental Biology, New York 21, New York, U.S.A.

THE USE OF TERATOGENS IN THE ANALYSIS OF ABNORMAL DEVELOPMENTAL MECHANISMS

F. CLARKE FRASER, B.Sc., M.Sc., Ph.D., M.D., C.M.

Department of Medical Genetics, The Montreal Children's Hospital, 937-8511 McGill University, Montreal, Canada

GENERAL PRINCIPLES IN EXPERIMENTAL TERATOLOGY

JAMES G. WILSON, Ph.D.

Department of Anatomy, University of Florida College of Medicine, Gainesville, Florida, U.S.A.

FETAL HORMONES AND MORPHOGENESIS

PROFESSOR ETIENNE WOLFF, M.D.

Laboratorie d'Embryologie Expérimentale, Collège de France, Nogent-sur-Marne, Seine, France

177

The Use of Teratogens in the Analysis of Abnormal Developmental Mechanisms

F. CLARKE FRASER, B.Sc., M.Sc., Ph.D., M.D., C.M.

The demonstration by Warkany and Nelson[28] that a maternal nutritional deficiency could produce malformations regularly in embryonic rats showed that the mammalian uterus was not as good a protective barrier for the embryo as had been thought, and suggested that environmental agents, as well as genes, might be teratogenically important in human beings. There followed a period when a wide variety of environmental agents were applied to a wide variety of mammalian species and were shown to produce a wide variety of malformations (reviewed by Kalter and Warkany.[17]) The time has now passed when one gets excited because yet another teratogen has been added to the list. The "helter-skelter approach" is being supplanted by the realization that teratogens, like genes, can be used as experimental tools to alter development in specific ways, and that, by studying the embryonic sequellae of such alterations, it is possible to learn something of normal developmental processes and how they can go wrong.

For example, trypan blue (originally tried as a means of simulating the teratogenic effects of rubella[10]) has been shown to produce malformations of the heart and the great vessels in rats,[30] and a study of the atrial and caval abnormalities so produced has suggested that they arose as the result of early displacement of the atrial chamber by an abnormal looping of the cardiac tube.[8] Many of the malformations resembled, anatomically, those seen in human beings, and so the experimental analysis suggests how the human malformations may have arisen. In this experiment, the mothers were treated early in pregnancy, and the embryos were examined near the end of pregnancy, the intervening chain of events being inferred from the end-results. It would be valuable to observe the embryos at the time when the primary defect is postulated to occur and thus test the hypothesis directly, but, since a minority of embryos are affected, it may be difficult to demonstrate that an abnormality seen in an embryo halfway through gestation would have resulted in a particular sort of malformation at birth. Comparison of strains, one of which produced a high frequency, and the other a low frequency, of malformations following exposure to the teratogen might be helpful here.

Monie et al.,[21] produced urinary tract abnormalities in about two thirds of the rat embryros from mothers treated with a pteroylglutamic acid (PGA) antagonist and studied their pathogenesis by observing abnormal embryos at various stages from shortly after treatment to near term. The first observed abnormality was malformation of the vertebral column, which apparently caused the umbilical arteries to interfere with craniad migration of the kidney, resulting in renal ectopia. Hydronephrosis and hydro-ureter could be interpreted as resulting from delay in or failure of disruption of the membrane which temporarily closes the opening of ureter into bladder. The experimentally induced urinary tract abnormalities have their counterpart in man, and the authors cautiously conclude that "the mechanisms concerned in their formation may be similar."

Turning to the central nervous system, the

pathogenesis of anencephaly has been studied by Giroud and Martinet[11] who used maternal treatment with large doses of vitamin A as a means of producing this defect in rats. The first abnormality is failure of the encephalic tube to close. Organogenesis and histogenesis proceed relatively normally in spite of this, so that all of the major structures of the brain are represented, but the brain is, so to speak, turned inside out. Later, degeneration sets in, and soon only debris and some nerves remain. Since similar stages occasionally have been reported in man, it is probable that the process (cranioschisis to exencephaly to anencephaly) is the same, at least in some cases.

Using another teratogen, trypan blue, Warkany *et al.*,[29] have analyzed, in a similar way, the pathogenesis of myelomeningocele in rats. Comparison of embryos at various ages, after treatment on the 8th, the 9th and the 10th days of gestation, showed that the neural tube on the 12th gestational day (when it normally closes) is already abnormal, with an irregular central canal, apparent overgrowth of the neural plate and lack of differentiation of vertebral primordia, similar to those described by Patten in an 8-mm. human embryo. This is followed by failure of the neural tube to close, with extensive overgrowth and eversion of the exposed nervous tissue. Degenerative changes occur towards the end of pregnancy, the exposed neural plate tissue is shed, and the supporting meninges become epithelialized and vascularized. A fluid-filled space develops between the pia of the neural plate and the dura covering the vertebrae. Thus, myelomeningocele is shown to begin as myeloschisis, followed by degeneration of the neural plate, and cyst formation in the subarachnoid space, and the pathogenesis of a lesion that could not be deduced from simply observing the final result has been clarified by the use of a teratogen to interrupt normal development. There are a great many other types of defect produced by teratogens in which embryologic studies of this sort would help to clarify the pathogenesis.

In our laboratory, we have taken a similar approach to study the causes of cleft palate in mice, with the added refinement that inbred strains were used in one of which (A/Jax) 100 per cent of the young had cleft palate following maternal treatment with cortisone; in the other (C57BL/6Jax) only 17 per cent of the young were affected. In both cases, treatment was begun 11 days after maternal insemination. Palate closure normally occurs around the end of day 14. Observations on treated embryos at the time of palate closure showed that movement of the shelves from the vertical plane, on either side of the tongue to the horizontal plane, above the tongue, was delayed, and that growth of the head continued so that when the shelves became horizontal they might be too far apart to meet.[27] In the A/Jax strain no treated embryos were seen with shelves touching, whereas in the C57BL/6 strain the majority of embryos did have the shelves meeting, but later than in untreated animals (Fig. 1). This interstrain comparison demonstrates far better than observations on only the C57BL/6 strain alone would have, that the pathogenesis of cleft palate in this case is delay in shelf movement rather than, say, a breakdown of shelf tissue after normal fusion. The comparison of strains that differ markedly in the frequency of malformations induced by a teratogen is a useful technic that could be exploited much more fully in the analysis of teratogenic mechanisms.

Finding an interstrain difference in response to a teratogen also emphasizes that even when an environmental agent is clearly implicated as the "cause" of a malformation, the genetic constitution of the reacting embryo also is involved, since it determines how susceptible the embryo will be to the effects of the teratogen. This raises the question of what differences between the strains underly the difference in response to the teratogen. Strain A/Jax and C57BL/6 differ in their coat color, spontaneous tumor incidence, various metabolic characteristics,[4,5,6] the types of spontaneously occurring malformations they exhibit, and in many other ways. Which ones are related to their difference in susceptibility to the teratogenic effects of cortisone?

One such difference seems to be the developmental stage at which palate closure occurs. In the C57BL/6 strain, closure begins earlier (perhaps 10 to 12 hours) than in the A/Jax strain (Fig. 1).[26] This correspondence also holds for a variety of crosses between the strains—[23] the lower the frequency of cortisone-induced cleft palate, the earlier the normal time of palate closure (Table 1). It might be thought, then, that the difference in cleft palate frequency could be due merely to the fact that the cortisone has longer to act when palate closure occurs later. However, this does not seem to be so, since the frequency of cleft palate is not increased in the C57BL/6 strain by beginning cortisone treat-

ment earlier than day 11.[14] It would seem, rather, that the force that builds up in the shelves and eventually enables them to push their way above the tongue builds up more effectively in the C57BL/6 strain, and that this is reflected in an earlier time of palate closure and in a greater resistance to the effects of cortisone.[27] Possibly the difference in behavior of the shelves is related to the distribution of acid mucopolysaccharide in them, but this has not been firmly established.

Another intriguing aspect of our studies on strain differences was the discovery that the maternal genotype, as well as the embryo's, is important in determining the embryo's reaction to the teratogen. Embryos from A/Jax mothers crossed to C57BL fathers had a higher frequency of cortisone-induced cleft palate (43%) than the genetically similar

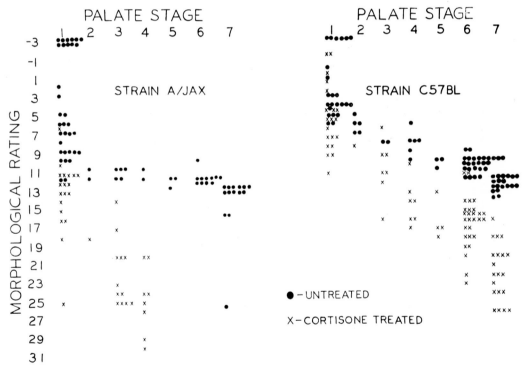

FIG. 1. The use of teratogens in the analysis of abnormal developmental mechanisms. Correlation of palate closure stage and developmental stage of embryo. Palate stages run from stage 1 (completely open) to 7 (closed). Morphologic rating refers to developmental stage of the embryo estimated from several external features (see Walker and Fraser, 1956, 1957). Palate closure occurs at more advanced developmental stages in embryos from mothers treated with cortisone (×) than in embryos from untreated mothers (●).

TABLE 1. Relation of Palate Stage to Morphologic Rating in Untreated Mouse Embryos of Various Genotypes. Palate Stages Run From 1 (Before Closure Begins) to 7 (Completely Closed). Morphologic Rating Refers to the Degree of Development of the Embryo as Indicated by Its External Features (Walker and Fraser, 1956). "% CP" Is the Frequency of Cortisone-Induced Cleft Palate in Mice of These Genotypes

Morphologic Rating	A X A Palate stage							A X C Palate stage							CA X A Palate stage						
	1	2	3	4	5	6	7	1	2	3	4	5	6	7	1	2	3	4	5	6	7
−3	12																				
−2																					
−1	1							1							1						
0								1							2						
1	1							2							3						
2	1							2							1						
3	3							2							16						
4	2							22							14						
5	2							11							3						
6	9							6							7						
7	7							3	4						10	1					
8	8	3						7	1	6	3	3	5		3	1	1	1		3	
9	3	1								1	1		11						1	6	
10	2	3	2	1	1	9	1			1			7	4			3		2	11	1
11		1	4	2		8	6						7	6						7	4
12						5	10						4	16						4	7
13				1			27							12							16
14							12							4							6
15							3							6							2
16							6							2							3
17							1							4							
18							1							4							
19							2														
20																					
"% CP"	100							45							25						

Morphologic Rating	AC X A Palate stage							C X C Palate stage							C X A Palate stage						
	1	2	3	4	5	6	7	1	2	3	4	5	6	7	1	2	3	4	5	6	7
−3																					
−2								4													
−1								2							3						
0								6							3						
1								2							7						
2	4							2							3						
3	4							2							8						
4	16							38	3						12	1					
5	6							1	1	1	1				4	1					
6	6							1	2	1	2				2			1			
7	13	1								2	5		3		4	2	1		7	2	
8	5	1	4	1						2	5	5	10	1	3				7	2	11
9	2		4	1	3	5		1			1	2	6	2						1	12
10			1			20	1			1			8	1						10	7
11						12	6						3	8						4	13
12						9	5							9							14
13							5							9							13
14							3							6							7
15							3							2							1
16							1							1							1
17							3														2
18							2														
19																					
20							1														
"% CP"	22							18							4						

embryos from C57BL mothers crossed to A/Jax fathers (4%). This difference corresponded to a difference in the time of palate closure in untreated embryos — those from the A/Jax × C57BL cross closed later than those from the C57BL × A/Jax (Table 1). This may be the first demonstration in mammals that the timing of a developmental process depends on the interaction of fetal and maternal genes. Again, the value of comparisons between animals of different genotypes is emphasized.

A second probable mechanism for the production of cleft palate was discovered as a result of attempts to inject cortisone directly into the embryo. It was found that removal of fluid from the amniotic sac may cause a cleft palate in the embryo concerned.[24,27] This result in rats was reported independently by Dokter[2] who also observed other types of malformation in embryos following amniotic sac puncture. The mechanism involved here still is not entirely clear, but the fact that the treated embryos appear constricted, and that the tongue appears to be pressed upward into the space between the palatine shelves, suggests that the cleft palate results from increased mechanical resistance provided by the tongue against shelf movement. Walker[25] has shown that the effect also occurs even when the punctured sac and embryo is removed from the uterus.

Cleft palate also may develop as a result of abnormally narrow palatine shelves which, although they may reach the horizontal position at the normal time, may be too narrow to meet. This seems to be the reason for the cleft palate that occurs in mice homozygous for the *ur* (urogenital) gene.[7]

It is possible that an abnormally wide head may prevent the palatine shelves from meeting, and there is some evidence that this may be the cause of at least some of the cleft palates caused by maternal PGA deficiency.[1]

Thus, cleft palate can be caused in a variety of ways, and, unfortunately, it may be quite impossible to tell, from the end-result, which mechanism was involved in a particular case. Furthermore, one cannot tell, from the time of normal palate closure, just when the embryo was exposed to the teratogen, except that probably it was not after the palate closed.

It may be helpful to think of palate closure and the ways it may go wrong as an example of quasicontinuous variation,[13] i.e., a con-

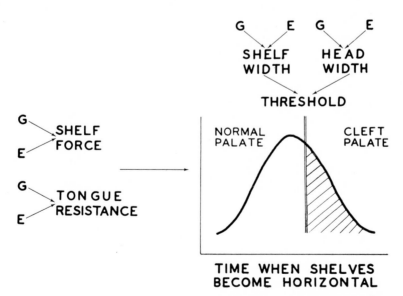

FIG. 2. The use of teratogens in the analysis of abnormal developmental mechanisms. Hypothetical diagram of factors influencing palate closure. For explanation see text.

tinuous distribution separated by a threshold into two separate groups. If the normal time at which the palatine shelves reach the horizontal position above the tongue forms a normal distribution (Fig. 2), then the stage after which it is too late for them to meet can be thought of as a threshold—embryos in which the shelves come up after this time will have cleft palate. Cortisone increases the frequency of cleft palate by delaying shelf movement—i.e., shifting the distribution to the right in relation to the threshold. Amniotic puncture does it by increasing the resistance of the tongue, which also shifts the distribution to the right. Narrow shelves or a wide head in effect move the threshold to the left. All these interacting elements can be altered both by genetic and environmental factors.[9] Obviously, it is dangerous to generalize about the causes of cleft palate.

Finally, I should like to discuss briefly the use of teratogens to analyze the biochemical aspects of development. Great opportunities exist for analyzing the biochemical requirements of embryos by applying, at specific developmental stages, chemicals of known pharmacologic properties. Landauer[18,19] has successfully exploited this approach in chicks, but only a beginning has been made in mammals.

Millen and Woollam,[20] for instance, have shown that insulin protects rats against the teratogenic effects of cortisone on the central nervous system, although in mice it seems to potentiate the teratogenic effects of cortisone on the palate.[15] Does this mean that the deleterious effects of cortisone on the central nervous system are mediated through a different pharmacologic property than its effect on the palate? It would seem that much might be learned about the biochemistry of teratogenesis by studying the potentiating and the inhibiting effects of pharmacologic agents on teratogens. Also, it would be interesting to compare the frequencies of cleft palate produced by a variety of the newer corticoids and see which of the biologic properties was related to their teratogenic

action. Incidentally, once this was established, the teratogenic potency of corticoids might provide a convenient method of assaying that particular property of corticoids.

The increasing availability of potent and specific antimetabolites for a variety of biologically important compounds provides another tool for studying the metabolic requirements of developmental processes, already being exploited by a number of workers (reviewed by Kalter and Warkany[17]). We have been using 6-aminonicotinamide, followed 2 hours later by a dose of nicotinamide, to produce a transitory inactivation of nicotinamide at precisely known gestational stages, and studying the resulting teratologic effects. The method provides some interesting possibilities for studying the biochemistry of the relationship between vitamin and analogue. For instance, it takes less nicotinamide to counteract the inhibiting effect of 6-aminonicotinamide when the nicotinamide is given simultaneously with than when it is given 2 hours after the analogue.[22] However, it is the teratologic implications we wish to discuss here. For one thing, it is interesting that interference with nicotinamide for as little as 2 hours (and maybe less) is highly teratogenic, even though it produces no visible effects on the mother. Must we not face the possibility that transitory, and clinically unrecognizable, metabolic deficiencies in humans in the first 8 weeks of pregnancy may be teratogenic? Is the occurrence of anencephaly more often in lower than in higher social classes related to the nutritional differences between them? On the other hand, if this is so, why is it that in countries with a high living standard and widespread use of vitamin supplements during pregnancy, the malformation rate remains uncompromisingly high?

The frequency of cleft palate produced by a transitory inactivation of nicotinamide is higher in the A/Jax strain than in the C57BL/6 strain,[12] and in the A/Jax × C57BL/6 than in the C57BL/6 × A/Jax hybrids,[3] just as it is when cortisone is used as a teratogen. On the other hand, galacto-flavin produces more cleft palates in the C57BL/6 strain than in the A/Jax strain.[16] This shows that the susceptibility of the A/Jax palate to cortisone and 6-aminonico-tinamide is not just a nonspecific instability to any environmental insult. It also suggests that galactoflavin interferes with palate clo-sure at a different metabolic point than cor-tisone and 6-aminonicotinamide, and that perhaps cortisone and 6-aminonicotinamide act on the same pathway. Since the 6-aminonicotinamide is known to interfere with DPN synthesis, this implies that corti-sone's teratogenicity may reside in its effect on DPN synthesis, or on some related proc-ess. Of course, we would not want to draw conclusions from these few comparisons, but the approach appears to be useful. By ob-serving the effects of a variety of teratogens on a number of strains and seeing which ones produce the same patterns of strain differ-ences in frequency of malformation, it should be possible to deduce which ones are affect-ing the same metabolic pathways, and get some idea of which pathways are involved.

The use of transitory exposures to meta-bolic inhibitors makes it possible to define the developmental stages most susceptible to interference much more precisely than was possible with agents such as cortisone which acted over a rather long period of gestation. Thus, a 2-hour maternal inactivation of nico-tinamide produces a high frequency of cleft palate on gestation day 13 in the A/Jax strain but a much lower frequency on day 12 and almost none on day 11 or 14.[12] Cleft lip is produced in A/Jax × C57BL hybrids on day 9.[3] Treatment of A/Jax mice on day 10 produces a very much higher frequency of resorption than treatment on any other day. Why does the embryo need more nicotinamide on day 10 in order to survive? These and many other questions remain to be answered, and the use of tera-togens in the analysis of developmental mechanisms should have a long and produc-tive future.

SUMMARY AND CONCLUSIONS

Teratogens can be used as tools to alter embryonic processes in very specific ways From the results of such developmental dis-turbances much has been and can be learned about normal development and the patho-genesis of malformations. The use of gene-tically susceptible animals in order to obtain a high frequency of the malformation con-cerned facilitates such analyses.

Comparison of strains that react differ-ently to a teratogen is a useful way to get further information about the factors that determine whether a given embryo is born malformed.

The same type of malformation can result from several different pathogenetic mechan-isms, and it may be impossible to tell, from the end-result, how the malformation arose.

Much can be learned about the metabolic processes involved in normal development, and how they are affected by teratogens, by comparing the effects of a variety of terato-gens, singly and in combinations, on a variety of genetic constitutions. The use of precisely timed, very short exposures of embryos to specific metabolic antagonists appears to be a promising method of analyzing the bio-chemical requirements of the embryo.

ACKNOWLEDGMENTS

Financial support from the National Research Council of Canada, the United States Public Health Service, and The National Foundation is gratefully acknowledged.

REFERENCES

1. Asling, C. W.: Genesis of maxillo-facial deformities in rats resulting from maternal dietary deficiency *in* Pruzansky, S. (ed.): Symp. on Cong. Anomalies of the Face and Assoc. Structures, pp. 173-188, Spring-field, Ill., Thomas, 1961.
2. Dokter, H. J.: Anti-thyreoide Stoffen enangeboren misvormingen, Amsterdam, Proefschrift, 1958.
3. Feiner, M.: Personal communication.
4. Fenton, P. F., Cowgill, G. R., Stone, M. A., and Justice, D. H.: The nutrition of the mouse. VIII. Studies on panto-thenic acid, biotin, inositol and p-amino-

benzoic acid, J. Nutr. **42**(2):257-269, 1950.

5. Fenton, P. F., Dickson, H. M., and Cowgill, G. R.: Glucose absorption in highly inbred strains of mice, Proc. Soc. Exp. Biol. Med. **80**:86-88, 1952.

6. Fenton, P. F., and Dowling, M. T.: Studies on obesity. I. Nutritional obesity in mice, J. Nutr. **49**(2):319-331, 1953.

7. Fitch, N.: An embryological analysis of two mutants in the house mouse, both producing cleft palate, J. Exp. Zool. **136** (2):329-361, 1957.

8. Fox, M. H., and Goss, C. M.: Experimentally produced malformations of the heart and great vessels in rat fetuses. Atrial and caval abnormalities, Anat. Rec. **129**(3):309-332, 1957.

9. Fraser, F. C., Walker, B. E., and Trasler, D. G.: Experimental production of congenital cleft palate: genetic and environmental factors, Pediatrics **19**(No. 4, Pt. II): 782-787, 1957.

10. Gillman, J., Gilbert, C., and Gillman, T.: A preliminary report on hydrocephalus, spina bifida and other congenital anomalies in the rat produced by trypan blue, S. Afr. J. Med. Sci. **13**:47-90, 1948.

11. Giroud, A., and Martinet, M.: Morphogenese de l'anancephalie, Arch. Anat. Micr. Morph. Exp. **46**(3):247-264, 1957.

12. Goldstein, M.: Personal communication.

13. Gruneberg, H.: Quasi-continuous variation in the mouse, Symp. Genet., Pavia **3**:215-227, 1952.

14. Kalter, H.: The inheritance of susceptibility to the teratogenic action of cortisone in mice, Genetics **39**(2):185-196, 1954.

15. ———: Preliminary studies on the metabolic factors involved in the production of cleft palate in mice, Genetics **39**:975, 1954.

16. Kalter, H., and Warkany, J.: Congenital malformations in inbred strains of mice induced by riboflavin-deficient, galactoflavin-containing diets, J. Exp. Zool. **136** (3):531-566, 1957.

17. ———: Experimental production of congenital malformations in mammals by metabolic procedures, Physiol. Rev. **39**: 69-115, 1959.

18. Landauer, W.: On the chemical production of developmental abnormalities and of phenocopies in chicken embryos, J. Cell. Comp. Physiol. **43**(1):261-305, 1954.

19. ———: Niacin antagonists and chick development, J. Exp. Zool. **136**(3):509-530, 1957.

20. Millen, J. W., and Woollam, D. H. M.: Insulin-cortisone relationship in experimental teratogenesis, Nature (Lond) **181**: 418, 1958.

21. Monie, I. W., Nelson, M. M., and Evans, H. M.: Abnormalities of the urinary system of rat embryos resulting from transitory deficiency of pteroylglutamic acid during gestation, Anat. Rec. **127**(4):711-724, 1957.

22. Pinsky, L., and Fraser, F. C.: Congenital malformations following a two-hour inactivation of nicotinamide by its analogue, 6-aminonicotinamide in pregnant mice, Brit. M. J. (in press).

23. Trasler, D. G., and Fraser, F. C.: Factors underlying strain, reciprocal cross, and maternal weight differences in embryo susceptibility to cortisone-induced cleft palate in mice, Proc. 10th Int. Cong. Gen. **2**:296-297, 1958.

24. Trasler, D. G., Walker, B. E., and Fraser, F. C.: Congenital malformations produced by amniotic-sac puncture, Science **124**: 439, 1956.

25. Walker, B. E.: Effects on palate development of mechanical interference with the fetal environment, Science **130**:981, 1959.

26. Walker, B. E., and Fraser, F. C.: Closure of the secondary palate in three strains of mice, J. Embryol. Exp. Morph. **4**:176-189, 1956.

27. ———: The embryology of cortisone-induced cleft palate, J. Embryol. Exp. Morph. **5**(2):201-209, 1957.

28. Warkany, J., and Nelson, R. C.: Appearance of skeletal abnormalities in the offspring of rats reared on a deficient diet, Science **92**:383-384, 1940.

29. Warkany, J., Wilson, J. G., and Geiger, J. F.: Myeloschisis and myelomeningocele produced experimentally in the rat, J. Comp. Neurol. **109**(1):35-64, 1958.

30. Wilson, J. G.: Teratogenic activity of several azo dyes chemically related to trypan blue, Anat. Rec. **123**(3):313-334, 1955.

General Principles in Experimental Teratology

JAMES G. WILSON, Ph.D.

The considerable literature on the subject of experimental teratology has been reviewed by Gruenwald,[18] Giroud,[11] Kalter and Warkany,[25] and Wilson[56] and variously discussed under such headings as classes of agents used, possible mechanisms of action and types of malformations produced. An attempt is made here to analyze these results for generalizations which might be applicable to all or most teratologic situations. The following are presented not as definitive laws of teratology but rather as general principles which, for the time being, may impart an element of unity in what is rapidly becoming a diverse and confusing field.

1. **The Embryologic Stage at the Time an Agent Acts Determines Which Tissues Are Susceptible to Teratogenesis.** This generality was propounded strongly by Stockard[45] after he observed in the developing sea minnow that such agents as hypoxia and reduced temperature caused similar malformations at a given stage, but that the types of malformations changed when these or other agents were applied at other developmental stages. In recent years, it has become necessary to modify Stockard's original hypothesis, particularly as applied to the embryos of higher vertebrates. During cleavage and early germ-layer stages of mammals, for example, the embryos seem to be resistant to teratogenesis. This has been shown repeatedly with a variety of agents such as irradiation,[20,40,54] vitamin deficiencies,[4,37] vitamin excess[5] and many others. In the only known exceptions, ocular defects appeared in a few rats subjected to hypoxia on days 1 to 8 of gestation,[53] and monstrous development occurred in all of a single litter of hamsters subjected to hypothermia on day 2 of gestation.[43]

Why early mammalian embryos are immune to teratogenesis is not known. It probably has something to do with whether individual cells in the embryo have become predetermined to form specific parts of the future organism or whether they retain, at least to some degree, the original totipotency of the fertilized egg. For want of a more precise term, this presumed change in cellular potentiality is called the *beginning of differentiation*. When an agent is applied before this change occurs, no specific tissue or organ defect can be produced because as yet no cells have been designated to form such tissues and organs. All cells are alike, that is, have the same metabolic needs, and all would be expected to react alike to a teratogenic insult. The outcome would be death or retardation of growth but not malformation.[58] In mammals, differentiation begins several days after conception: as early as 5½ days in the hamster and the mouse, as late as 9 days in the rabbit.

As differentiation begins, the embryo abruptly becomes susceptible to most teratogenic agents and, at or soon after this time, many agents produce their highest incidence of malformations.[4,5,20,21,37,40,54] This is probably due to the fact that many individual organs have a period of particular susceptibility to extrinsic influences which coincides with early developmental events in the organ. To identify this most susceptible period, minimal doses of the teratogenic agent must be used.[27,40,54] Large doses cause the defect in question to appear on days other than that of greatest susceptibility.[40,52] Some organs

187

under the right conditions of treatment may be induced to show more than one susceptible period.[27,41] Thus, although malformations seem to be produced with greatest ease when organs or organ-systems are in primordial stages, it is by no means always the case that overt developmental events can be correlated with the time an agent is active. Renal anomalies can be induced by irradiating rat embryos on the 9th day, but the metanephros does not appear even in rudimentary form until the 12th day.[59] Skeletal abnormalities have been produced by a variety of means many hours before any skeletal structure other than the notochord is recognizable.[32,42]

Susceptibility to teratogenesis decreases as differentiation proceeds.[7,9,22,54,60] In other words, larger doses of the agent are required to produce comparable malformations, if indeed comparable ones can be produced at all. Not only individual organs, but the embryo as a whole becomes progressively more resistant to teratogenesis.[20,37] For example, exposure of rat embryos to 100 r of x-rays on the 9th day of gestation caused many types of malformations in virtually all of the young, the same treatment on the 10th day caused somewhat fewer malformations in 75 per cent of the animals, whereas the same treatment of the 11th day did not produce any malformations.[54]

The syndrome of malformations associated with an agent may change when the agent is applied at successively later times in gestation, as has been well shown in experiments with short-term vitamin deficiencies applied at various times in gestation.[36,37] These changes reflect the fact that different organs undergo susceptible periods at different times. The duration of action of the teratogenic influence also affects the composition of the syndrome. Vitamin A deficiency terminated on the 10th day by therapeutic doses of the vitamin resulted only in heart abnormalities, but allowing the deficiency to continue to the 15th day resulted in abnormalities of the eyes, the aortic arches, the diaphragm, the lungs and several genitourinary organs.[60]

2. **Teratogenic Agents Interfere With Particular Phases of Metabolism, Which Often Produces Characteristic Patterns of Malformations.** The phases of metabolism affected are not always known and, in fact, our limited knowledge of the mechanisms of action of most agents prevents final substantiation of this principle at present. Whether or not the mechanisms are known, the fact remains that many agents produce specific arrays of malformations. Ancel[1] and Landauer[27] have reported on many different chemical agents which in chicks produce typical patterns of abnormalities. Also, in mammals the patterns produced by various agents may be strikingly different, particularly if detection methods other than gross inspection are used. A careful observer would not be likely to confuse the array of defects produced in rats by maternal vitamin A deficiency[34,50] with that caused by maternal riboflavin deficiency,[12,51] or either of these with that resulting from pantothenic acid deficiency.[3,38] The syndrome of irradiation defects in the rat[54] bears only superficial resemblance to that produced by trypan blue,[55] and neither closely resembles those produced by the various antimetabolites.[33] Although frequently there are defects common to the syndromes caused by different agents, usually there are other defects which are not duplicated. In addition to qualitative differences, there also may be clear-cut variations of a quantitative nature.

However, it must not be overlooked that similar patterns of defects are sometimes produced by chemically different agents. Runner[39] obtained surprisingly constant patterns of skeletal deformities in mice following the use of either folic acid antagonist, iodoacetate, fasting or insulin. After administering various nutrients as antidotes, he concluded that all of the agents had effected a common chain of reactions in the citric acid cycle, probably at different levels. Several other investigators also have concluded that similarity in the patterns of defects produced by different agents indicates relatedness in the pathways of action.[27,32,41] On the other hand, compounds closely related both in chemical reactivity and in biologic properties do not always produce identical malformations. Murphy[32] used 5 alkylating agents on pregnant rats and noted that many of the same types of defects occurred after all, but that definite quantitative differences also occurred.

The best evidence presently available on the specific nature of the relationship between a chemical teratogenic agent and the metabolic needs of the tissues upon which it acts comes from a series of experiments by Landauer.[27,29] He undertook to protect the embryo against the effects of known teratogens by administering specific supplements and found that riboflavin protected against 6-aminonicotinamide and 3-acetyl-pyridine, nicotinamide against insulin, sulfanilamide and eserine, and 1-proline against nicotine. On this basis, he concluded that teratogenic effects occur as a consequence of interference with localized metabolic needs and further postulated that many, if not all, such interferences were with enzymatic processes. He was able to demonstrate that insulin acted in a specific way at at least two steps in the development of the chick. During an early stage when rumplessness was found to be a frequent result of insulin treatment, the simultaneous administration of pyruvic acid protected against the teratogenic action. At a later susceptible period, when micromelia and beak defects were common following insulin treatment, pyruvic acid was of no protective value, but nicotinamide, which had been ineffective earlier, now was able to prevent the abnormalities characteristic of this stage.

The time at which an agent acts or fails to act also is indicative of specificity. Nelson et al.[36] pointed out that riboflavin deficiency during days 7 to 9 of gestation in rats caused no malformations but that pteroylglutamic acid deficiency during the same period

caused a high rate of malformations. Landauer[27] reported that 3 teratogens—pilocarpine, insulin and boric acid—produced similar long-bone defects in the legs of chicks when given at various times during early incubation but that the time of maximal effect differed by several hours for each of the 3 agents.

Further, indirect evidence for the specificity of action of teratogenic agents can be deduced from the fact that many substances and factors, regardless of how large or unphysiologic the dose may be, are not able to cause malformation.[25,56] This implies that for teratogenesis to occur a definite relationship must exist between the agent and the needs of the embryo.

3. **Teratogenic Agents Often, If Not Always, Act In a Complementary Fashion With the Genotype of the Embryo To Produce Malformations.** This principle is most evident in strains of laboratory animals which without any treatment exhibit a low incidence of a "spontaneous" malformation and when subjected to a teratogenic agent show a marked increase in this incidence. Runner[39] observed that the 129 strain of mice regularly showed a 2 per cent occurrence of axial skeletal defects, but when known teratogens were applied the occurrence of this type of abnormality was increased 10 to 15 times. Other examples have been given by Anderson,[2] Landauer[28] and Ingalls et al.[21] Russell[41] recognized this principle and pointed out that the converse also is true, namely, that a feature which shows little or no natural variability is likely to be quite resistant to change under the influence of extrinsic factors. Landauer[28] has suggested that when experimentally induced malformations closely mimic naturally occurring mutations, the corresponding normal sequence of developmental events is in "precarious equilibrium."

The commonly observed fact that different strains of animals of the same species may respond to the same agent to differing degrees is explained best in terms of the unlike genetic background against which the agent acts. Fraser and Fainstat[9] have observed this in several strains of mice treated similarly with cortisone during pregnancy. Gunberg[19] reported variations in mortality as well as malformations among 3 strains of laboratory rats (2 of them actually substrains) injected with trypan blue under standard conditions. An illuminating experiment was performed by Kalter,[22] who injected the same dose of cortisone into 2 strains of pregnant mice, with the result that strain A gave birth to offspring 100 per cent of which had cleft palate, while the young of strain C57BL showed only 19 per cent with cleft palate. When the 2 strains were crossed so that C57 males bred with A females, 43 per cent of the young had cleft palate, which is about what might be expected. However, when the cross was reversed, that is, a C57 female with an A male, the incidence dropped to only 4 per cent. Thus, it is apparent that the uterine environment as well as the genotype of the embryo is important in determining cleft palate after cortisone injection.

The nature of the interaction between the genes of the embryo and the extrinsic agent in producing malformations is not known, but certain possibilities have been suggested. In discussing phenocopies, that is, induced abnormalities that simulate naturally occurring ones, Goldschmidt[16] concluded that "the hypothesis can hardly be avoided that all phenocopies are due to a bringing into light of already present, nonpenetrant, subthreshold . . . mutants." Landauer[29] proposes the alternative view that . . . "phenocopies represent the end-result of an interference with the activity of the gene or genes for normal or mutant phenotype, observed in the phenotype of the control material." It has been suggested by Fraser *et al.,*[10] and Kalter[24] that a majority of spontaneously occurring malformations are the result not of single genetic or single extrinsic factors, but of a combination of many genetic and many environmental factors. The use of multiple agents in small doses has not been studied

widely, but a movement in this direction is seen in the recent reports in which two or more extrinsic agents in minimally effective doses have been used simultaneously.[6,13,31,62]

4. **Intra-uterine Mortality Tends To Vary Directly With the Rate of Malformations.** In a large proportion of the experiments in which observations have been made, embryonic death rate was found to run generally parallel with the rate of malformation.[14,17,29,30,31,35,36,37,48,55,57] Like malformations, mortality decreases as embryonic age at the time of teratogenic treatment increases.[23,54] Strains of mice which were found to be highly sensitive to the teratogenic effects of cortisone were also highly susceptible to its lethal effects and, conversely, the resistant strains were resistant to both effects.[9]

Often some degree of concurrence can be demonstrated even when a close parallel is not evident. A teratogen may be effective in producing death before the embryo attains a sufficient stage of differentiation for malformations to occur,[23,37,58] but after susceptibility to teratogenesis begins, the parallelism between death and developmental defects becomes apparent. In a few instances, agents such as pantothenic acid deficiency[38] and x-irradiation[40] have been found to result in the resorption of entire litters in proportion to the teratogenic effect, but to have relatively slight effect on the death rate of individuals in surviving litters. Murphy[32] noted considerable variability in the relationship between the minimal teratogenic dose and the LD_{50} dose for the embryos when 5 alkylating agents were applied under uniform experimental conditions in pregnant rats. In a few experiments, it was found that regardless of dose the predominant effect was embryonic death and that malformations were relatively infrequent.[8,15,47]

The question arises, are intra-uterine death and malformations merely different manifestations of the same primary injury, or are they two separate and distinct reactions of the embryo to the agent? There is no doubt but that they are different phenomena in some instances. Smithberg[44] used fasting as an agent and produced abnormalities of the axial skeleton in 30 per cent of the offspring of prepubertal mice in which pregnancy was maintained by progesterone injection. The malformation rate remained constant whether 1 or 2 mg. of progesterone was used, but mortality was twice as high with 1 mg. as with 2, demonstrating that the two effects can vary independently. Grabowski and Parr[17] observed a high incidence of immediate death among chick embryos exposed to hypoxia which they felt had nothing to do with the malformations observed later. They regarded many of the delayed deaths as due either to undetected classes of malformations or to "physiological difficulties arising at the time of treatment and becoming acute at a later period." Zwilling and De Bell[63] observed that the teratogenic effect of sulfanilamide increased as dosage increased but the lethal effect did not.

The fact remains that in a large proportion of experimental situations death and deformity occur together and respond to teratogenic stimuli in such a way as to suggest a common cause. When embryonic stages are examined after teratogenic treatment, many severe types of malformations are found which are rarely seen if the offspring are allowed to go to term.[26,60,61] Undoubtedly, this means that some malformations themselves cause death in utero. It does not rule out the likelihood that some of the increased mortality is unrelated to malformation.

5. **An Agent Which Is Very Damaging To the Embryo May Be Relatively Harmless To the Mother.** An excellent example of this principle can be drawn from human teratology, namely, the occurrence of severe malformations after subclinical infection during pregnancy with German measles. Similar situations have been observed with regularity in experimental teratology.[14] Pregnant females have been affected only mildly, if at all, by such potent teratogens as cortisone,[9] folic acid deficiency produced by PGA an-

tagonist,[35,37] pantothenic acid deficiency[30,38] hypervitaminosis A,[5] and riboflavin deficiency produced by the antagonist galactoflavin.[25]

However, the mothers are not always spared. Murphy,[32] using several teratogenic antimetabolites, found great variability in the LD_{50} response of the mother as compared with that of her embryos, ranging from a 1:1 ratio for thiadiazol to a 530:1 ratio for 1-norlucine. Warkany and Roth[49] have emphasized that vitamin A deficiency of sufficient severity to cause malformations is tolerated poorly by the mother. Thus, the pregnant female sometimes may be affected appreciably, but even in these cases there is no justification for the outworn notion that the embryo lives as a favored parasite upon the mother, able to obtain scarce materials at her expense.[56]

COMMENT

Five general principles have been found to be applicable to most situations in experimental teratology. The first three, those relating to the developmental stage of the embryo, the nature of the teratogenic agent and the genotype of the embryo, appear to act in conjunction to determine the types and the frequencies of malformation which will result from treatment with a given agent. The fourth attempts to define the relationship between two different responses of the embryo to teratogenic treatment, namely, malformation on the one hand and prenatal death on the other. The fifth concerns the extent to which the reaction of the embryo to an agent can be correlated with that in the maternal animal. An area of teratology conspicuously missing from this list of principles is that dealing with mechanisms of action. It is anticipated that this subject will receive increasingly more attention, and doubtless it will be possible soon to begin formulating fundamental generalities in this sphere. Then the ultimate aim of all teratology, the prevention of malformations, may be within sight.

REFERENCES

1. Ancel, P.: La Chimiotératogenèse chez les Vertébrés, Paris, Doin, 1950.
2. Anderson, D. H.: Effects of diet during pregnancy upon the incidence of congenital hereditary diaphragmatic hernia in the rat, Am. J. Path. 25:163-185, 1949.
3. Boisselot, J.: Malformations congénitales provoquées chez le rat par une insuffisance en acide pantothénique du régime maternal, Compt. rend. Soc. biol. 142:928-929, 1948.
4. Cheng, D. W., Chang, L. F., and Bairnson, T. A.: Gross observations on developing abnormal embryos induced by maternal vitamin E deficiency, Anat. Rec. 129:167-186, 1957.
5. Cohlan, S. Q.: Congenital anomalies in the rat produced by excessive intake of vitamin A during pregnancy, Pediatrics 13:556-567, 1954.
6. ————: Failure of cortisone and insulin to affect the teratogenesis of hypervitaminosis A in the rat, Nature (submitted), 1960.
7. Dagg, C. P., and Karnofsky, D. A.: Teratogenic effects of azaserine on the chick embryo, J. Exp. Zool. 130:555, 1955.
8. Ferm, V. H.: Teratogenic effects of trypan blue on hamster embryos, J. Embryol. Exp. Morph. 6:284, 1958.
9. Fraser, F. C., and Fainstat, T. D.: Production of congenital defects in the offspring of pregnant mice treated with cortisone, Pediatrics 8:527-533, 1951.
10. Fraser, F. C., Walker, B. E., and Trasler, D. G.: The experimental production of congenital cleft palate: genetic and environmental factors, Pediatrics 19:782-787, 1957.
11. Giroud, A.: Les malformations congénitales et leur causes, Biol. méd. 44:1-86, 1955.
12. Giroud, A., and Boisselot, J.: Répercussions de l'avitaminose B2 sur l'embryon du rat, Arch. franç. pédiat. 4:317-327, 1947.
13. Giroud, A., Lefebvres-Boisselot, J., and Dupuis, R.: Un régime polyvitamine est-il moins tératogene qu'un régime depourvu d'une seule vitamin B, Compt. rend. Soc. biol. 151:2085, 1957.
14. Giroud, A., and Martinet, M.: Malformations diverses du foetus de rat suivant les stades d'administration de vitamine A en excès, Compt. rend. Soc. biol. 149:1088, 1955.
15. ————: Répercussions de l'hypervitaminose A chez l'embryon de lapin, Compt. rend. Soc. biol. 152:931, 1958.
16. Goldschmidt, R. B.: Problematics of the phenomenon of phenocopy, J. Madras Univ. 27B:17-24, 1957 (cited by Landauer, Am. Natural. 92:205, 1958).
17. Grabowski, T., and Parr, J.: The teratogenic effects of graded doses of hypoxia on the chick embryo, Am. J. Anat. 103:313-348, 1958.
18. Gruenwald, P.: Mechanisms of abnormal development, Arch. Path. 44:398-664, 1947.
19. Gunberg, D. L.: Variations in the teratogenic effects of trypan blue administered to pregnant rats of different strain and substrain origin, Anat. Rec. 130:310 (abstract), 1958.
20. Hicks, S. F.: Developmental malformations produced by radiation. A timetable of their development, Am. J. Roentgenol. 69:272-293, 1953.
21. Ingalls, T. H., and Curley, F. L.: Principles governing the genesis of congenital malformations induced in mice by anoxia, New England J. Med. 257:1121-1127, 1957.
22. Kalter, H.: The inheritance of susceptibility to the teratogenic action of cortisone in mice, Genetics 39:185, 1954.
23. ————: Factors influencing the frequency of cortisone-induced cleft palate in mice, J. Exp. Zool. 134:449-468, 1957.
24. ————: The multiple causation of congenital malformations. Paper presented at the Teratology Conference in New York, April 9-10, 1960.
25. Kalter, H., and Warkany, J.: Experimental production of congenital malformations in mammals by metabolic procedures, Physiol. Rev. 39:69-115, 1959.
26. Kaven, A.: Das Auftreten von Gehirnmissbildungen nach Röntgenbestrahlung von Mäuseembryonen, Z. Menschl. Vererb. -u. Konstitutions 22:247-257, 1938.
27. Landauer, W.: On the chemical production of developmental abnormalities and of phenocopies in chicken embryos.
28. ————: Phenocopies and genotype, with special reference to sporadically-occurring developmental variants, Am. Natural. 91:79-90, 1957.
29. ————: On phenocopies, their developmental physiology and genetic meaning, Am. Natural. 92:201-213, 1958.

30. Lefebvres-Boisselot, J.: Role tératogene de la déficience en acide pantothénique chez le rat, Am. J. Med. **52**:225-298, 1951.

31. Millen, J. W., and Woollam, D. H. M.: Influence of cortisone on teratogenic effects of hypervitaminosis A, Brit. M. J. **2**:196, 1957.

32. Murphy, L. M.: A comparison of the teratogenic effects of five polyfunctional alkylating agents on the rat fetus, Pediatrics **23**:231-244, 1959.

33. Murphy, L. M., Dagg, C. P., and Karnofsky, D.: Comparison of teratogenic chemicals in the rat and chick embryos, Pediatrics **19**:701-714, 1957.

34. Nelson, M. M.: Production of congenital anomalies in mammals by maternal dietary deficiencies, Pediatrics **19**:764-776, 1957.

35. Nelson, M. M., Asling, C. W., and Evans, H. M.: Production of multiple congenital abnormalities in young by maternal pteroylglutamic acid deficiency during gestation, J. Nutr. **48**:61-80, 1952.

36. Nelson, M. M., Baird, C. D. C., and Wright, H. V.: Multiple congenital abnormalities in the rat resulting from riboflavin deficiency induced by the antimetabolite galactoflavin, J. Nutr. **58**:125-134, 1956.

37. Nelson, M. M., Wright, H. V., Asling, C. W., and Evans, H. M.: Multiple congenital abnormalities resulting from transitory deficiency of pteroylglutamic acid during gestation in the rat, J. Nutr. **56**:349-370, 1955.

38. Nelson, M. M., Wright, H. V., Baird, C. D. C., and Evans, H. M.: Teratogenic effects of pantothenic acid deficiency in the rat, J. Nutr. **62**:395-405, 1957.

39. Runner, M. N.: Inheritance of susceptibility to congenital deformity. Metabolic clues provided by experiments with teratogenic agents, Pediatrics **23**:245-251, 1959.

40. Russell, L. B.: X-ray induced developmental abnormalities in the mouse and their use in the analysis of embryological patterns. I. External and gross visceral changes, J. Exp. Zool. **114**:545-602, 1950.

41. ———: X-ray induced developmental abnormalities in the mouse and their use in the analysis of embryological patterns. II. Abnormalities of the vertebral column and thorax, J. Exp. Zool. **131**:329-390, 1956.

42. Russell, L. B., and Russell, W. L.: An analysis of the changing radiation response

of the developing mouse embryo, J. Cell. Comp. Physiol. **43**:(Suppl. 1)103-150, 1954.

43. Smith, A. U.: The effects on foetal development of freezing pregnant hamsters (*Masocricatus auratus*), J. Embryol. Exp. Morph. **5**:311-323, 1957.

44. Smithberg, M.: Unpublished data, 1960.

45. Stockard, C. R.: Developmental rate and structural expression: an experimental study of twins, "double monsters" and single deformities, and the interaction among embryonic organs during their origin and development, Am. J. Anat. **28**:115-277, 1921.

46. Thiersch, J. B.: Effect of certain 2, 4 diaminopyrimidine antagonists of folic acid on pregnancy and rat fetus, Proc. Soc. Exp. Biol. Med. **87**:571-577, 1954.

47. ———: Effect of o-diazo acetyl-l-serine on rat litter, Proc. Soc. Exp. Biol. Med. **94**:27-32, 1957.

48. Waddington, C. H., and Carter, T. C.: Malformations in mouse embryos induced by trypan blue, Nature, (Lond) **169**:27-28, 1952.

49. Warkany, J., and Roth, C. B.: Congenital malformations induced in rats by maternal vitamin A deficiency, J. Nutr. **35**:1-12, 1948.

50. Warkany, J., Roth, C. B., and Wilson, J. G.: Multiple congenital malformations: a consideration of etiologic factors, Pediatrics **1**:462-471, 1948.

51. Warkany, J., and Schraffenberger, E.: Congenital malformations induced in rats by maternal nutritional deficiency. VI. Preventive factor. J. Nutr. **27**:477-484, 1944.

52. ———: Congenital malformations induced in rats by roentgen rays, Am. J. Roentgenol. **57**:455-463, 1947.

53. Werthemann, A., and Reiniger, M.: Über Augenentwicklungsstörungen bei Rattenembryonen durch Sauerstoffmangel in der Frühschwangerschaft, Acta Anat. **11**:329-347, 1950.

54. Wilson, J. G.: Differentiation and the reaction of rat embryos to radiation, J. Cell. Comp. Physiol. **43**:(Suppl. 1) 11-38, 1954.

55. ———: Teratogenic activity of several azo dyes chemically related to trypan blue, Anat. Rec. **123**:313-334, 1955.

56. ———: Experimental studies on congenital malformations, J. Chron. Dis. **10**:111-130, 1959.

57. Wilson, J. G., and Barch, S.: Fetal death and maldevelopment resulting from maternal vitamin A deficiency in the rat, Proc. Soc. Exp. Biol. Med. 72:687-693, 1949.

58. Wilson, J. G., Brent, R. L, and Jordan, C. H.: Differentiation as a determinant of the reaction of rat embryos to X-irradiation, Proc. Soc. Exp. Biol. Med. 82: 67-70, 1953.

59. Wilson, J. G., Jordan, H. C., and Brent, R. L.: Effects of irradiation on embryonic development. II. X-rays on the ninth day of gestation in the rat, Am. J. Anat. 92: 153-187, 1953.

60. Wilson, J. G., and Warkany, J.: Aortic arch and cardiac anomalies in the off- spring of vitamin A deficient rats, Am. J. Anat. 85:113-155, 1949.

61. Wilson, J. G., Roth, C. B., and Warkany, J.: An analysis of the syndrome of malformations induced by maternal vitamin A deficiency. Effects of restoration of vitamin A at various times during gestation, Am. J. Anat. 92:189-217, 1953.

62. Wollam, D. H. M., Millen, J. W., and Fozzard, J. A. F.: The influence of cortisone on the teratogenic activity of X radiation, Brit. J. Radiol. 32:47-48, 1959.

63. Zwilling, E., and De Bell, E.: Micromelia and growth retardation as independent effects of sulfanilimide in chick embryos, J. Exp. Zool. 115:59, 1950.

Fetal Hormones and Morphogenesis

ETIENNE WOLFF, M.D.

The first stages of development are independent of the action of embryonic hormones because the endocrine glands themselves are not yet differentiated. This independence continues through much of the developmental process; general growth and organ differentiation are autonomous until a stage occurring after the middle of the gestation period of rodents and the incubation period of birds. However, one should set aside the action of the genital hormones, which is exerted at a much earlier stage than that of the other endocrine glands. Their effect is strong in normal morphogenesis and teratogenesis, while the action of other hormones occurs later and is more discrete and much less well known. We shall study separately the genital hormones and those secreted by the other endocrine glands.

THE MORPHOGENETIC AND TERATOGENETIC ACTION OF THE SEX HORMONES

The predominant influence of the sex hormones on the morphogenesis of the sexual characteristics of the embryo has been demonstrated in all groups of vertebrates by experiments with castration, injection, grafts, parabiosis and organ culture. It may be said that these procedures made it possible to obtain all the known spontaneous sexual malformations, from the simple alteration of the external genitalia to the complete and definitive inversion of sex in certain species. It is very noteworthy that, on the whole, crystalline hormones extracted from adults had effects of the same type and intensity as the hormones secreted by the embryonic gonads, the chemical nature of which is still being debated. We will study successively the morphogenetic effect of these hormones on the gonads, the genital tract, the external genitalia and on other early somatic sexual characteristics.

The most outstanding experiments were performed in 3 groups of vertebrates: amphibians, birds and mammals.

EFFECT ON THE GENITAL GLANDS

In Amphibians, experiments with grafts and parabiosis have been performed since 1925 and, in our times, principally by Burns, Witschi and Humphrey. They demonstrated that a hormonal substance passes from one partner to the other in parabiosis or from a graft to the host, or from the host to the graft. In general, it is the male gonad that tends to modify the sex of the female partner. But such effects are not produced exclusively from the female to the male. The work of Witschi,[47,48,49] Witschi and McCurdy,[50] and Humphrey,[20] has shown that it is possible to induce an inverse transformation, i.e., from the male to the female, if the female partner in parabiosis is much larger than the male (following parabiosis between two animals of different species or different ages), or if one implants small fragments of a testicular bud in a whole female gonad. Therefore, the effect of sexual inversion has a quantitative basis as well as a qualitative one.

Between 1942 and 1945, Humphrey[17-19] succeeded in raising axolotls (*Amblystoma mexicanum*) of female genetic sex to sexual maturity; the gonads of one of them had been transformed into a testicle by a male gonad of the same species. The female host, transformed into a functional male, was bred with a normal male. This cross produced 25 per cent males and 75 per cent females, leading to the genetic formula for the axolotl: ZZ for the male, WZ for the female.

The injection of crystalline sex hormones of the steroid group provoked very noteworthy sexual inversions as observed by many authors, including Padoa,[32] Gallien,[10] Witschi,[47] Foote,[5] Mintz,[31] etc. Various effects were noted:

1. Masculinization of females by androgenic hormones, especially in the Salientia of the Ranidae family.

2. Feminization by estrogenic hormones in certain species of Urodela and Salientia. It has been shown that such transformation is temporary in certain species and permanent in others, such as in the Urodela, *Pleurodelidae waltii*[13] or in the Salientia, *Xenopus laevis*.[3,12,14] In both cases, the males transformed into females could be crossed with normal males. The breeding produced only males, which verified the genetic formula ZZ for the male.

3. Paradoxic effects of the sex hormones. Certain androgenic or estrogenic hormones exerted effects contrary to those which were to be expected from the nature of the hormone. Thus, a high dose of estradiol caused the masculinization of the females of *Rana esculenta*.[8,9,32] Testosterone consistently feminized the larvae of *Amblystoma* and *Pleurodelidae*.[5,6,10,11] A toxic effect of these substances on certain species may be the explanation for this paradoxic effect. This toxic effect causes necrosis of the medulla and the adjacent tissues. However, the remaining part of the cortex, liberated from the inhibitory action of the medulla, is sufficient to form an ovary. The male hormone acts by selective destruction.

The first experiments on sexual inversion were carried out on birds in 1935 by V. Dantchakoff,[4] B. Willier *et al.*,[46] and by Et. Wolff and Ginglinger.[55,56] They showed, for the first time, that inversion of the sex of male embryos was possible with the aid of estrogenic steroids. Depending on the dose of hormone injected and the stage of the treatment, every degree of intersexuality was obtained, from a testicle surrounded by a thin ovarian cortex to a typical ovary. Such transformation is unstable and reversible after hatching. The male gonads, transformed into ovaries or ovotestes, resume their testicular development. The continuation of ovarian development has not yet been achieved, even with continued injections.

The androgenic hormones have no masculinizing effect on female gonads. They have, at best, an inhibitory effect on the cortex. Some of them have a paradoxic effect, such as androsterone, which feminizes males (Et. Wolff *et al.*).[64]

Etienne Wolff,[52] has shown, by experiments with coelomic grafts, that the embryonic female gonads have exactly the same feminizing effect as the estrogenic substances. Similarly, the secretions of the male gonads have no significant effect on the gonads of female embryos. The in-vitro parabiosis experiments[53,54,57-60] between gonads of different sex confirm these conclusions.

In mammals, nature's experiment with freemartins[26,27,28] has shown that in the case of parabiosis between twins of opposite sex, the male fetus secretes a hormone capable of masculinizing the female fetus. No experiments carried out on eutherian mammals, and especially on rodents, have yet been capable of reproducing this natural phenomenon. However, in-vivo parabiosis experiments carried out by McIntyre[30] and Holyoke,[15] or in-vitro parabiosis,[16] have shown inhibition of the ovary by the associated male gonad.

On the other hand, in Marsupiala, R. K. Burns[1,2] was able to transform into ovotestes the testicles of young opossums inoculated with an estrogenic hormone at birth.

It may be concluded from these investigations that sexual determination is, in general, more stable as one rises in the vertebrate scale.

EFFECT ON THE GENITAL TRACT AND THE EXTERNAL GENITALIA

In all vertebrate groups, sexual differentiation of the genital tract and the external genitalia is dependent upon the hormones secreted by the gonads. This has been demonstrated particularly by experiments with embryonic castration and in-vitro cultures. We specifically cite the work of Jost[21-25] and Raynaud,[36,37,38,39] Price and Pannabecker[33-35] with mammals, and of Et. Wolff *et al.*[65-67] with birds.

Bilateral castration of male rabbit fetuses before the 20th day causes the female genital tract to persist, the disappearance of the entire male tract and rudimentation of the external genitalia (genital tubercle). In female fetuses, castration does not change the morphology of the female tract but arrests its growth. Unilateral castration of males results in the maintenance of the female tract on the operated side, and the male tract on the side where a gonad remains.[21] These results show that the hormones secreted by the gonads have a relatively weak range of action. They are propagated by diffusion rather than by the circulatory system. Such localized effects are attested to by cases of true hermaphroditism observed in humans. When there is a male gonad on one side and a female gonad on the other, the genital tract is often male on one side and female on the other. Generally, the effect of the male hormone is dominant. It causes regression of the female canals and maintenance of the male passages. These results were confirmed by the experiments of Price and Pannabecker on the culture of the genital tract of the rat, in the absence or the presence of gonads of the same or the opposite sex.

In birds, early castration of male embryos results in the preservation of the female Müller's ducts. On the other hand, the castration of female embryos permits the genital tubercle to be maintained and to develop into a penis analogous to that of the male. Therefore, testicular secretion causes regression of Müller's ducts, whereas ovarian secretion inhibits the development of the genital tubercle. These results are confirmed by in-vitro cultures.[29,51,64]

EFFECTS ON OTHER EARLY SOMATIC CHARACTERISTICS

Two examples are typical: The syrinx of the duck and the mammary glands of the mouse.

Castration and culture experiments[51] have shown that, in the absence of any hormone, the syrinx of birds develops according to the male pattern, voluminous and asymmetrical. The female hormones of the embryo or the adult inhibit the development of the syrinx. The male form of the syrinx is neutral or ahormonal.

Castration of the mouse embryo (Raynaud,[36,39-43]) does not impede the growth of the mammary glands; they develop according to the female pattern in both sexes. The male hormone normally causes regression of the mammary buds. It is not the female hormone which stimulates their primary development. On the contrary, an excess of female steroid hormone causes all kinds of malformations of the mammary glands, particularly abortion of the epithelial buds.

* * *

From this section, one may conclude that embryonic sex hormones, as well as adult steroid hormones, can produce all of the possible forms of aberration of the embryo's sexual characteristics, just as they habitually govern their normal morphogenesis.

* * *

EFFECT OF THE OTHER ENDOCRINE GLANDS

The key morphogenetic role of the thyroid and the pituitary glands at the time of metamorphosis of the larvae of Batrachia should be recalled. No morphogenetic effect of such importance is manifested in Amniota. The action of the fetal endocrine glands is more discrete, and their deficiencies are manifested particularly by metabolic disorders of the other organs.

The normal morphogenetic action of certain fetal hormones should be distinguished from the teratogenic action of certain hormonal substances administered in excess.

NORMAL MORPHOGENETIC ACTION

Removal of the pituitary and the thyroid has only a minor effect on the general growth of bird and mammal embryos. Nevertheless, the removal of the pituitary gland causes, in addition to disturbances of carbohydrate metabolism, hypofunction and atrophy of the thyroid, deficiency of gonadal secretions and, consequently, side-effects on the genital tract and the somatic sexual characteristics.[25,45]

TERATOGENETIC ACTION OF CERTAIN HORMONES INJECTED IN EXCESS

Jost[23] has demonstrated the teratogenetic action of hypertensive hormones (postpituitary acetone powder, vasopressin, adrenalin) injected into the rabbit fetus. This causes "acroblapsia" and hemorrhagic malformation of the extremities.

Fraser, Fainstadt and Kalter,[7] injecting cortisone or hydroxycorticosterone into mice at different stages of gestation produced various malformations in the embryos, particularly cleft palates (100% of the mice of race A, treated on the 11th day).

These results may be related to the general phenomena of chemoteratogenesis. Nevertheless, they show the specific effect of certain hormonal substances which possibly may occur spontaneously in cases of hyperfunction of the fetal endocrine glands.

REFERENCES

1. Burns, R. K.: Sex transformation in the Opossum: some new results and a retrospect, Arch. Anat. Micr. Morph. Exp. 39: 467-483, 1950.
2. ———: Experimental reversal of sex in the gonads of the Opossum *Didelphis virginiana,* Proc. Nat. Acad. Sc. USA 41: 669-676, 1955.
3. Chang, C. Y., and Witschi, E.: Breeding of sex-reversed males of *Xenopus laevis,* Proc. Soc. Exp. Biol. Med. 89:150-152, 1955.
4. Dantchakoff, V.: Sur l'inversion sexuelle expérimentale de l'ébauche testiculaire, chez l'embryon de poulet, Compt. rend. Acad. sc. 200:1983-1985, 1935.
5. Foote, C. L.: Response of gonads and gonaducts of Amblystoma larvae to treatment with sex hormones, Proc. Soc. Exp. Biol. Med. 43:519-523, 1940.
6. ———: Modification of sex development in the marbled salamanders by administration of synthetic sex-hormones, J. Exp. Zool. 86:291-319, 1941.
7. Fraser, F., Fainstat, T., and Kalter, H.: The experimental production of congenital defects with particular reference to cleft palate, Etudes néo-natales 2:43-54, 1953.
8. Gallien L.: Sur l'action amphisexuelle de la dihydrofolliculine dans la différenciation du sexe chez les Batraciens, Compt. rend. Acad. sc. 211:665, 1940.
9. ———: Recherches expérimentales sur l'action amphisexuelle de l'hormone femelle (oestradiol) dans la différenciation du sexe chez *Rana temporaria,* Bull. biol. 75: 370-397, 1941.
10. ———: Action amphisexuelle de la prégnéninolone chez *Discoglossus pictus,* Compt. rend. Acad. sc. 227:1418-1420, 1948.
11. ———: Inversion du sexe et effet paradoxal (féminisation) chez l'Urodèle *Pleurodeles waltlii M.,* traité par le propionate de testosterone, Compt. rend. Acad. sc. 231:1092-1094, 1950.
12. ———: Inversion totale du sexe chez *Xenopus laevis D.* à la suite d'un traitement gynogène par le benzoate d'oestradiol, administré pendant la vie larvaire, Compt. rend. Acad. sc. 237:1565-1566, 1953.
13. ———: Inversion expérimentale du sexe sous l'action des hormones sexuelles chez le Triton *Pleurodeles waltlii M.* Analyse des conséquences génétiques, Bull. biol. 88:1-51, 1954.
14. ———: Inversion expérimentale du sexe chez un Anoure inférieur *Xenopus laevis D.* Analyse des conséquences génétiques, Bull. biol. 90:163-181, 1956.
15. Holyoke, E. A.: The differentiation of embryonic ovaries and testes grafted to-

gether in adult hosts in the rabbit, Anat. Rec. **124**:307, 1956.

16. Holyoke, E. A., and Beber, B. A.: Culture of gonads of mammalian embryos, Science **128**:1082, 1958.

17. Humphrey, R.: Sex inversion in the amphibia, Biol. Symp. **9**:81-105, 1942.

18. ———: Sex of the offspring fathered by two Amblystoma females experimentally converted into males, Anat. Rec. **82**:77, 1942.

19. ———: Sex determination in Ambystomid Salamanders: a study of the progeny of females experimentally converted into males, Am. J. Anat. **76**:33-36, 1945.

20. ———: Male homogamety in the Mexican Axolotl: a study of the progeny obtained when germ cells of a genetic male are incorporated in a developing ovary, J. Exp. Zool. **134**:91-101, 1957.

21. Jost, A.: Recherches sur la différenciation sexuelle de l'embryon de lapin. II. Action des androgènes de synthèse sur l'histogénèse génitale, Arch. anat. Micr. morph. exp. **36**:241-270, 1947.

22. ———: Recherches sur la différenciation sexuelle de l'embryon de lapin. IV. Organogenèse sexuelle masculine après décapitation du foetus, Arch. anat. Micr. morph. exp. **40**:247-281, 1951.

23. ———: Dégénérescence des extrêmités du foetus du rat provoquée par l'adrénaline, Compt. rend. Acad. sc. **236**:1510-1512, 1953.

24. ———: La dégénérescence des extrêmités du foetus de rat sous des actions hormonales (acroblapsie expérimentale) et la théorie des bulles myélencéphaliques de Bonnevie, Arch. franç pédiat. **10**: 1953.

25. ———: Problems of fetal endocrinology: the gonadal and hypophyseal hormones, Recent Progr. Hormone Res. **8**:379-418, 1953.

26. Keller, K., and Tandler, J.: Über das Verhalten der Eihäute bei der Zwillingsträchtigkeit des Rindes, Mschr. Ver. Tierärz. Ost. **3**:513-526, 1916.

27. Lillie, F. R.: The theory of the free-martin, Science **43**:611, 1916.

28. ———: The free-martin; a study of the action of sex hormones in the foetal life of cattle, J. Exp. Zool. **23**:317-452, 1917.

29. Lutz-Ostertag, Y.: Contribution à l'étude du développement et de la régression des canaux de Müller chez l'embryon d'oiseau, Bull. biol. **88**:333-412, 1954.

30. McIntyre, M. N.: Effect of the testis on ovarian differentiation in heterosexual embryonic rat gonad transplants, Anat. Rec. **124**:27-45, 1956.

31. Mintz, B.: Effects of testosterone propionate on sex development in female Amblystoma larvae, Physiol. Zool. **20**:355-373, 1947.

32. Padoa, E.: Feminizzazione e mascolinizzazione di girmi di *Rana esculenta* in funzione della dose di diidrofollicolina loro somministrata, Monit. zool. ital. **53**: 210-213, 1942.

33. Price, D., and Pannabecker, R.: Organ culture studies of foetal rat reproductive tracts, Ciba Foundation Coll. Ageing **2**: 3-13, 1956.

34. ———: A study of sex differentiation in the fetal rat, Sympos. Chemical Basis Develop, pp. 774-778, Baltimore, Johns Hopkins, 1958.

35. ———: Comparative responsiveness of homologous sex ducts and accessory glands of fetal rats in culture, Arch. anat. Micr. morph. exp. **48bis**:223-244, 1959.

36. Raynaud, A.: Intersexualité obtenue expérimentalement chez la souris femelle par action hormonale, Bull. biol. **72**:297-354, 1938.

37. ———: Effet des injections d'hormones sexuelles à la souris gravide sur le développement des ébauches de la glande mammaire de l'embryon. I. Action des substances androgènes, Ann. Endocr. **8**:248-253, 1947.

38. ———: Effet des injections d'hormones sexuelles à la souris gravide, sur le développement des ébauches de la glande mammaire des embryons. II. Action de fortes doses de substances oestrogènes. Ann. endocr. (Par.) **8**:318-329, 1947.

39. ———: Nouvelles observations sur l'appareil mammaire des foetus de souris provenant de mères ayant reçu des injections de testostérone pendant la gestation, Ann. endocr. (Par) **10**:54-62, 1949.

40. Raynaud, A., and Raynaud, J.: Transformation sous l'influence d'une hormone oestrogène, des ébauches mammaires à cordon primaire unique du foetus de souris, en ébauches à bourgeons multiples ou à 2 cordons mammaires primaires, Compt. rend. Acad. sc. **229**:191-193, 1954.

41. ———: La production expérimentale de malformations mammaires chez les foetus de souris par l'action des hormones sexuelles, Ann. Inst. Pasteur **90**:39-219, 1956.

42. ———: Les stades foetaux successifs de l'inhibition du développement des ébauches mammaires de la souris sous l'effet d'une

hormone oestrogène, Compt. rend. Acad. sc. **243**:424-426, 1956.

43. ———: Sur les modifications précoces apportées par l'hormone oestrogène, dans la structure des ébauches mammaires des foetus de souris, Bull. Soc. zool. franç **82**:204-222, 1957.

44. Tandler, J., and Keller, K.: Über das Verhalten des Chorions bei verschiedengeschlechtlicher Zwillingsgravidität des Rindes und über die Morphologie des Genitales der weiblichen Tiere, welche einer solchen Gravidität entstammen, Deutsch. Tierätztl. Wchnschr. **19**:148-149, 1911.

45. Watterson, R. L. (ed.): Endocrines in Development, Chicago, Univ. Chicago Press, 1959.

46. Willier, B. H., Gallagher, T. F., and Koch, F. C.: Sex modification in the chick embryo resulting from injections of male and female hormones, Proc. Nat. Acad. Sc. **21**:625-631, 1935.

47. Witschi, E.: Sex-reversal in parabiotic twins of the American wood frog, Biol. Bull. **52**:137-146, 1927.

48. ———: Parabiosis in amphibians; sex inversion due to developmental inhibition, Anat. Rec. **44**:253, 1929.

49. ———: Studies on sex differentiation and sex determination in Amphibians. V. Range of the cortex-medulla antagonism in parabiotic twins of Ranidae and Hylidae, J. Exp. Zool. **58**:113-145, 1931.

50. Witschi, E., and McCurdy, H. M.: Sex differentiation in heterogenous parabiotic twins *in* Essays in Biology, pp. 657-674, California, Univ. California, Press, 1943.

51. Wolff, Em.: La différenciation sexuelle normale et le conditionnement hormonal des caractères somatiques sexuels précoces, tubercule génital et syrinx chez l'embryon de canard, Bull. biol. **84**:113-193, 1950.

52. Wolff, Etienne: Recherches sur l'intersexualité expérimentale produite par la méthode des greffes de gonades à l'embryon de poulet, Arch. anat. Micr. morph. exp. **36**:69-90, 1947.

53. ———: L'évolution des canaux de Müller de l'embryon d'oiseau après castration précoce, Compt. rend. Soc. biol. **143**:1239-1241, 1949.

54. ———: Le rôle des hormones embryonnaires dans la différenciation sexuelle des Oiseaux. Coll. intern. Differ. sex., Arch. Anat. Micr. Morph. exp. **39**:426-450, 1950.

55. Wolff, Etienne, and Ginglinger, A.: Sur la transformation des poulets mâles en inter-

sexués par injection d'hormone femelle (folliculine) aux embryons, Arch. anat. hist. embr. **20**:219-278, 1935.

56. ———: Sur la production expérimentale d'intersexués par l'injection de folliculine à l'embryon de poulet, Compt. rend. Acad. sc. **200**:2118-2120, 1935.

57. Wolff, Etienne, and Haffen, K.: Sur la culture in vitro des glandes génitales des embryons d'Oiseau: obtention de la différenciation sexuelle normale et de l'intersexualité expérimentale des gonades explantées, Compt. rend. Acad. sc. **233**:439-441, 1951.

58. ———: Sur le développement et la différenciation sexuelle des gonades embryonnaires d'oiseau en culture in vitro, J. Exp. Zool. **119**:381-399, 1952.

59. ———: Sur l'intersexualité expérimentale des gonades embryonnaires de canard cultivées in vitro, Arch. anat. micr. morph. exper. **41**:184-207, 1952.

60. ———: Action féminisante de la gonade droite de l'embryon femelle de canard en culture in vitro, Compt. rend. Soc. biol. **146**:1772-1774, 1952.

61. Wolff, Etienne, and Lutz-Ostertag, Y.: La différenciation et la régression des canaux de Müller de l'embryon de poulet en culture in vitro, Compt. rend. Assoc. Anat. **72**:214-228, 1953.

62. Wolff, Etienne, Lutz-Ostertag, Y., and Haffen, K.: Sur la culture in vitro des canaux de Müller de l'embryon de poulet, Compt. rend. Soc. biol. **146**:1791-1793, 1952.

63. Wolff, Etienne, Ostertag, Y., and Pfleger, D.: Sur la régression in vitro des canaux de Müller de l'embryon mâle de poulet, Compt. rend. Acad. sc. **229**:1263-1265, 1949.

64. ———: Sur les conditiones de la régression in vitro des canaux de Müller de l'embryon mâle de poulet, Compt. rend. Soc. biol. **144**:280-282, 1950.

65. Wolff, Etienne, Strudel, G., and Wolff, Em.: L'action des hormones androgènes sur la différenciation sexuelle des embryons de poulet, Arch. anat. hist. embr. **31**:237-310, 1948.

66. Wolff, Etienne, and Wolff, Em.: The effects of castration on bird embryos, J. Exp. Zool. **116**:59-97, 1951.

67. ———: Mise en évidence d'une action féminisante de la gonade droite chez l'embryon femelle des oiseaux, par les expériences d'hémicastration, Compt. rend. Soc. biol. **145**:1218-1219, 1951.

SESSION V

Discussion

Moderator

PAUL A. WEISS, M.D.

Member and Professor, The Rockfeller Institute, Head, Laboratory of Developmental Biology, New York 21, New York, U.S.A.

Panel Members

PROFESSOR JAMES W. MILLEN, M.D.

Department of Pathology, New England Deaconess Home, Boston, Massachusetts, U.S.A.

S. P. HICKS, M.D.

Reader in Anatomy, Anatomy School, University of Cambridge, Cambridge, U.K.

SALOME G. WAELSCH, Ph.D.

Professor of Genetics (in Anatomy), Albert Einstein College of Medicine, Eastchester Road and Morris Park Avenue, New York 61, New York, U.S.A.

JAMES G. WILSON, M.D.

Department of Anatomy, University of Florida, College of Medicine, Gainesville, Florida, U.S.A.

201

DR. MILLEN: First, I would expand Dr. Fraser's statement that mammalian teratology is no longer concerned exclusively with the description of experimentally produced malformations. Almost every malformation mentioned at this Conference has been reproduced experimentally in mammals, and now teratogens are being used to analyze developmental processes.

The incidence of malformations is fortunately small and, therefore, it is necessary to increase it for experimental purposes. This can be done by selective breeding or by use of a teratogen such as vitamin A. Then we can study the effects of other substances upon the incidence of particular malformations.

It is unlikely that any single, external environmental factor can be held responsible for more than a minute fraction of congenital malformations. But the pregnant female provides a highly complex chemical environment for the embryo which, during the most critical period of gestation, is under the influence of the pituitary, the adrenal cortex, the thyroid and the pancreas. Pregnancy results in a profound disturbance of the maternal endocrine system and, conceivably, hormonal imbalance may lead to malformation. Professor Hoet has provided convincing evidence of the increased incidence of malformations among babies whose mothers' blood sugar is raised during pregnancy. Dr. Wolff has referred to the effects of sex hormones on development. Also, it is suggestive that certain malformations occur more commonly in one sex than in the other.

This brings us to a point referred to by Dr. Wilson. It used to be thought that the fetus was insulated, at least from metabolic disturbance. Now, clearly, this is not so; the homeostasis of the fetus is only relatively secure. The fetus may be killed or maimed by substances which are normal physiologic constituents of the body, when given in quantities which appear to be insufficient to harm the mother. In part, the solution of the problem of congenital malformations must lie in fuller knowledge of the interaction of hormones and hormone substrates in developmental processes.

Dr. Woollam and I have some evidence that administration of thyroxine can reduce the incidence of harelip in the Strong A line of mice. These studies provide some grounds for hope; although we are unable at present to control the human genetic constitution, we can attempt to prevent the expression of genetic defects.

DR. HICKS: I should like to refer to two matters: one an expression of concern about the restrictive use of the words "congenital malformation" and "teratogenesis"; the other concerning the use of antimetabolites.

Use of the terms "congenital malformation" and "teratogenesis" tends to limit our thinking to anatomic abnormalities expressed between conception and birth. There are practical reasons for this, but it leads to a short-sighted approach to problems of abnormal development. For example, such a point of view would exclude consideration of diabetes mellitus, Huntington's chorea, and abnormalities of behavior. Abnormalities of behavior are the most important group of developmental disorders that our society faces. The anatomic aspects of diabetes mellitus and Huntington's chorea are overshadowed by the molecular and the functional manifestations, but both are congenital, in the sense that they are present at conception and at birth in genetic form even if not expressed until later in life.

Second, I would discuss briefly the use of antimetabolites to produce abnormalities of development, chiefly anatomic ones. Many investigators confuse the effects of an antimetabolite with the effects of a deficiency of the corresponding normal metabolite. Probably antimetabolites never, or almost never, imitate their corresponding natural deficiencies in experimental mammals. Dr. Fraser and Dr. Wilson were careful to make the distinction between deficiencies and conditions caused by antimetabolites (which they also called analogues and agents). Two examples from our own experience will illustrate the point. Acetylpyridine, aminonicotinamide and pyridine sulfonic acid are considered to be antimetabolites to nicotinic acid and its amide and are incorporated into appropriate pyridine nucleotide enzymes in vitro. When given to living animals, they produce different pathologic lesions. The genetic background of the animals can modify the differences further. Similarly, methylamine sulfoxamine, which is an antagonist of both glutamic acid and methionine, produces one kind of lesion in certain genotypes, and ethionine does something different. Among many reasons for this, most important must be the individuality of the antimetabolite molecule itself.

DR. WAELSCH: As Dr. Weiss mentioned, separation of normal from abnormal development is not possible. The experimental production of abnormalities, that is, deviations from normal development, made possible the causal analysis of normal development. Equally, the study of genetically and environmentally produced abnormalities has enabled analysis of mechanisms of normal development, particularly in organisms such as mammals which are not easily approached by direct experimental methods.

Dr. Fraser underlined this point in relation to the development of the normal palate, about which we know much more as a result of his studies of genetically and environmentally produced abnormalities of the palate. I would stress one or two points which he and Dr. Wilson have made. One of the most important considerations is the specificity of the effect. A large variety of agents interfere with development and produce abnormalities which frequently cannot be separated from one another. These malformations often owe their similarity not so much to the similarity of the agents employed, or of the mechanisms by which they arise, but rather to the limited number of ways in which the organism is able to respond to the disturbance. One must not confuse the limited number of possible responses with the specificity of the effect of an agent. Therefore, one wonders, how much the use of a diversity of teratogenic agents can contribute to the study of normal and abnormal development.

A model approach to this problem is that which Dr. Landauer used in his studies of the relationship of disturbed carbohydrate metabolism and abnormalities of limb structures. The abnormalities were described, their development studied, and the pharmacology and the metabolic and biochemical effects of the agents examined. Finally, the correlation of these studies permitted conclusions about the mechanism by which these malformations arise.

Also, I would underline a point made by Dr. Wilson, viz., the resistance of embryos in early stages to teratogenic agents. Is this really resistance or simply a lethal effect of the teratogens? A variety of teratogenic agents have lethal effects on early stages; in mice, the embryos frequently fail to implant. But even if there is resistance, the cells of the early embryo are highly pluripotent.

I would comment also on Dr. Wilson's observation that differentiation has to produce a visible difference before it can be assumed to have occurred. Differentiation of cells may occur before a visible difference sets in. Therefore, one wonders whether it is correct to say that all embryonic cells have the same metabolic needs before visible differentiation.

Dr. Wilson also spoke of the relation between malformations and intra-uterine deaths. Intra-uterine death must be due to malformation or some change of morphogenesis. Therefore, the two effects are not independent, and the malformations which survive are the less extreme ones.

Does Dr. Wolff consider feasible the study of the correlation between chromosomal abnormalities, fetal hormones and morphogenesis? In collaboration with Madame Wolff, he has developed beautiful organ tissue culture methods. Do these methods lend themselves to a study of the type of fetal hormone production in tissues with chromosomal abnormalities and the correlation with morphogenesis?

Two final questions: Could Dr. Millen give more details of the insulin data which I believe are still controversial? Would Dr. Wolff comment briefly on Dr. Jost's interesting work on intra-uterine amputations as a result of hormonal defects?

DR. WILSON: The first question which Dr. Waelsch directed to me concerns the reaction of the early undifferentiated mammalian embryo. There certainly is a lethal effect, as well as retardation of growth. This had led to the suggestion that the reaction of the embryo prior to cellular differentiation can be only by cellular death. If a sufficient number, perhaps a critical number, of cells is destroyed by the agent, one might expect death. If fewer than the critical number are destroyed, the embryo might be expected to survive, but with delay in development in proportion to the the number of cells lost.

The second question concerns the possibility, or the probability, that chemical differentiation precedes morphologic differentiation. Experimental evidence favors this view. However, we have spoken of differentiation in terms of the teratogenic criterion: how soon can an effect on an embryo be expected to result in aberration of development? Our present methods do not provide detailed evidence, but I believe that differentiation precedes recognizable change in form.

The third question was concerned with the relationship between intra-uterine death and malformations. There probably are several types of intra-uterine death. The work of Grabowski and Paar, in which chick embryos were exposed to anoxia, has shown clearly that there is a high incidence of immediate deaths which these authors describe as physiologic deaths. One must conclude

that this probably is not the result of a malformation in the anatomic or morphologic sense but follows a major physiologic derangement. Many experiments have shown variations in embryonic response to an effective agent. One day after irradiation, for example, one finds animals which have survived for a few hours and exhibit gross defects: 2 days later a different group of embryos may have died or be about to die, showing different defects. I refer particularly to the work of Dr. Russell and of myself in which embryos were examined at 1-day intervals following irradiation.

MODERATOR WEISS: As embryonic cell damage leads to death if the cells affected are vital and to malformations if they are not, it seems to me that a clear distinction can be made between the two effects. Also, as morphogenesis results from the synthesis and the arrangement of molecules, I think it is important to recognize that discrimination between morphologic and chemical criteria is artificial, although it may be useful in practice.

DR. FRASER: Dr. Hicks has criticized the use of the term "malformation". However, its use can be justified. Malformations raise problems of organogenesis and morphogenesis which are additional to those related to conditions such as diabetes and Huntington's chorea.

DR. WOLFF: Attention was drawn to the fact that the sex hormones explain normal development rather than developmental anomalies. However, they explain both, and it should be remembered that the sexual differentiation depends on the sex genes, while the hormones are merely messengers, intermediaries between gene determination and sexual differentiation. Until recent years, we have been at a loss when attempting to explain anomalies such as the Klinefelter syndrome or the Turner syndrome, but now that we know that there are chromosomal anomalies we are in a better position to understand what is happening. No doubt it is the genes that are the underlying cause of anomalous hormone secretions in these XXY and XO syndromes. The fact that the hormone secretion is disturbed by this anomalous chromosome formula strikingly shows that the genes first determine sexual differentiation, while the hormones are merely intermediaries. Therefore, we believe that these recent discoveries in cytology may explain the anomalies of hormone secretion.

Dr. Waelsch asked whether our method of organ culture in vitro might make it possible to study the type of fetal hormone production in tissues with chromosomal abnormalities. Theoretically, this would be possible if we had at our disposal, for example, gonads affected by the Klinefelter syndrome. Also, it would be possible with a bird or a mammal which showed genetic intersexuality. In this case, I believe that we might succeed in demonstrating a disturbance in hormone secretion in a culture. In some crossings of ducks and turkeys there are genetic anomalies in sexual differentiation which could be used for this purpose.

Dr. Waelsch also asked about the work of Jost who performed intra-uterine amputations and ablations, in which the embryo was decapitated and the hypophysis suppressed. We also have effected these early hypophyseal suppressions in bird embryos. Briefly, the results of the work in birds and mammals are as follows:

The general development of the body and growth remain unaffected.

Some organs are affected: we find hypoplasia of the hypophysis, which causes thyroid hypoplasia and signs of adrenal and pancreatic insufficiency.

In late gestation or late incubation, the absence of the hypophysis causes insufficiency of gonadal secretions, which becomes manifest particularly in the development of the male genital tubercle.

In a hypophysectomized rabbit embryo, Jost has shown that the urethral groove on the male genital tubercle fails to close. The result is hypospadias. Watterson found that ablation of the hypophysis has the same effect on development of the genital tubercle of the chick embryo.

MODERATOR WEISS: Dr. Harris asks Dr. Fraser: Should cleft palate be regarded as a manifestation of abnormal skull development or as the result of local factors affecting the palatine shelves? Dr. Fraser suggests that cortisone has a local action on the shelves. Has he any definite proof for this?

DR. FRASER: It is impossible to answer the first question in general terms. Dr. Waelsch has observed cleft palates of genetic origin which are clearly associated with major malformations of the skull.

In answer to the second question, I think that the cortisone does interfere with development of the palate, perhaps because the palate is the only part of the skull that is susceptible to the action of the cortisone at this time.

MODERATOR WEISS: Dr. Leck asks: Cortisone reduces fibrillogenesis in healing connective tissue, vitamin A inhibits keratin synthesis, and trypan blue increases the viscosity of some fibrillar proteins. Is it possible that these substances cause cleft palate, exencephalus and spina bifida by affecting the fibrillar proteins, which (according to some findings by Fraser, Brachet and others) may mediate the forces which cause approximation of the palatine and the neural folds?

DR. FRASER: This is an attractive idea. I have not examined results of teratogens other than cortisone. Microscopically, we have not observed effects on fibrillogenesis.

MODERATOR WEISS: Dr. Christie asks: Dr. Fraser stated that the development of a particular malformation could be followed by the removal of embryos at various stages from treated mothers. Could he state how one can be certain that malformation will occur in a particular embryo, especially where the course of development of the malformation is devious or deviant?

DR. FRASER: For this purpose we must rely on strains in which frequency of the malformation differs. If the corresponding abnormality is seen early in development—frequently in the highest susceptible strain and less frequently in the resistant strain—this provides strong evidence that there is a causal relation. Also, in the high frequency strain, one can follow the morphogenetic process at successive stages.

MODERATOR WEISS: Dr. Kesson asks: Would Dr. Wolff kindly repeat his remarks concerning the freemartin in cattle and its pathogenesis? Also Dr. Carpenter asks: The freemartin phenomenon was said to be due to steroid hormones originating in the male. Has this been established? Could it not equally well be due to migration of germ cells like that of erythrocytes and their precursors which causes incompatibility and chimerism?

DR. WOLFF: We know that bovine twins of different sex are dizygotes, and that the male twin influences the female twin in a constant way, masculinizing it almost completely. However, masculinization is never complete because freemartins are always sterile. The primary manifestation of this action of the male gonad on the female gonad is a transformation of the latter into a testis which is generally sterile but which, in some cases, shows gonocytes. This experiment of nature (which has been the starting-point of all experiments on hormonal intersexuality) has not been repeated in other mammals. Investigators have succeeded only in inhibiting female development in mouse embryos, without transforming the gonads to testes. In answer to the second question, migration of germ cells could not have occurred. The germ cells do not carry the genes of sexuality; they do not determine sexual differentiation but are neuter and can be transformed into male or female gynocytes, according to the conditions which they encounter in the gonad.

MODERATOR WEISS: Professor Daumiere asks: If it is true that differentiation of gonads can be induced by gonadal hormones, how is sex thought to influence development? Have there been any experiments in which primordial gonocytes or extra-embryonic endoblasts were influenced by gonadal hormones?

DR. WOLFF: In mammals, the gonocytes do not pass through the circulation as they do in birds; they pass from the umbilical vesicle to the genital excrescences at a time when there is no circulation. Hence, it seems impossible that gonocytes should be capable of migrating from one embryo to another.

MODERATOR WEISS: Dr. Potter suggested that the excess of female anencephalics may result from maldevelopment of the hypophysis in genetically masculine individuals.

DR. WOLFF: This is impossible. There is no hypophyseal activity at the stage at which anencephaly occurs, and sexual differentiation occurs before the hypophysis exerts its influence. In primary sexual differentiation, which occurs in the gonads, the hypophysis is not active. If the hypophysis exerts an influence, it is only in a very late stage, and it can influence only the differentiation of secondary sex characters such as the genital tubercle.

MODERATOR WEISS Dr. Runner asks: Is extrapolation from animal experiments on teratogenesis to human development permissible?

DR. WILSON: There is a considerable degree of overlap between the types of agents which cause malformations in man and those used in experimental animals. Radiation produces similar malformations in both, affecting primarily the central nervous system and secondarily the extremities. In parallel with the observations on rubella in man, the Newcastle disease virus, the blue tongue virus and the influenza A virus, all have been shown to be effective in rodents and/or chicks.

Also, there is a parallel in the case of endocrine influences. The data referred to by Dr. Wolff can be compared with the observations that in man synthetic progestogens may cause pseudohermaphroditism. Finally, the antimetabolic aminopterin—a folic acid antagonist which is among the most widely used agents in laboratory animals—has been shown to be effective in human beings. On these grounds, it seems justified to base conclusions about man on experience of experimental animals. However, no instance of nutritional deficiency causing malformations in man has been recorded so far, whereas some of our best information on experimental teratology has come from investigation of nutritional deficiencies. Also, advanced maternal age must be considered to be a teratogenic agent in man; there is no evidence that it is significant in other mammalian species.

MODERATOR WEISS: Dr. Regal asks: Can we compare malformations in plants with those in animals?

DR. FRASER: I believe that much can be learned from knowledge of morphogenesis in plants. For example, the phenomenon of branching in plants may throw some light on hyperdactylism. Nevertheless, we must be careful in applying experimental evidence to man.

MODERATOR WEISS: Dr. Radik asks: What is the significance of the observation that carcinogens and mutagens and carcinostatic and cytostatic agents are also teratogenic agents?

We can say little more than that they alter the course of development, in some cases causing death, in others malformations and in still others tumors. We know the action of mutagens but not of carinogens.

In closing these four sessions I would give a personal view of our present position and objectives. A malformation is something that is misformed or badly formed, affecting the viability, the durability, or the survival of the individual. It is misleading to speak as though malformations are due entirely to something done to the embryo. Malformations can be understood only in terms of the developing system. They arise as modifications of this system, not as additions to it or subtractions from it.

Development proceeds essentially as a se-

quence of events, all of which are interrelated. If the blueprint is at fault, the best execution will not lead to a durable result. Equally, if the blueprint is correct and the execution deficient, the result will be unsatisfactory.

Our main need at present is to ask practical questions. This requires avoidance of the false antithesis between such terms as genetic and environmental, hormonal and genetic, normal and abnormal; for we know now that no single answer will settle the problems with which we are concerned.

Development is an assembly line process which can proceed only if raw materials from various sources are brought together in the right places at the right times. The molecules, the cells and the tissues of the embryo are constantly interacting mechanically or biochemically, through direct contact or diffusible agents. The inductions mentioned earlier are examples of these interactions. This discussion has shown how experimentally produced malformations can be used to study them.

Malformations can result only from disturbance of the harmony of the embryonic processes. These processes have a time schedule and a space pattern. If the time schedule of one part is disturbed, that of the other part is also affected. If it gets beyond the stage where it can be repaired, a defect results. Many examples of faulty development are attributable to errors of timing or of spacing.

Clearly, we are dealing with a complex system in which at the outset there is a genome trapped in a chromosome, a chromosome trapped in a nucleus and a nucleus trapped in egg-cytoplasm. Anything that happens subsequently bears the imprint of the interactions which have gone before. Hence, there is constant interaction between the genome and its environment; and the cells of an egg never can be exactly the same after interaction has begun.

The background against which teratogenic agents or radiation are applied to an embryo is changing constantly. Therefore, it is misleading to ask whether an action is genetic or hormonal, since the cells are not protected from actions of other cells during their previous development. Moreover, hormones are products of other cells and, as such, have experienced the same genetic-environmental interactions. It is more rewarding to study development with these facts in mind than to look for single critical events.

The same considerations apply to the relation between the normal and the abnormal. Each cell experiences unique and unpredictable contigencies and at corresponding stages differs somewhat from every other one. Hence, we are dealing with a statistical distribution in which it is convenient to speak of the outliers as malformations. Considered developmentally, the much admired cupid-bow mouth has an affinity to cleft palate.

Also, some malformations are produced by events which are considered as normal when they occur elsewhere; for example, the heart is formed by the fusion of bilateral cardiac rudiments, but fusion of the eyes constitutes the malformation of cyclopia.

The study of malformations can contribute to knowledge of development, while knowledge of development can assist in the understanding of malformations. Therefore, I hope that we are at the beginning of a period of fruitful collaboration between the embryologist and the pathologist.

SESSION VI

Maternal Fetal Interactions

Moderator
LOUIS B. FLEXNER, M.D.
Professor and Chairman, Department of Anatomy, School of Medicine,
University of Pennsylvania, Philadelphia, Pennsylvania, U.S.A.

MATERNAL EFFECTS IN MAMMALS AND THEIR EXPERIMENTAL ANALYSIS
DR. ANNE McLAREN, M.D.
Institute of Animal Genetics, West Mains Road, Edinburgh, Scotland, United Kingdom

PROTEIN TRANSFER AND SELECTION
DR. W. A. HEMMINGS
University of North Wales, Bangor, North Wales, United Kingdom

STUDIES ON SYNCYTIAL TROPHOBLAST OF HUMAN PLACENTA
LEWIS THOMAS, M.D.
Professor and Chairman, Department of Medicine, New York University Bellevue
Medical Center, Director, Third and Fourth Divisions, New York 16, New York, U.S.A.

Maternal Effects in Mammals
and Their Experimental Analysis

ANNE McLAREN, M.D.

With the exception of Siamese twinning and certain rare cases of placental anastomosis, the most intimate physiologic association between vertebrate animals is the association of mother and fetus in mammals. To what extent the mother and the fetus interact and, in particular, to what extent the developing embryos are influenced by the maternal environment in which they find themselves, are therefore questions which merit attention. Of the few characters susceptible to prenatal maternal influence which so far have been recognized, still fewer have been subjected to experimental analysis so that our knowledge of when and how such influences are exerted is still extremely sparse. Today, I want to consider what categories of maternal influence are available for investigation, what experimental means we have at our disposal for their analysis, and what results have been obtained so far.

For all we know, every character in the mammalian organism may be under the influence of the maternal environment. Only when the influence shows *variation* can we recognize a maternal effect and investigate it. For ease of discussion, rather than because I think the distinction has any profound significance, I shall consider first those instances of maternal influence which are recognized as a result of alterations in the mother's environment (experimentally induced or not), then those which are recognized as a consequence of differences in genetic constitution.

A large body of experimental work exists on the effects upon the development of the young of subjecting the mother to acute or chronic environmental insults during pregnancy. The type of insult varies widely. When Jacob (Genesis Chap. 30), motivated not by a spirit of pure scientific enquiry, held striped rods in front of the sheep and the goats of Laban's flock at the moment of conception, the young were born striped and speckled. The more recent literature has been reviewed excellently by Wilson,[66] who divides the type of agent used into physical factors, maternal nutritional deficiencies, growth inhibitors and specific antagonists, infectious agents, hormone injections and endocrine states, and miscellaneous chemicals and drugs. The effects on the embryo range from minor malformations to death. This field is covered amply elsewhere in this Conference. In any case, the relevance of much of the work to the topic of maternal effects is lessened by the very frequent difficulty of deciding whether the agent is acting through the mother in any but the most trivial sense: that is whether it is acting by way of modifications in the maternal physiology, or whether it is acting on the embryo directly. In the case of x-rays, one of the most widely studied of environmental insults, it seems likely that the principal effects are exerted on the embryo directly.

It is usually impossible to settle this question by experimental manipulation of the embryo and the mother, since most environmental agents are effective only if applied after the embryo has implanted, and at this stage of pregnancy the embryo is rarely

211

amenable to experimental interference. An exception is to be found in the work of Shah,[58] illustrated in Figure 1. If female rabbits are exposed to a high temperature for 6 days after mating (i.e., for the period of gestation between fertilization and implantation) a large proportion of their embryos die at a later stage of gestation. By transferring such embryos at the end of 6 days to the uteri of rabbits kept at a normal temperature, and conversely by transferring untreated 6-day embryos to the uteri of heated females, Shah was able to establish conclusively that the high temperature was not exerting any direct adverse effect on the embryos but was acting via the mother. Again, Smith[59] observed a litter of grossly abnormal fetuses in a female hamster which had been frozen for 45 min-

utes at a very early stage of pregnancy. No experimental analysis has been carried out here, but, if the effect is confirmed, it will be tempting to suppose that in this case also we are dealing not with a direct teratogenic effect on the embryos but with a case of maternal influence dependent on the environment of the mother.

An interesting category concerns the possible effect upon the embryos of active or passive immunization of the mother. Gluecksohn-Waelsch[16] reported abnormalities of the nervous system in embryo mice whose mothers had been actively immunized against brain tissue. Ivanyi and his colleagues[27] and Frenzl et al.[15] induced experimental erythroblastosis fetalis in rabbits and rats, respectively, both by active immunization of the female with the erythrocytes of

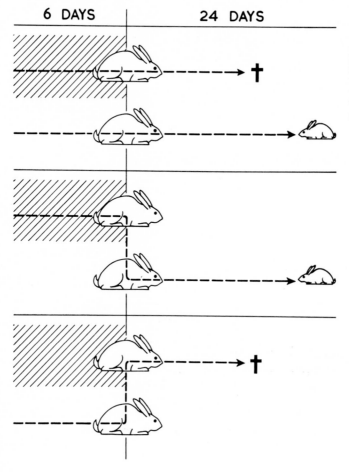

FIG. 1. Analysis by embryo transfer of the effect of exposing pregnant rabbits to a high temperature (Shah[58]). Shaded areas indicate that the animal was kept at a high temperature for the first 6 days after mating. See text for explanation.

the male with which it had mated and by passive immunization with antierythrocyte immune serum. On the other hand, Mitchison[41] failed to find any ill effect on F_1 hybrid mouse embryos of immunizing the mother with red cells or tumors from the paternal strain.

Several instances are known of maternal effects which vary with the age or the parity of the mother. Wright[67] found an effect of maternal age (not parity) in the guinea pig upon the manifestation of polydactyly and also upon the expression of a spotting factor. Holt[24] showed that the manifestation of a recessive polydactyl gene in mice decreased with increasing maternal age. (In this as in some other cases, the effects of age and parity are not distinguished.) Other characters influenced by maternal age in mice are the manifestation of harelip and cleft palate,[47] and the sacralization of the 27th vertebra in the Bagg albino strain.[18] Environmental factors which cause nonsystematic fluctuations from litter to litter of the same female also may affect the number of presacral vertebrae,[35] as well as the size of the 3rd molars.[19] Russell,[53] again in mice, found effects of maternal age upon postnatal growth, upon the incidence of juvenile diarrhea, and upon prenatal and postnatal survival of WW anemics. In the first 2 cases, advancing maternal age was advantageous, and in the 3rd it was disadvantageous.

In man, birth weight[30] and the incidence of a number of miscellaneous congenital deformities vary with the age and the parity of the mother. So does the incidence of dizygotic twins, which might be considered an indirect effect of maternal age on, for instance, birth weight. Of course, the best-known instance in man is mongolism, where Penrose[44] has established that the dependence is on maternal age itself and is independent of parity. Every increase of 5 years after the age of 25 more than doubles the probability that a mongol child will be born. The interest of this case is increased by the recent finding[28] that mongols have a diploid number of 47 chromosomes, the extra chromosome being a small acrocentric autosome. It still is entirely unknown whether the age-dependent maternal effect operates in the first instance on the chromosomes, on the cytoplasm, or on the uterine environment. For instance, the last might modify the development of the mongol phenotype

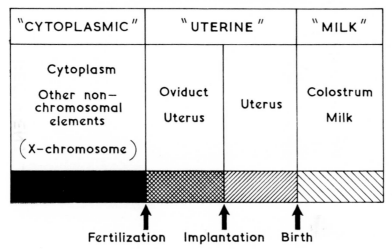

FIG. 2. Classification of maternal effects on mammals according to the route by which they operate.

in embryos of appropriate chromosomal constitution.

Before turning to the consideration of maternal effects which vary with the genetic constitution of the mother, I shall digress and consider what experimental means are available for the analysis of maternal effects. In particular, I shall discuss how one can identify the stage of development of the young at which the mother is exerting her influence.

A female mammal may influence her young before fertilization, between fertilization and birth, and after birth (Fig. 2). I propose to exclude any effects mediated through the chromosomes, such as sex-linkage effects. Without prejudice to such sophistications as the possible influence of the nucleoplasm, I shall refer to all prefertilization effects as "cytoplasmic." Similarly, I shall refer to effects exerted between fertilization and birth as "uterine," while bearing in mind that part of this period is spent in the oviduct in many species. In addition to the passage of substances such as soluble foodstuffs across the placental barrier, there are other routes by which the mother may influence her young in utero. Brambell[5] has reviewed the various routes by which, in rabbits, protein molecules may pass intact from mother to young. Postnatally, by far the most important maternal influences are those mediated through the central nervous system: for instance, instruction of the

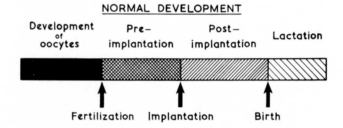

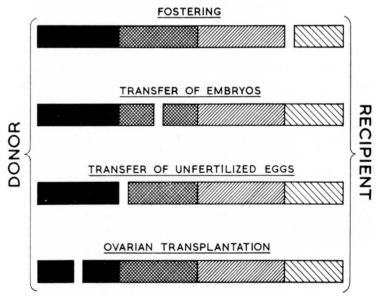

FIG. 3. Some of the technics available for the experimental analysis of maternal effects in mammals.

young by the mother and imitation of the mother by the young. These, too, we shall exclude. Postnatal influences exerted through the process of lactation I shall term "milk" effects.

Sometimes it is obvious whether a cytoplasmic, a uterine or a milk effect is involved, without further experimental analysis. An effect which can be recognized at or before birth cannot be due to milk. An effect resulting from an environmental insult administered during pregnancy cannot be cytoplasmic; if it also can be recognized before birth, it must be uterine. Usually, however, the diagnosis demands experimental interference. The technics most relevant (Fig. 3) are cross-fostering, which for full rigor must be carried out before the mother has had a chance to suckle her young (for instance, they may be delivered by Cesarean section), transfer of early embryos (*see* McLaren and Michie[36] for references; also Tarkowski[61] for an alternative technic in mice), transfer of unfertilized eggs,[52] and transplantation of ovaries.[43,50] Recently, technics have been developed[3,31] whereby ovaries may be grafted not only within inbred strains or from parental strains into F_1's but between genetically unrelated females.

Let us imagine a maternal effect such that the offspring of a female of type A are characteristically different from the offspring of a female of type B. Types A and B may be genetically different, or different in age, or maintained on different diets: the source of the difference is for the moment irrelevant. Let us suppose that we have no indication as to what type of maternal effect is involved. If we cross-foster by exchanging offspring between A and B females at birth, a positive result will establish a milk effect; but if the young do not respond, we cannot distinguish between a uterine and a cytoplasmic effect. Transfer of unfertilized eggs will discriminate between a uterine effect (where the young will resemble young of the recipient female or "uterine

foster-mother") and a cytoplasmic effect (where they will resemble young of the donor female or true mother). Transfer of early embryos will achieve the same discrimination, except that it cannot unequivocally establish a cytoplasmic effect; the embryos owe to their true mother some of their postfertilization environment, in addition to their cytoplasm. In the case of ovarian transplantation, if the young from the grafted ovary resemble young of the donor strain, we may be confident that the effect is a cytoplasmic one and, moreover, one which is not influenced by the altered biologic environment to which the grafted ovary has been exposed. But if the young are affected by the treatment, we cannot assert that the effect must be a uterine or a milk one, since the cytoplasm of the developing oocyte might have been influenced by the host at a stage prior to fertilization.

These experimental technics have been used fairly widely for purposes not directly relevant to the study of maternal effects. For example, ovarian transplantation has been applied to the study of aging,[29] and to the genetic analysis of conditions where the female dies before reproducing,[57,60] or even dies before birth.[55] Embryo and egg transfer has made possible the rearing of young from female mice which produce viable ova but cannot support pregnancy.[51] Embryo transfer has been used extensively in the fields of reproductive and developmental physiology[1,9,10,34,37,38,62] and has potential practical application in animal breeding (see Hammond[21]).

However, application of these technics to the analysis of maternal effects has been very limited. Of the instances of maternal influence cited so far (i.e., those where the influence varies with the mother's environment, using the term environment in a wide sense to include the age of the mother), none has been analyzed in this way. Shah's embryo transfers[58] established that it was a maternal effect with which he was dealing: the fact that it was a uterine effect was then obvious from the circumstances of the case, since the heat treatment had been applied after conception. It seems likely that, for instance, in maternal age effects or effects of chronic nutritional deficiencies, altered conditions of the uterine environment will play the major role; but it would be extremely interesting to know whether alterations also take place in the properties of the cytoplasm.

More has been done along these lines for maternal effects which vary with the genetic constitution of the mother. The basic situation here is an F_1 cross between two genetically dissimilar types: the young will be genetically similar to one another whichever way around the cross is made, except for sex-linked factors. Differences between reciprocal hybrids (once sex-linkage is ruled out) therefore will provide evidence of a maternal effect or, in principle, of a paternal effect, but this possibility has yet to be demonstrated in mammals. However, Penrose[45] has reported a paternal age effect on the incidence of acrocephalosyndactyly in man. The character most widely studied in this context is birth weight. Following the well-known demonstration by Walton and Hammond[64] that birth weight and subsequent growth in Shetland pony × Shire horse crosses depend almost entirely on the breed of the mother, similar though less marked maternal effects on birth weight have been found in rabbits, mice, sheep, cows and humans (for references and discussion, see McLaren and Michie[39]). In mice,[7] rabbits[63] and sheep,[25] transfer of embryos has shown a uterine effect on birth weight. Brumby's study also suggests the possibility of a cytoplasmic influence on growth rate which, if confirmed, would constitute the first reported evidence of the role of the cytoplasm in mammals.

Birth weight is doubly under maternal control in polytocous mammals, since here the rate of growth of the fetuses is related inversely to the number in the litter, and this itself depends on the environment and the genetic constitution of the mother. The increased incidence of binovular twins with maternal age has been mentioned already. To take an environmental example, the experimental induction of superovulation in mice by treatment of the female with gonadotrophins greatly depresses mean fetal weight.[22] In a normal mouse colony, the interrelation between body weight and number in the litter acts as a stabilizing factor. Big females shed more eggs and have numerically larger litters; females from large litters grow more slowly and shed fewer eggs.

Maternal control of over-all prenatal growth rate presumably is mediated through nutritional channels. There is indirect evidence[39] that the pattern of blood supply to the uterus may play an important role. A generalized nutritional influence of this sort is of interest in its own right, and of considerable significance in the field of animal breeding; but from the point of view of gaining some new understanding of morphogenesis, greater interest attaches to maternal effects which involve more specific morphologic or physiologic characteristics.

In all species, some quantitative characteristics other than birth weight also will be "nutritional," in the sense of being closely dependent on birth weight and, therefore, influenced by maternal and other factors which affect prenatal growth. For instance, of the various skeletal characters in mice which Deol and Truslove[12] found to be affected by unbalanced feeding of the mother while pregnant, about one half were correlated with general body size.

A quantitative trait which certainly is not "nutritional" in the simple sense and is not correlated with birth weight, yet is often under maternal control, is the number of lumbar vertebrae. In some inbred strains, the majority of mice have 5 lumbar vertebrae, in other strains, 6. In most strain combinations tested, the F_1 progeny tend to resemble the maternal strain;[56] this cannot be due to a milk effect, as the character is established by birth. Young born from pure-line ovaries transplanted into F_1 hosts[54] showed a host effect on number of lumbar vertebrae; but as explained earlier, this result is compatible with either a uterine or a cytoplasmic effect. In a different strain combination (Fig. 4), transfer of F_1 embryos to recipient females of the paternal strain has established that the specific influence of the mother is exerted, not through the cytoplasm, but entirely through the uterine environment.[37] How a specific morphogenetic influence of this nature can be transmitted via the uterine environment remains wholly obscure.

Other quantitative characters for which reciprocal differences not due to sex linkage have been demonstrated in mice include susceptibility to cortisone treatment,[14] and tail ring number.[13,32] No experimental analysis of these maternal effects has been carried out as yet. The claim by Cloudman[11] to

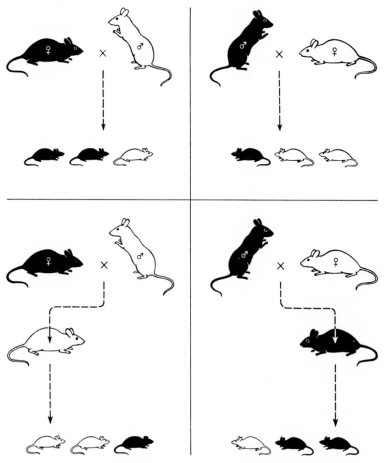

Fig. 4. Diagram to illustrate the experiment of McLaren and Michie.[37] Mice with 5 and 6 lumbar vertebrae are represented as black and white respectively. The 2 upper pictures represent reciprocal crosses between the C3H and C57BC strains of mice, which have predominantly 5 and 6 lumbar vertebrae respectively. The F_1 progeny tend to resemble the maternal strain in vertebral type. In the 2 lower pictures, F_1 hybrid embryos are transferred to uterine foster-mothers of the paternal strain, and when born are found to resemble their foster-mothers rather than their true mothers in vertebral type.

have achieved by embryo transfer an alteration which endured over several generations in the susceptibility of pure-strain mice to transplanted tumors needs confirmation before it can be accepted.

Using the gene *Yellow* in mice, which in homozygous form is lethal at an early embryonic stage, Robertson[49] was able to prolong the life of homozygous embryos to some degree by transplanting ovaries into normal wild-type females. This shows that the viability of the mutants is influenced by the uterine environment as well as by their own genotype. On the other hand, the reciprocal difference in manifestation of *Fused,* reported by Reed,[48] whereby more of the genetically *Fused* mice are phenotypically normal when the mother is *Fused* than when the mother is herself normal (a patroclinous effect), has never been analyzed experimentally.

Crosses between different mammalian species provide very many cases of reciprocal differences in viability, fertility, physiology and morphology (e.g., horse × donkey, sheep × goat, bison × yak, bison × cow, interspecific crosses in Peromyscus and Llama; for references, *see* Gray[17]). The sheep × goat combination also has been studied by means of embryo transfer.[65] A female goat mated to a male sheep becomes pregnant, but the hybrid embryo dies before the end of gestation. The reverse cross is invariably sterile, so that the hybrid embryo, if it develops at all, dies before implantation. Goat embryos which were transferred to sheep uteri died soon after implantation, while sheep embryos in goat uteri developed for a longer period of time. Transfers of hybrid embryos were not carried out. Lopyrin, Loginova and Karpov[33] have reported the successful birth of a lamb after sheep eggs were transferred to a female goat. Interspecific embryo transfers also have been performed by Briones and Beatty[6] and by Averill, Adams and Rowson.[4] In both cases, only the very early development was studied. The work of Averill *et al.*[4] suggests that the differences in rate of cleavage between the sheep and the rabbit embryo is inherent in the embryo itself and is not influenced by the mother.

Hemolytic disease of the newborn, which might be expected to affect species crosses, has been reported in mules.[8] Of course, the same condition arises in man, in association particularly with the Rh system, and also with other blood group antigens such as Kell (*see* Race and Sanger[46] for references). Because of its clinical importance, the Rh condition is the most studied of all maternal effects in the human species. Essentially, a woman carrying a fetus which possesses a blood group antigen absent in herself may become immunized against her child, and then antibodies from the mother may react back upon the child to produce the characteristic hemolytic anemia. No naturally occurring system of this type is known in laboratory animals: the attempts to produce such a situation experimentally have been mentioned earlier. Recently, however, Hollander and Gowen[23] have reported an apparent case of maternal-fetal incompatibility in mice. Females homozygous for the recessive gene *hairloss* exert some adverse influence upon their phenotypically normal offspring, leading to heavy mortality both before and immediately after birth. *Hairloss* young, on the other hand, are unaffected. Although no experimental analysis has been undertaken as yet, it seems possible that the maternal influence has an immunologic basis.

The final category of maternal effects which we must consider concerns the differences between reciprocal F_1 progenies of mice in cancer susceptibility. A widely known example is the case of "milk factor" or mammary tumor inciter, which confers susceptibility to spontaneous mammary cancer in some strains of mice. Cross-fostering experiments have shown both that the responsible agent is transmitted through the milk and also that it is *not* transmitted via the uterus or the cytoplasm. Susceptibility to leukemia also shows a maternal effect in some strain crosses (*see* Grüneberg[20] for references); the maternal influence appears to consist of a leukemia inhibitor which may be transmitted from the low-leukemia female either before or after birth. To my knowledge, egg or embryo transfers have not yet been done.

The mammary tumor agent also is present in the semen of high-cancer strain males. When such males are mated to low-cancer strain females, or when semen from them is injected, the offspring may show a high incidence of tumors even though the mother herself does not develop a tumor. However, transmission must be via the mother, and not directly to the young in utero, since the incidence of tumors increases in later litters, whether or not the subsequent matings are with a high-cancer strain male.[42] This lag effect presumably is due to the time required for propagation of the agent in the mother. Thus, the apparent paternal effect can be analyzed into transmission of the agent from the male to the female, giving rise to a maternal effect, exerted probably via the milk.

At the outset, I proposed to classify maternal effects into those which depend on variations in the mother's environment, and those which depend on variations in the genetic constitution of the mother. The case

Origin	Type	Example
Environmental	Acute insults	X-rays Trypan blue Antimetabolites Infection
	Chronic insults	Dietary deficiencies Immunization Endocrine disturbances
	Age and parity	Polydactyly and spotting Cleft palate Incidence of twins Mongolism
Genetic	Within species	* Birth weight * Lumbar vertebrae * Tail rings * Cortisone susceptibility * Leukaemia "Fused" in mice "Yellow" in mice Rh Hairloss
	Between species	* Many differences
Maternal		Milk factor Cloudman's claim

FIG. 5. Classification of maternal effects in mammals according to their origin, i.e., they owe their recognition according to the type of alteration of the mother. Examples marked with an asterisk could in part depend on variations in the maternal environment to which the mother was subjected, as well as to variations in her genetic constitution.

of milk factor highlights an important qualification to this scheme. The transmission of milk factor from a mother to her young depends *not* on the genetic constitution of the mother but on the type of maternal environment (in this instance, postnatal nutrition) which *her* mother provided for her. The classification outlined in Figure 5 includes the maternal environment to which the mother herself was subjected as a separate category. In theory, it constitutes just one among many environmental factors which influenced her; but in practice such instances are classed more conveniently with those which depend on the mother's genetic constitution, since often it is impossible to separate the one from the other. It is known now that the milk factor can transmit susceptibility over many generations, independent of genotype; but before the appropriate tests had been done, it might have been thought that only females of a particular genetic constitution would be able to transmit the factor. In the case of maternal effects on birth weight, leukemia susceptibility, number of tail rings in mice, number of lumbar vertebrae, interspecific hybrids and hemolytic anemia, the property of the mother which enables her to exert the maternal effect might be due at least in part not to her genes but to her own maternal environment. In the case of Rhesus, it is known that the incidence of affected children of a Rhesus-negative mother varies according to the Rhesus group of the mother's own mother. It seems unlikely that the uterine effect on the number of lumbar vertebrae in mice is more than a 1-generation effect, but the critical test has not yet been done. A possible further instance has been reported by Alzamora *et al.,* in Ingalls.[26] The incidence of babies born with heart defects is increased in Peru, at high altitudes, possibly because of low oxygen tension.[2] The fetuses of mothers with heart defects themselves tend to suffer from hypoxia-induced heart defects, so that to some extent the initial environmental stimulus stretches over more than one generation.

Thus, the mammals have open to them an alternative pathway of inheritance, a somatic, maternal, nonchromosomal pathway. There seems to be no reason why this alternative pathway should be occupied only by such characters as mammary cancer and heart disease. For instance, it could lead to the possibility of cumulative acclimatization to changed conditions of life. To what extent mammals have availed themselves of this opportunity must await future research.

REFERENCES

1. Adams, E. E.: Egg transfer and fertility in the rabbit, Proc. 3rd Int. Congr. Anim. Repr., pp. 5-6, Cambridge, 1956.
2. Alzamora, V., *et al.*: On the possible influence of great altitudes on the determination of certain cardiovascular anomalies, Pediatrics **12**:259-262, 1953.
3. Amand, W. St., and Smith, L. H.: Interstrain ovarian transplantation in lethally irradiated mice after bone marrow therapy, Nature (Lond) **184**:1503-1504, 1959.
4. Averill, R. L. W., Adams, C. E., and Rowson, L. E. A.: Transfer of mammalian ova between species, Nature (Lond) **176**:167, 1955.
5. Brambell, F. W. R.: Transport of proteins across the fetal membranes, Symp. Quant. Biol. **19**:71-81, 1954.
6. Briones, H., and Beatty, R. A.: Interspecific transfers of rodent eggs, J. Exp. Zool. **125**:99-118, 1954.
7. Brumby, P. J.: The influence of the maternal environment on growth in mice, Hered. **14**:1-18, 1960.
8. Caroli, J., and Bessis, M.: Rev. Hemat. (Par) **2**:207-228, 1947.
9. Chang, M. C.: Development and fate of transferred rabbit ova or blastocyst in relation to the ovulation time of recipients, J. Exp. Zool. **114**:197-226, 1950.
10. ———: Fertilizability of rabbit ova and the effects of temperature in vitro on their subsequent fertilization and activation in vivo, J. Exp. Zool. **121**:351-382, 1952.
11. Cloudman, A. M.: The effect of an extra-chromosomal influence upon transplanted spontaneous tumours in mice, Science **93**:380, 1941.
12. Deol, M. S., and Truslove, G. M.: Genetical studies on the skeleton of the mouse.

XX. Maternal physiology and variation in the skeleton of C5-BL mice, J. Genetics **55**:288-312, 1957.

13. Fortuyn, A. B. D.: A cross of gene environment as a means of studying the inheritance of some quantitative characters in *Mus musculus*, Genetica **21**:243-279, 1939.

14. Fraser, F. C., Kalter, H., Walker, B. E., and Fainstat, T. D.: The experimental production of cleft palate with cortisone and other hormones, J. Cell. Comp. Physiol. **43**:(Suppl.)237-259, 1954.

15. Frenzl, B., Kren, V., Stark, O., Smetana, K., and Kraus, R.: Experimental erythroblastosis foetalis in rats, Folia. Biol., Praha **6**:135-143, 1960.

16. Glueksohn-Waelsch, S.: The effect of maternal immunization against organ tissues on embryonic differentiation in the mouse, J. Embryol. Exp. Morph. **5**:83-92, 1957.

17. Gray, A. P.: Mammalian Hybrids, Commonwealth Agricultural Bureaux, Farnham Royal, England, 1954.

18. Green, E. L.: Genetic and non-genetic factors which influence the type of skeleton in an inbred strain of mice, Genetics **26**:192-222, 1941.

19. Grüneberg, H.: The genetics of a tooth defect in the mouse, Proc. Roy. Soc. (Biol) **138**:437-451, 1951.

20. ———: The Genetics of the Mouse, ed. 2, The Hague, Martinus Nijhoff, 1952.

21. Hammond, J.: Problems concerning the transplantation of fertilized ova or "artificial pregnancy," An. Fac. Med. Lima **35**:810-819, 1950.

22. Healy, M. J. R., McLaren, A., and Michie, D.: Foetal growth in the mouse, Proc. Roy. Soc. (Biol), October, 1961.

23. Hollander, W. F., and Gowen, J. W.: A single-gene antagonism between mother and fetus in the mouse, Proc. Soc. Exp. Biol. Med. **101**:425-428, 1959.

24. Holt, S. B.: The effect of maternal age on the manifestation of a polydactyl gene in mice, Ann. Eugen. **14**:144-157, 1948.

25. Hunter, G. L.: The maternal influence on size in sheep, J. Agric. Sci. **48**:36-60, 1956.

26. Ingalls, T. H.: Environmental influences in causation of congenital anomalies, Ciba Symp. on Congenital Malformations, pp. 51-77, Boston, Little, Brown, 1960.

27. Ivanji, P., Tomaskova, M., Smetana, K., Soukup, F., Brozman, M., and Ivanji, J.: Experimental erythroblastosis foetalis in rabbits, Folia Biol. (Praha) **4**:369-380, 1958.

28. Jacobs, P. A., Baikie, A. G., Court Brown, W. M., and Strong, J. A.: The somatic chromosomes in Mongolism, Lancet **1**:710, 1959.

29. Jones, E. C., and Krohn, P. L.: Influence of the anterior pituitary on the ageing process in the ovary, Nature (Lond) **183**: 1155-1158, 1959.

30. Karn, M. N., and Penrose, L. S.: Birth weight and gestation time in relation to maternal age, parity and infant survival, Ann. Eugen. **6**:147-164, 1951.

31. Krohn, P. L.: Litters from C$_3$H and CBA ovaries orthotopically transplanted into tolerant A strain mice, Nature (Lond) **181**:1671-1672, 1958.

32. Law, L. W.: The effect of specific genes on the size character tail ring number in *Mus musculus*, Genetica **21**:1-15, 1939.

33. Lopyrin, A. I., Loginova, N. V., and Karpov, P. L.: The effect of changed conditions during embryogenesis on growth and development of lambs, Sovet. Zootch. **6**:83-95, 1951. (*See:* Animal Breeding Abstr., Edinburgh **20**:729, 1952.)

34. McLaren, A., and Biggers, J. D.: Successful development and birth of mice cultivated in vitro as early embryos, Nature (Lond) **182**:877-878, 1958.

35. McLaren, A., and Michie, D.: Factors affecting vertebral variation in mice. 1. Variation within an inbred strain, J. Embryol. Exp. Morph. **2**:149-160, 1954.

36. ———: Studies on the transfer of fertilized mouse eggs to uterine foster-mothers. I. Factors affecting the implantation and survival of native and transferred eggs, J. Exp. Biol. **33**:394-416, 1956.

37. ———: Factors affecting vertebral variation in mice. 4. Experimental proof of the uterine basis of a maternal effect, J. Embryol. Exp. Morph. **6**:645-659, 1958.

38. ———: Studies on the transfer of fertilized mouse eggs to uterine foster-mothers. II. The effect of transferring large number of eggs, J. Exp. Biol. **36**:40-50, 1959.

39. ———: Control of prenatal growth in mammals, Nature (Lond) **187**:363-365, 1961.

40. Michie, D., and McLaren, A.: Experiments with egg transfer in the mouse, Stud. Fertil. **10**:141-149, 1959.

41. Mitchison, N. A.: The effect on the offspring of maternal immunization in mice, J. Genet. **51**:406-420, 1953.

42. Muhlbock, O.: Studies on transmission of mouse mammary tumor agent by male parent, J. Nat. Canc. Inst. **12**:819-837, 1952.

43. Parkes, A. S.: Ovarian homografting between mice of different strains, J. Endocr. **14**:(Suppl.)21-22, 1956.

44. Penrose, L. S.: The relative aetiological importance of birth order and maternal age in Mongolism, Proc. Roy. Soc. (Biol) **115**:431-450, 1934.

45. ————: Genetical causes of malformation and the search for their origins, Ciba Symp. on Congenital Malformations, pp. 22-31, Little, Brown, Boston, 1960.

46. Race, R. R., and Sanger, R.: Blood Groups in Man, Oxford, Blackwell, 1950-1958.

47. Reed, S. C.: Harelip in the house mouse. I. Effects of the external and internal environments, Genetics **21**:339-360, 1936.

48. ————: The inheritance and expression of Fused, a new mutation in the house mouse, Genetics **22**:1-13, 1937.

49. Robertson, G. G.: An analysis of the development of homozygous yellow mouse embryos, J. Exp. Zool. **89**:197-231, 1942.

50. ————: Homoplastic ovarian transplantability in the house mouse, Proc. Soc. Exp. Biol. Med. **59**:30-31, 1945.

51. Runner, M. N., and Gates, A.: Sterile, obese mothers, J. Hered. **45**:51-58, 1954.

52. Runner, M. N., and Palm, J.: Transplantation and survival of unfertilized ova of the mouse in relation to postovulatory age, J. Exp. Zool. **124**:303-316, 1953.

53. Russell, E. S.: Search for new cases of parental and seasonal influences upon variations within inbred strains, Ann. New York Acad. Sc. **57**:597-605, 1954.

54. Russell, W. L.: Maternal influence on number of lumbar vertebrae in mice raised from transplanted ovaries, Genetics **33**:627-628, 1948 (Abstr.).

55. Russell, W. L., and Gower, J. S.: Offspring from transplanted ovaries of fetal mice homozygous for a lethal gene (*Sp*) that kills before birth, Genetics **35**:133-134, 1950 (Abstr.).

56. Russell, W. L., and Green, E. L.: A skeletal difference between reciprocal F_1 hybrids from a cross of two inbred strains of mice, Genetics **28**:87, 1943 (Abstr.).

57. Russell, W. L., Russell, L. B., and Gower, J. S.: Exceptional inheritance of a sex-linked gene in the mouse explained on the basis that the X/O sex-chromosome constitution is female, Proc. Nat. Acad. Sci. USA **45**:554-560, 1959.

58. Shah, M. K.: Reciprocal egg transplantations to study the embryo-uterine relationship in heat-induced failure of pregnancy in rabbits, Nature (Lond) **177**:1134-1135, 1956.

59. Smith, A. U.: The effects on foetal development of freezing pregnant hamsters (Mesocricetus auratus), J. Embryol. Exp. Morph. **5**:311-323, 1957.

60. Stevens, L. C., Russell, E. S., and Southard, J. L.: Evidence on inheritance of muscular dystrophy in an inbred strain of mice using ovarian transplantation, Proc. Soc. Exp. Biol. Med. **95**:161-164, 1957.

61. Tarkowski, A. K.: Experiments on the transplantation of ova in mice, Acta theriolog. **2**:251-267, 1959.

62. ————: Experiments on the development of isolated blastomeres of mouse eggs, Nature (Lond) **184**:1286-1287, 1959.

63. Venge, O.: Studies of the maternal influence on the birth weight in rabbits, Acta zool. **31**:1-148, 1950.

64. Walton, A., and Hammond, J.: The maternal effects on growth and conformation in Shire horse-Shetland pony crosses, Proc. Roy. Soc. (Biol) **125**:311-335, 1938.

65. Warwick, B. L., and Berry, R. O.: Intergeneric and intra-specific embryo transfer in sheep and goats, Proceedings of the First National Egg Transfer Breeding Conference, pp. 5-12, 1949.

66. Wilson, J. G.: Experimental studies on congenital malformations, J. Chron. Dis. **10**:111-130, 1959.

67. Wright, S.: Effects of age of parents upon characteristics of the guinea pig, Am. Nat. **60**:552-559, 1926.

Protein Transfer and Selection

DR. W. A. HEMMINGS

Transfer of antibody from mother to young was demonstrated first by the pioneer work of Ehrlich in the mouse.[11] The interest taken in this field by many subsequent workers has greatly widened our understanding, and the present state of knowledge of man and the common domestic and laboratory animals has been summarized in a number of recent reviews.[2,3,4,5,10,16,19]

Immune transfer is a phenomenon common, perhaps universal among mammals. It is of great importance in securing the survival of the young against pathogenic affront immediately after birth and in some cases may play a wider part in fetal nutrition. On the other hand, serious disorder may result where an iso-antibody is transferred. Although the function is restricted to a short period of life and is carried out before birth by extra-embryonic membranes which may be regarded as specialized in this sense, its mechanism necessarily poses problems of general nature, such as arise from any consideration of the production and the utilization of the complex group of molecules which form the serum proteins. Cellular absorption of large molecules must occur in immunization, in the growth of the oocyte and at the targets of the protein hormones. The unique value of the structures which effect the immune transfer lie in the massive quantity of protein handled and in their easy accessibility in most cases for experiment.

The location of transfer, and the time, vary in different species. The ungulates are born with no antibody and little gamma globulin but derive these in one massive dose from the colostrum, the small intestine being permeable to protein for a brief period after birth. In the rabbit and the guinea pig, all transfer occurs before birth. The maternal supply is secreted into the lumen of the uterus and absorbed by the yolk-sac splanchnopleure. The latter is a well-vascularized membrane, of similar morphologic derivation to the gut walls, which forms the outer surface of the conceptus in the latter part of gestation in these species. The mouse and the rat also possess this route, but the contribution it makes is small compared with the supply from the colostrum and the milk absorbed by the small intestine after birth. In the Rhesus monkey, the gut is impermeable to protein, the yolk-sac is vestigial, and the wholly prenatal transfer must be considered a function of that versatile organ the allantochorionic placenta. Presumably, this holds true for man.[1] Among carnivores, it is known only that the dog receives its passive immunity after birth; slight prenatal transmission also has been reported.

It must not be assumed necessarily that the mechanism of transfer is similar in all cases, though it now appears to be accepted generally that an active cellular transport is always involved. Cytologic studies show the microvillous cell border and cytoplasmic vacuolation indicative of intense droplet ingestion, and in some cases labeled material has been shown to be absorbed into the vacuoles under experimental conditions.[9] Unfortunately, the treatment of the protein within the cell is still very obscure. However, one type of observation distinguishes two modes of entry of antibody. In some cases, particularly in the ungulate gut, it appears that whatever antibody is presented to the endoderm cell is passed on to the circulation, as though the cell were operating simply as a pump. In other cases, which include all those of prenatal passage quoted above as well as gut absorption in the mouse and the rat, different antibodies may be found at quite distinct concentration in the blood. Thus, in man, maternal bacterial antitoxins normally reach approximate equality of concentration in the fetal blood at full term, whereas some bacterial agglutinins seem to fall far below this level. In particular contrast are the blood group iso-agglutinins: both Rh- and A B O-saline-agglutinating or complete antibodies pass considerably less readily than do the incomplete or blocking antibodies which are responsible for hemolytic disorder. It is clear that a more complex model of cellular activity than that of the micropump will be required to explain these instances if, as at first sight appears to be the case, an actual molecular separation is being carried out during the process of transmission.

The evidence from animal experiments indicates that such separation does occur. Thus, 2 antibodies in an artificial mixture of sera, presented to the yolk-sac endoderm of the rabbit fetus by injection into the lumen of the uterus, may achieve quite distinct concentrations in the fetal circulation: for example, equine diphtheria antitoxin reaches less than 1/50th of the concentration of homologous tetanus antitoxin in these circumstances. This experimental effect of selection between closely similar molecules has been shown also in the guinea pig, the mouse and the rat. It is associated primarily with the species of origin of the molecule rather than with the type of antibody, though multiple antibodies in the one serum have been shown to suffer selection. Where the study was extended to whole gamma globulin preparations isotopically labeled with iodine, the fetal circulating con-

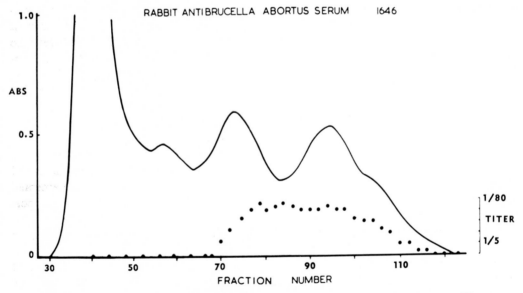

Fig. 1. Quantitative immunoelectrophoresis of rabbit hyperimmune serum. Electrophoresis carried out on cellulose powder columns by the method of Porath. Ordinate: protein concentration. Abscissa: volume eluted from column, the albumin peak being on the extreme left. Dots indicate antibody concentration according to the secondary ordinate scale.

This antibody is transmitted to the fetal circulation, where it shows the same wide range of mobility. It sediments exclusively as 7S material in the ultracentrifuge.

centration of bovine gamma globulin was low, confirming observations with antibodies which are a constituent of that fraction. However, the labeled heterologous protein is absorbed equally with the homologous by the membrane, a finding quite in agreement with the concept that absorption occurs by pinocytosis.[13] Yet, the differential must be set up before the protein enters the circulation, since foreign protein appears to be treated indifferently in the fetal serum during the experimental period. When homologous and heterologous globulin—measured both as antitoxin and as isotopic labels— are injected simultaneously into the fetal circulation, they are found at the same relative concentrations a day later.[15] This evi-

dence implicates the endoderm cells as the effective agents in setting up the differential, for no other continuous cellular barrier exists in the yolk-sac splanchnopleure.

In keeping with the finding that heterologous protein reaches the blood in far lower amount, the total body count of the fetus is far lower than after administration of homologous globulin. Neither is it found to remain in the membrane: there is a vigorous proteolytic activity in the endoderm which destroys the serologic label and releases the isotopic one as a breakdown product freely exchanging with the maternal circulation across the placenta. Proteolysis and protein transfer are concurrent in the endoderm but not necessarily associated, for

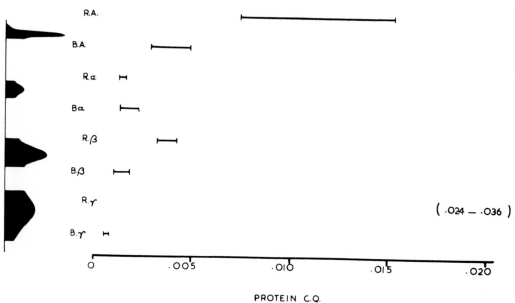

CONCENTRATION OF HOMOLOGOUS AND BOVINE SERUM PROTEIN IN FETAL SERUM

24 HOURS AFTER I.U. INJECTION

FIG. 2. Transport of electrophoretically prepared fractions of serum in the rabbit. Preparations were iodinated with I^{131} at the level of 0.5 atom per molecule immediately prior to injection. The ordinate indicates the mobility of the fraction of rabbit (R) or bovine (B) serum cut from a run such as Fig. 1. The abscissa is a scale of concentration achieved in the fetal circulation. (The value for rabbit gamma globulin is too high for convenient representation and is given as figures in parenthesis.) (Hemmings: In press).

approximately ⅘ of the experimental dose of labeled homologous globulin also is destroyed within the membrane. From this point of view, the difference of treatment of the heterologous protein is that it suffers a somewhat higher proportion of proteolysis. These findings do not explain the transfer, especially in its selective aspect, but rather underline it in contrast with the autotrophic role of the yolk-sac.

All components, even of homologous serum protein, do not pass equally to the fetal blood. Study of the labeled major components, separated by zone electrophoresis, shows that albumin also enters the fetal blood of the rabbit in substantial amount, while alpha and beta globulins, although transmitted, appear at considerably lower levels. Compared with the corresponding fractions of bovine serum, with the possible exception of albumin, they do not show the strong species differential char-

acteristic of the gamma globulin. It is as though the rabbit endoderm cell were rather indifferent toward the alpha and the beta globulins and will accept the foreign alternative if it is offered; it has a preference for albumin of its own kind but draws a firm distinction between gamma globulins. Similar information on species selection in other prenatal systems is not available at present, but in the monkey it has been shown that homologous albumin, relative to gamma globulin, enters less freely than in the rabbit, and alpha and beta globulins do not appear to be represented.[1] Evidently, here also the differential between homologous fractions is very marked. However, in the guinea pig, all components of maternal serum appear to reach the fetus.[8]

Investigation of the effect of a controlled minor change of the molecule may be expected to help our understanding of selection. One such modification is iodination.

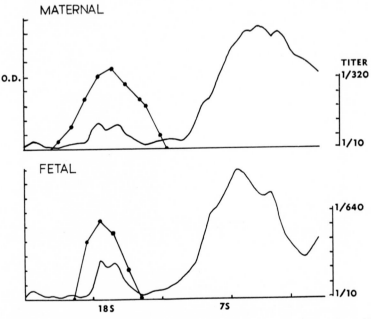

FIG. 3. Transport of homologous macroglobulin antibody in the rabbit. Zone ultracentrifugation of paired serum samples from an immune pregnant animal. Ordinate, protein concentration (continuous line) or antibody titre (connected dots). Abscissa, volume eluted from centrifuge tube. (Hemmings, in press).

An antibody tested in vitro may receive up to 40 atoms of iodine before its reactivity and the original specificity as an antigen are lost. It will be treated then as foreign by its original donor and stimulate antibody production. A much lighter degree of iodination (6 atoms per molecule) brings about a decline of the half-life of gamma globulin when returned to the circulation.[17] Tests of the gut of the young mouse show that it is able to distinguish very sharply between molecules identical save in difference of the number of substituted atoms.[14] Transmission is indistinguishable from normal below the mean level of 0.5 atom per molecule, but above this level a sharp drop is brought about. The entry is reduced approximately one order by substitution of 5 atoms, as though the molecule were widely heterologous. Thus, the loss of a small number of tyrosine residues by modification leads to dramatic change of treatment in the endoderm cell; instead of being transmitted, the molecule is now subjected to proteolysis.

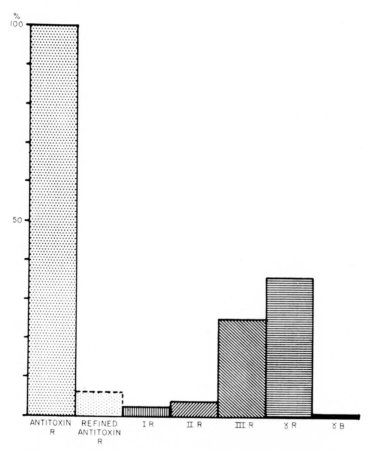

Fig. 4. Selective transport of fragments of homologous gamma globulin in the rabbit. Ordinate, concentration achieved in the fetal circulation, relative to that of homologous antitoxin. Abscissa, from L to R, homologous antitoxin, homologous antitoxin after pepsin refinement, Porter fractions I, II, III, normal rabbit gamma globulin prepared by salting, and normal bovine gamma globulin prepared by salting. With the exception of the antitoxins, samples were labelled before injection as specified in legend for Figure 3. (From Brambell *et al.*[7])

Partial degradation of antibody is known to affect its transmission adversely. Pepsin refinement of homologous antitoxin reduces the passage from maternal to fetal circulation in the guinea pig.[12] Similarly, in the rabbit a pepsinized homologous diphtheria antitoxin administered to the uterus simultaneously with untreated tetanus antitoxin does not achieve concentrations of the same order.[6] The cause underlying these findings may be over-all damage to the molecule or the loss, in the reduction of molecular weight which accompanies pepsin refinement, of specific regions which normally determine transmission.

The action of crystalline papain on immune rabbit gamma globulin has been shown to be a very limited degradation into three components of approximately equal size. Two of these have antibody activity; the third has not but alone retains the ability to react specifically with an antibody prepared against rabbit gamma globulin. This third fraction has been crystallized.[18]

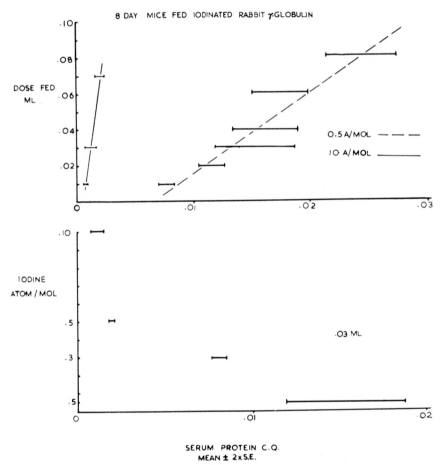

FIG. 5. Selective uptake from the gut of young mice of rabbitt gamma globulin iodinated at different levels. (A) The regression of serum concentration with dose at 2 levels of iodination. Within each relationship each group was composed of 6 mice, being 1 sibling from each of 6 litters. Continuous regression line, iodination of 10 atoms/mol, b = 49.4. Broken regression, iodination of 0.5 atom/mol, b = 4.4. (B) The lowering of serum concentration with increased iodination at standard level of dosage. (From: Hemmings, W. A.: Nature 186:399, Fig. 1.)

Transmission of these three fragments has been measured in the rabbit by trace-labeling, and it is clear that the third fragment reaches concentrations in the fetal circulation approximately an order greater than the other two and closely similar to that of the whole gamma globulin. Clearly, it is part, or all, of this component which determines the transmission of the original molecule.[7]

These lines of evidence show the endoderm cell to behave in a widely varying manner according to the molecular structure of the protein entering it. The separations it achieves, although accompanied by a deplorable loss of material, match our present technics and may exercise their improvement in the foreseeable future.

REFERENCES

1. Bangham, D. R., Hobbs, K. R., and Terry, R. J.: Selective placental transfer of serum proteins in the rhesus, Lancet **2**:315, 1958.
2. Brambell, F. W. R.: The passive immunity of the young mammal, Biol. Rev. **33**:488-531, 1958.
3. Brambell, F. W. R., and Hemmings, W. A.: Active transport through embryonic membrane, Symp. Soc. Exp. Biol. **8**:476-489, 1954.
4. ———: The transmission of antibodies from mother to fetus *in* Villee, C. A. (ed.): The Placenta and Fetal Membranes, Baltimore, Williams and Wilkins, 1960.
5. Brambell, F. W. R., Hemmings, W. A., and Henderson, M.: Antibodies and Embryos, London, Athlone, 1951.
6. Brambell, F. W. R., Hemmings, W. A., and Oakley, C. L.: The relative transmission of natural and pepsin-refined homologous antitoxin from the uterine cavity to the foetal circulation in the rabbit, Proc. Roy. Soc. (Biol) **150**:312-317, 1959.
7. Brambell, F. W. R., Hemmings, W. A., Oakley, C. L., and Porter, R. R.: The relative transmission of the fractions of papain hydrolysed homologous gamma globulin from the uterine cavity to the foetal circulation in the rabbit, Proc. Roy. Soc. (Biol) **151**:478-482, 1960.
8. Dancis, J., and Shafran, M.: The origin of plasma proteins in the guinea pig fetus, J. Clin. Invest. **37**:1093, 1958.
9. Dempsey, E. W.: Electron microscopy of the visceral yolk-sac epithelium of the guinea pig, Am. J. Anat. **93**:331-363, 1953.
10. Edsall, G.: Active and passive immunity of the infant, Ann. New York Acad. Sc. **66**:32-43, 1956.
11. Ehrlich, P.: Ueber Immunität durch Vererbung and Saügung, Ztschr. Hyg. **12**:183-203, 1892.
12. Hartley, P.: The behaviour of different types of homologous and heterologous diphtheria antitoxin when administered to pregnant guinea pigs, Monthly Bull. Minist. Health (Lond) **7**:45-53, 1948.
13. Hemmings, W. A.: Protein selection in the yolk-sac splanchnopleure of the rabbit: the total uptake estimated as loss from the uterus, Proc. Roy. Soc. (Biol) **148**:76-83, 1957.
14. ———: Selection of iodinated protein in the young mouse, Nature (Lond) **186**:399, 1960.
15. Hemmings, W. A., and Oakley, C. L.: Protein selection in the yolk-sac splanchnopleure of the rabbit: The fate of globulin injected into the foetal circulation, Proc. Roy. Soc. (Biol) **146**:573-579, 1957.
16. Kekwick, R. A.: The serum proteins of the fetus and young of some mammals, Adv. Prot. Chem. **14**:231-254, 1959.
17. McFarlane, A. S.: Labelling of plasma proteins with radioactive iodine, J. Biochem. **62**:135-143, 1955.
18. Porter, R. R.: The hydrolysis of rabbit gamma globulin and antibodies with crystalline papain, J. Biochem. **73**:119-126, 1959.
19. Vahlquist, B.: Placental transfer of antibodies in human beings, Etudes neo-natal **1**:31-46, 1952.

Studies on Syncytial Trophoblast of Human Placenta

LEWIS THOMAS, M.D.

Schmorl,[6] in 1893, first described the finding of multinucleated, syncytial cell masses in the pulmonary capillaries of women dying at various stages of pregnancy, and pointed out the similarity of these cells to the syncytial trophoblast of the fetal placenta. Since then, others have reported similar observations,[1,3,5,7] and there is general agreement that occasionally tags and fragments of syncytium may come away from the chorionic villi and be swept into the maternal circulation during human pregnancy.

The histologic appearance of the chorionic villi of the human placenta is compatible with the view that the syncytial trophoblast is capable of leaving the villi and entering the maternal blood. Throughout pregnancy, numerous "sprouts" of syncytium appear to be attached to the villi by thin strands of cytoplasm, and many seem actually to be lying free in the intervillous space.

The present study was undertaken in order to learn whether the migration of trophoblast into the intervillous space, and thence to the maternal blood stream, occurs as a normal and regular event in pregnancy. The most direct approach to the problem seemed to be to search for these cells in the blood draining the pregnant uterus.

MATERIALS AND METHODS

Blood has been obtained at the time of cesarean section or laparotomy from the uterine veins in 25 pregnant women, at stages of pregnancy ranging from the 18th week to term. The preparation of blood smears was carried out by methods similar to those used by Moore[4] for the detection of neoplastic cells in the blood of patients with cancer. A 5-ml. sample of blood was drawn, by syringe and needle, from a uterine vein situated in the broad ligament, well away from the lateral border of the uterus. Care was taken to avoid pressure and handling of the uterus in obtaining the blood. The sample was placed in a tube containing 0.5 ml. of 1 per cent Versene (ethylenediaminetetraacetic acid) solution, mixed and 1 ml. of 5 per cent human fibrinogen was then added to cause sedimentation of the erythrocytes. The tube was incubated for 15 minutes at 37° C., and the supernatant plasma containing leukocytes was drawn off and sedimented by low-speed centrifugation for 5 minutes. The sedimented buffy coat was smeared on 5 microscopic slides, fixed in equal parts of 95 per cent alcohol and ether, and stained by the Papanicoulou technic.

In several cases, blood also was obtained from the placental site by passing a needle through the intact wall of the uterus. In two instances, the ovarian veins were tapped, since these much dilated vessels appeared to have become anastomotic channels for a major part of the uterine venous return.

Control samples of blood were obtained in each case from a femoral vein, or from the inferior vena cava below the level of entry of the uterine veins. In addition, femoral and inferior vena cava blood was obtained from nonpregnant women hospitalized for a variety of reasons; in several of these, the uterus had been removed previously.

RESULTS

In 20 of the 25 pregnant women from whom uterine vein blood was obtained, extremely large, multinucleated cells with the morphologic appearance of syncytial trophoblast were identified readily in each blood smear. They were easily distinguishable from megakaryocytes (which were found to occur with frequency in the vena cava blood) by their relatively enormous size and by the numerous discrete, oval, clearly separated, deeply basophilic nuclei which they contained. The cytoplasm was eosinophilic, and most of the cells possessed a membrane. The size of the trophoblasts varied somewhat, but most measured between 50 and 200 micra in diameter. The smaller cells contained approximately 20 nuclei, while in the larger ones, the nuclei were so numerous and closely packed together as to be uncountable.

Similar multinucleated cells were found in blood obtained directly from the placental site by needle aspiration through the intact uterus.

The trophoblasts seemed to be more numerous in the uterine vein blood of early pregnancy than in samples taken at term. In two cases examined early in the 2nd trimester, it was estimated that at least one trophoblast was contained in each ml. of blood in the venous return from the uterus.

Blood drawn from the inferior vena cava by catheterization through the femoral vein was examined in 32 pregnant women in whom laparotomy was not performed. In 2 cases, unmistakable trophoblasts were found; in several others, there were smaller multinucleated cells which could not be distinguished with certainty from megakaryocytes.

No cells resembling trophoblasts were encountered in any blood samples from the femoral vein itself in 40 cases nor in venous blood taken from the antecubital vein in 90 pregnant women, indicating that the cells do not pass through the lungs into the peripheral circulation. This finding is not surprising in view of the large size of the majority of trophoblasts.

LYSIS OF SYNCYTIAL TROPHOBLAST BY PROTEOLYTIC ENZYMES

In view of the considerable number of trophoblasts which are continually leaving the placenta and entering the maternal blood, and the large size of these cells, it must be assumed that some mechanism exists for their rapid destruction, for otherwise they would rapidly occlude the capillary blood of the mother's lungs. An accidental observation made in the course of this study may provide a clue as to this mechanism.

An attempt was being made to isolate trophoblasts from minced suspensions of fresh placental tissue, in order to study certain antigenic properties of the cells. To facilitate separation of the cells, trypsin was added after the fashion of its use in tissue culture preparations. However, instead of bringing about separation, the syncytial trophoblast was observed to undergo complete disintegration and lysis within a few minutes after the addition of trypsin.

Further study of the observation has revealed the following findings. Crystalline trypsin, in a concentration of 100 mcg. per ml., causes lysis of syncytial trophoblasts in 3 to 4 minutes. Concentrations of as low as 1 mcg. also will lyse the cells, but 2 hours incubation at 37° C. is required. Lysis begins with the formation of large, clear vacuoles in the base of the cells; these become confluent, the cell border fragments, and then the cytoplasmic and the nuclear contents are discharged through the broken surface. The end-result is a "naked" villus, with vessels and mesenchymal cells intact but with no external lining of trophoblast.

Similar cytolysis was demonstrated with crystalline chymotrypsin, in concentrations similar to those of trypsin. Human plasmin, activated with streptokinase, caused disintegration of trophoblasts within approximately 30 minutes.

The vulnerability of syncytial trophoblasts to proteolytic enzymes seems to be a unique property of these cells; other types of cells, if viable, are resistant to trypsin and plasmin. The question as to the viability of the trophoblast remains to be settled conclusively, although preliminary tissue culture experiments in the laboratory indicate that at least some of the syncytial trophoblasts of term placentas are capable of migration and amitotic division.

It seems possible that proteolysis in vivo may account for the rapid disappearance of trophoblasts from the maternal blood, and for their failure to accumulate in dense aggregates in the maternal lungs.

TISSUE CULTURE OF TROPHOBLAST

Initial attempts to cultivate trophoblast in tissue culture, employing explants of human placenta obtained at normal term deliveries, were unsuccessful in most instances. On three occasions, spindle-shaped cells grew out from the explants and developed multinucleated progeny with somewhat the appearance of syncytial trophoblast, these cells did not survive beyond 3 weeks and could not be transferred by subculture.

At the suggestion of Dr. William Thiede, of the University of Rochester, cultures were set up after trypsinization of young (12 to 16 week) human placental homogenates. The trypsin treatment was sufficient to cause disintegration of all syncytial trophoblast in these preparations, leaving intact a mixed population of unidentifiable single-nucleated cells. On culture of these, in Eagle's medium supplemented by human serum, multiplication of large numbers of spindle-shaped cells occurred during the first 4 days of culture. On the 5th and the 6th days, these cells became multinucleated, and the nuclei arranged themselves in a regular arrangement around the periphery of large,

circular cytoplasmic masses. Syncytial cells containing 10 to 30 nuclei were seen in abundance, with an appearance strikingly similar to syncytial trophoblasts. Once these multinucleated cells were formed, further growth of the culture ceased, and the culture died within the next several days.

No mitotic figures were observed at any time during the growth of the trophoblast cultures. The nucleoli were observed to become elongated, and then to split into 2 or 3 globular masses before new nuclei were formed. The possibility that the cells may be dividing by amitotic division is under investigation by time-lapse cinematography.

COMMENT

The fetal placenta, in the human, occupies throughout pregnancy, the anatomic position of a homograft, in which the blood of the mother must circulate through an extensive vascular compartment lined by the cells of an antigenically distinct individual, the fetus. It is possible that the trophoblast may be an immunologically immature cell in which the antigens determining histoincompatibility never succeed in developing, although the circumstance would be a special one for these cells, since all other fetal tissues become antigenically recognizable some time before birth. If it should be that the trophoblast does, in fact, possess antigens different from those of the mother, the phenomenon of migration of trophoblasts into the maternal blood might have a useful immunologic function. Billingham and Brent[2] have shown that the survival of skin homografts in mice can be prolonged greatly if the recipients are given intravenous injections of large numbers of viable cells from the donor prior to grafting. It may be that the invasion of maternal blood by trophoblasts plays a comparable role in maintaining a state of desensitization, or immunologic unresponsiveness, by exposing the mother to a constant excess of fetal antigen.

It has been suggested above that proteolytic enzymes may bring about disintegration of the trophoblasts once they have entered the mother's blood, thus protecting the lungs against an intolerable accumulation of these cells. This hypothesis, which is based entirely on the chance observation that intact trophoblasts are lysed rapidly after exposure to trypsin, opens up a new approach to the study of abnormalities of pregnancy, such as eclampsia, in which proteolysis and/or thromboplastin release have been suggested as possible underlying pathologic mechanisms.

SUMMARY

Syncytial trophoblasts have been found in smears of uterine vein blood of 20 pregnant women, at various stages of pregnancy. The numbers of cells encountered indicates that at least one cell is contained in each ml. of venous blood leaving the uterus.

Syncytial trophoblasts can be disintegrated rapidly by exposure to trypsin, chymotrypsin or plasmin. It is suggested that this vulnerability may indicate a mechanism for their lysis in vivo, after they enter the maternal blood.

A possible immunologic function is suggested for the migration of trophoblasts into the mother's blood.

REFERENCES

1. Bardawil, W. A., and Toy, B. L.: The natural history of choriocarcinoma: problems of immunity and spontaneous regression, trophoblast and its tumors, Ann. New York Acad. Sc. 80:197, 1959.
2. Billingham, R. E., and Brent, L.: Studies on epidermal cell suspensions, with particular reference to problems of transplantation immunity, Ann. New York Acad. Sc. 64:799, 1957.
3. Leusden, P.: Beitrag zur pathologischen Anatomie der Puerperaleklampsie, Virchows Arch. path. Anat. 142:1, 1895.
4. Moore, G. W., Sandberg, A., and Schubarg, J. R.: Clinical and experimental observations of the occurrence and fate of tumor cells in the blood stream, Ann. Surg. 146:580, 1957.
5. Park, W. W.: Experimental trophoblastic embolism of the lungs, J. Path. & Bact. 75:257, 1958.
6. Schmorl, G.: Pathologische—Anatomische Untersuchungen Über Pueperal-Eklampsie, Leipsig, bie Vogel, 1893.
7. Thomas, L., Douglas, G. W., Carr, M. C., and Cullen, N. M.: Migration of fetal trophoblasts into maternal blood, Fed. Proc. 18:601, 1959.

SESSION VI

Discussion

Moderator

LOUIS B. FLEXNER, M.D.

Professor and Chairman, Department of Anatomy, School of Medicine, University of Pennsylvania, Philadelphia, Pennsylvania, U.S.A.

Panel Members

DR. W. W. PARK, M.D.

Department of Pathology, St. Andrew's University, Dundee, Scotland, United Kingdom

DR. GEOFFREY S. DAWES, M.D.

Director, Nuffield Institute for Medical Research, University of Oxford, Oxford, United Kingdom

DR. R. R. A. COOMBS, M.R.C.V.S.

Assistant Director of Research, Department of Pathology, University of Cambridge, Cambridge, United Kingdom

235

DR. PARK: As a pathologist, my interest centers largely on the placenta, particularly the pathologic placenta which, perhaps has not received the attention that it deserves. In many congenital malformations, the placenta must at least transmit the harmful agents, and in doing so the placenta itself may be affected. If this happens, the damaged placental cells may act upon the embryo.

I found Dr. McLaren's division of possible causes of congenital malformations helpful, and I would comment on its application to hydatidiform mole which should be regarded as a congenital malformation. In speaking of malformations, we are apt to ignore the fact that the cells of the trophoblast are as much a part of the conceptus as is the fetus itself. The so-called classic hydatidiform mole is an arresting object. It may be very large, but lesser degrees are recognized, and the conceptus may show only occasional swollen, liquefied chorionic villi. We do not know whether these lesser degrees of hydropic change reflect lesser degrees of the cytoplasmic or the uterine effects that lead to the formation of the classic hydatidiform mole.

Some years ago, I examined a series of hydatidiform moles in the collection at Baltimore in an attempt to determine their sex. The method used was identification of the sex chromatin particle. At that time, I concluded that the placentas of both sexes probably could become hydatidiform moles. However, some recent work by Dr. Klinger of Basel, using a newer and much improved technic, suggests that only female conceptuses may do this. From other observations of my own, on better material than I had had originally, I am inclined to agree that the classic mole tends to occur predominantly in female conceptuses—if all conceptuses whose stromal cells and trophoblastic cells contain one or more sex chromatin particles can be regarded as female. This reservation is necessary because it is becoming increasingly difficult to define the terms "male" and "female," and it is just possible that some chromosomal aberration, causing the sex chromatin particle to appear, is an intrinsic part of the abnormality that leads to the development of a hydatidiform mole. The unusual sex incidence, subject to the reservation just referred to, makes it important to decide whether abortuses with varing degrees of hydropic change have essentially the same abnormality as that exhibited by the classic mole.

One rare phenomenon has acquired a new significance in the light of these observations. This is the birth of a recognizably male fetus, accompanied by a hydatidiform placenta, without evidence of twin pregnancy. If the fetus and the hydatidiform placenta are accompanied by a second placenta, obviously a twin pregnancy has occurred. But in the situation to which I refer, there is only one fetus and one placenta; the fetus is recognizably male, and the placenta is undeniably hydatidiform.

The significance of this occurrence, however rare, has yet to be decided, but I have no doubt of its importance. For if mainly female conceptuses give rise to hydatidiform moles, we have here a situation which is virtually unique: an abnormality acting upon predominantly female conceptuses and associated with overgrowth of the trophoblast, an overgrowth which is often premalignant or frankly malignant.

In examining the series of early human and macaque embryos at the Carnegie Institution's Department of Embryology, I was not able to find sex-chromatin in the embryo or in its membranes before about the 10th day of development. Theoretically, in the case of the female conceptus, it should appear in the zygote. Just possibly all the embryos were males, but as there were 14 (10 human and 4 macaque) this seems to be very unlikely.

Sex chromatin was first detected in the trophoblast on the 11th day, in the villi on the 13th day and in the embryo itself on the 14th day. Thereafter, it was seen with increasing frequency. So far as I know, this observation has not yet been confirmed by other workers.

These results suggest that the appearance or the nonappearance of sex-chromatin in embryonic tissue may be unusually sensitive to degeneration or to delay in fixation, and these findings in early embryos must be interpreted cautiously. However, most of the embryos in the Carnegie collection were fixed rapidly, and, although some of the sections have faded, they are well stained. If there is an initial period at the onset of development when the sex chromosomes are engaged in activity that prevents formation of a sex chromatin particle, the chromosomes in general may be particularly vulnerable at this time. It would be very difficult then to decide whether an abnormality that arose during this period was nuclear or cytoplasmic or uterine or, for that matter, tubal. Conceivably during this period, either some intrinsic chromosomal aberration becomes manifest or something gains access to the cells to cause chromosomal aberration via the somatic, maternal nonchromosomal pathway.

So far, it is difficult to discern any clues about the hydatidiform mole from external evidence. Rare cases are on record of women who gave birth to a succession of hydatidiform moles. But cases usually are sporadic and may be preceded and followed by normal pregnancies.

Dr. James Wilson referred to pteroylglutamic acid deficiency as an almost universal teratogen. It seems to be established beyond reasonable doubt that the incidence of hydatidiform mole is unusually high in tropical regions. The Armed Forces Institute of Pathology conducted an extensive survey in the Philippines, the East Indies, China and Malaya and found a much-increased incidence. The same finding has been reported from West Africa. Conceivably, dietary factors are involved, possibly pteroylglutamic acid deficiency.

Now, I would refer to the work of Dr.

Thomas on the presence of trophoblastic cells in venous blood from the pregnant uterus. These studies have provided useful in-vivo confirmation of an occurrence about which all knowledge hitherto has been based on postmortem evidence. I was interested in his observation that particles of syncytium seem to be more numerous in the uterine venous blood of early pregnancy. In a recent investigation of trophoblastic pulmonary embolism on postmortem material, we considered whether the stage or the duration of the pregnancy might have an influence on the amount of trophoblast passed to the lungs. (The trophoblast is most active during the early weeks of pregnancy.) This was one of four factors which we thought might be influential, the others being: the nature of the disease that caused death; the degree of uterine contraction during labor; and the time which had elapsed between parturition and death.

There were 220 patients in our series: our diagrams show the number of patients dying at different stages of pregnancy, the proportion whose lungs contained trophoblast, and the amount of trophoblast present in the lungs. Of course, it was necessary to devise some quantitative measure of the amount of trophoblast; we used the number of particles of trophoblast visible in 1,000 square millimeters of lung section (referred to as "the trophoblastic index").

Mainly of historical interest is Schmorl's original illustration of the presence of trophoblast in pulmonary vessels. His photomicrographs were not very good, but the drawing could not be bettered today. The multinucleated masses are similar to the structures shown by Dr. Thomas.

Next, we observe the incidence of particles of trophoblast in the lung in patients who died before delivery. There were 54 cases. Among the 10 patients in the 1st trimester, the proportion showing trophoblast in the lungs was small, and the amounts were not great. The ectopic ones contribute nothing significant. Trophoblast was found in the lungs of about one half of the deaths that occurred in the 2nd and the 3rd trimester. The amounts found were greater in the 2nd trimester than in the 1st and very great in the 3rd. This finding differs from Dr. Thomas' observation that most trophoblast is present in the early stages of pregnancy.

Our findings in women who died during or after labor were that about 70 per cent of patients who died in labor or less than 24 hours later had trophoblast in their lungs, and the amounts were very great. In 1 case, the trophoblastic index was 240, 3 times as great as that in any other patient. The amounts of trophoblast declined sharply after the 3rd day, and none was seen in the lungs of patients who died later than the 2nd week after parturition.

Since the trophoblast was found in such small numbers after the first 3 days, the average life of a particle of trophoblast probably is no more than about 3 days. The patient who had a trophoblastic index of 240 had eclampsia, but although the lungs contained vast quantities of trophoblast in the capillaries, she did not die from a pulmonary circulatory obstruction but from a massive cerebral hemorrhage.

The results obtained in abortions were not constant, probably because of the inaccuracy of the history and the uncertain length of time for which placental debris may be retained in the uterus.

As to the mechanism of destruction, Dr. Thomas mentioned that these particles are selectively susceptible to proteolytic enzymes, and that the end-result is a naked villus with vessels and mesenchymal cells intact. I wondered about the role of the basement membrane of the trophoblast in connection with protein transfer. What happens to the protein molecules when they have been passed on by the epithelial cell and are confronted with the basement membrane? There must be some mechanism for the removal of trophoblast, and it must involve loss of protein. But whether it is a mechanism peculiar to the pregnant woman

is doubtful, if only for the reason that the so-called pulmonary megakaryocytes are removed equally effectively and can be found in the lungs postmortem in virtually every patient.

On the nature of immunity mechanisms, I again find myself in conflict with Dr. Lewis Thomas. It is interesting to speculate, as he has done, on the possible significance of the phenomenon of trophoblastic embolism to the lung in relation to the placenta considered as a homograft. When actively acquired tolerance is induced by injection of a cell suspension into an immature animal, the animal is, as it were, being warned in advance of the graft that is yet to come. This cannot apply in pregnancy in women. I can see no way in which the mother can be warned in advance of the nature of the tissues of the embryo which are to be grafted onto her endometrium during pregnancy, and the first few days are crucial. At this time, implantation is or is not established. Either trophoblast is antigenically impotent, or there must be some as yet undiscovered defensive mechanism. The escape of trophoblast to the lung may have some reinforcing effect on such a defensive mechanism, though I doubt whether trophoblast within the maternal pulmonary capillaries can do anything that cannot be done equally well at the placental site. I suspect that, immunologically, embolism to the lungs by trophoblast is irrelevant.

REFERENCE

1. Klinger, H. P.: Neue Ergebnisse der Sex-Chromatin-Forschung an Placenta und Eihäuten, Gynaecologia **146:**328-335, 1958.

Dr. Dawes: The factors which determine the environment in which the fetus lives constitute a rather subtle environment because it depends not only upon how the mother is prepared but also upon how the fetus reacts to it.

Classic physiology has long recognized

that the adult animal maintains its own internal environment. It maintains the levels of various components in its blood and tissue fluids: electrolytes (including acids and bases), carbohydrate, hormones, water, oxygen and carbon dioxide. A question which inevitably arises is whether the embryo is passive or whether, in some way, it can regulate its own environment.

At present, little quantitative information is available on this subject, and more will be needed if we are to understand the action of some teratogenic agents. For example, if the mature sheep fetus is subjected to a mild degree of hypoxia, compensatory changes follow: a rise of blood pressure, an increase of heart rate, a change in the oxygen-carrying capacity of the blood and an increase in umbilical blood flow. However, at about 60 days' gestation, the fetus does not react in the same way. Blood pressure and heart rate do not increase, and there is no change in the oxygen-carrying capacity of its blood. Moreover, some years ago, Jost removed the head of a rabbit in utero at about 20 days' gestation. The rabbit survived and developed until term. Also, Dr. Levi-Montalcini reported survival of animals after elimination of the sympathetic nervous system.

These experiments suggest that the central nervous system is not as important in intra-uterine life as it is after birth. This raised the question whether the fetus in utero is able to regulate its own environment. We have no quantitative evidence, but the fact that the fetus grows and adapts itself during the whole of the intra-uterine period is suggestive.

We have little information about the nature of the mechanisms concerned in this regulation, but two observations are interesting. First, Dr. Hemmings has described the selective transfer of proteins across the placenta and other fetal organs. Second, McCance and his colleagues have shown recently that in the pig and the rabbit the mesonephros secretes isotonic urine. This is collected into the allantoic sac, and the chorioallantoic membrane transfers sodium by an active process. These findings indicate for the first time some of the mechanisms by which the internal environment of the fetus may be regulated. Although the exact nature of these mechanisms is unknown, they seem to be located in the fetal membranes (including the placenta).

I would also refer to a disease known as Scrapie, which occurs spontaneously in sheep aged 3 to 5 years. The sheep rub their backsides and sides and lose their wool; the disease is invariably fatal in a period varying from a few months to about a year after it first appears. Other characteristic features are loss of weight and ataxia, and the condition probably is attributable to degenerative changes in the central nervous system. So far, there is no evidence that this disease is infective, but it has been shown that an extract of the body fluid or brain of an infected animal injected into an uninfected animal causes appearance of the disease. The disease has been transmitted to goats. Recent work suggests that the condition is heritable as an autosomal recessive characteristic.

Here, then, is a disease transmitted by tissue extracts even after these have been boiled or treated with chemical agents which destroy all known viruses. The cause is a filter-passing agent and apparently is heritable. This raises the possibility that some of the degenerative diseases of middle age may be of an analogous character; they may be both heritable and transmissible and possibly congenital.

REFERENCES

1. Crawford, J. D., and McCance, R. A.: Sodium transport by the chorio-allantoic membrane of the pig, J. Physiol. **151:** 458-471, 1960.
2. McCance, R. A., and Stanier, M.: The function of the metanephros of foetal rabbits and pigs, J. Physiol. 151:479-483, 1960.
3. McCance, R. A., and Widdowson, E. M.: The acid-base relationships of the foetal

fluids of the pig, J. Physiol. **151**:484-490, 1960.

4. Parry, H. B.: Scrapie. A transmissible hereditary disease of sheep, Nature (Lond) **185**:441-443, 1960.

5. Stanier, M.: The function of the mammalian mesonephros, J. Physiol. **151**:472-478, 1960.

Dr. COOMBS: Most of my remarks will be confined to one aspect of maternal effects, namely, immunologic effects, including those that are physiogenic and those that are pathogenic. They are relevant to our discussion if only as models of processes which might have their counterpart in the causation of congenital malformations. My own view is that if immunologic effects are pathogenic, they are more likely to result in infertility, early abortion and stillbirth than in malformations.

The time when an antibody is passed to the fetus is rather late in relation to the time when it might influence normal development. In hemolytic disease of the newborn, fetal red cells pass from the fetus to the mother and act as a sensitizing antigen. A more serious situation for the fetus and subsequent offspring might be created by the passage of immunologically competent maternal white cells in the opposite direction from the mother to the fetus. Even if not previously sensitized, they might create conditions in the fetus like those found in experimentally produced runt disease, although these conditions might occur only if the number of cells transferred was very large. But, if cells previously were specifically sensitized, a focal lesion might be set up. There are, of course, technics by which we now can differentiate and distinguish maternal cells from those of the fetus.

Dr. Hemmings dealt with the physiogenic effects. I ask him how the maternal antibody is secreted into the uterine cavity. Is it a simple transudation or a selective type of secretion? In the transfer of gamma globulin in the rabbit, across the endodermal cells of the yolk-sac splanchnopleure, Dr.

Hemmings and his colleagues have shown selection against heterologous gamma globulin. But even with what he considers to be a homologous type of protein, he also found that much of the protein is broken down, proteolized, and that only 1/5th passes into the fetus. Would Dr. Hemmings comment on the possibility that in these experiments he was not dealing with homologous protein but with a globulin of a foreign, antigenically distinct allotype?

Perhaps this question requires an explanation. Recent work has shown that iso-antigens are found not only in red cells but also in serum gamma globulin. The gamma globulin of one rabbit will produce antibodies in another rabbit. Therefore, the question arises whether some of the situations which have been studied by Dr. Hemmings were not homologous in respect of this particular system. If he chose rabbits of the same allotype, possibly more gamma globulin would be transferred.

In discussion of iso-antigens and the corresponding antibodies that may cause disease, we must distinguish between red cell and platelet iso-antigens. Dr. Garrett and I recently observed neonatal purpura due to an iso-immunization with platelet iso-antigens. Similarly, on leukocytes there are different iso-antigens, which could lead to a similar process. Those on the leukocytes are interesting because they also are found on the majority of the tissues of the body. Indeed, we have shown these same antigens on HeLa cells after about 8 years in culture. These antigens are almost as complicated and as specific as transplantation antigens.

The serum groups may be another source of incompatibility leading to fetal death. Finally, maternal antibodies passing to the fetus or the newborn child may produce a passive sensitivity to their antigens and lead to death if the child's tissues contain one of these antigens.

Dr. Thomas referred to the privileged position of the conceptus. Any information about the antigenic structure of the trophoblast will be of value. Do the transplantation antigens exist in trophoblast cells, and, if so, do they reach the mother? Dr. Thomas and I looked for the A-antigen in the trophoblasts of Group A fetuses with Group O mothers. We were unable to demonstrate the presence of this antigen on the outer membrane of the syncytiocytotrophoblast.

On Dr. Thomas' hypothesis, I should like to reserve judgment. I do not like to speak of desensitization before sensitization has been demonstrated. Like Dr. Park, I do not see the need to bring into the discussion the migration of the trophoblast throughout the mother's body. Why could the substance not be secreted by the syncytiotrophoblast in situ? I think the argument would be no less strong without reference to migration. Does Dr. Thomas mean by desensitization that the mother is desensitized to any homograft of the antigenic structure of the fetus? Would the mother accept a graft from the father over pregnancy?

REFERENCES

1. Garrett, J. V., Giles, H. McC., Coombs, R. R. A., and Gunner, B. W.: Neonatal purpura with platelet iso-antibody in maternal serum, Lancet 1:521, 1960.
2. Woodruff, M. F. A.: The Transplantation of Tissues and Organs, p. 125, Springfield, Ill., Thomas, 1960.

DR. THOMAS: I am not inclined to make an issue of the hypothesis that I proposed earlier. I sometimes lose faith in it altogether. I referred to it mainly to emphasize the need for some explanation for what I consider to be an extraordinary and potentially dangerous phenomenon. Each day during pregnancy, some 40 million nuclei are received into the maternal blood in normal pregnancy; in eclampsia this number is increased 20-fold.

I have been asked to comment on the relationship between the stage of pregnancy and the numbers of cells in the blood. I do not think that there are very important differences. There are somewhat more and larger cells in the blood specimens from early pregnancy than at term, but I am not sure that the difference is significant. It is nothing like so great as the difference between normal subjects and patients with eclampsia.

I have also been asked to comment on the antigenicity of the trophoblast. Is the trophoblast destroyed in the customary 10 to 12 days when it is transplanted between members of the same species? In part, I can answer this from personal experience. In guinea pigs which are not inbred, survival of the placenta implanted subcutaneously is somewhat longer than that of an ordinary skin graft. It is destroyed and rejected after about 20 days, instead of 12 days, which is the normal period in the guinea pig. Woodruff was unable to modify normal pregnancy; that is to say, he could not bring about rejection of the placenta itself by this type of immunization.

It is difficult to draw any conclusions at present about the antigens of the trophoblast itself, because no one has been able to provide us with a pure suspension of trophoblasts. In homograft experiments, and in the type of experiments which Dr. Coombs and I attempted a few years ago, much confusion is introduced by the presence of other tissue elements, including the stroma of the chorionic villi, and until we can get a pure suspension of trophoblast, it will be impossible to find out much more about the antigenecity of this tissue. It is worth noting that the placenta does contain some kind of antigen which gives rise to nephrotoxic signs, as was shown several years ago by Seegal. But we do not yet know the origin of the responsible antigen; it may be in the basement membrane or in the trophoblast.

REFERENCE

Seegal, B. C., and Loeb, E. N.: The production of chronic glomerulonephritis in rats by injection of rabbit anti-rat placenta, J. Exp. Med. 84:211, 1946.

DR. HEMMINGS: Dr. Coombs asked about the secretion of antibody. The answer must be that the uterine lumen may be regarded as a lymphatic component of the body, since the transfer of antibodies to and from the lumen has been shown to be massive. Davis has drawn attention to another special mechanism, in that the giant cells are budded off from the chorionic region, loaded with material and thereafter disintegrate in the uterus.

I would like to investigate Dr. Coombs's second question with suitable genetic material. Our data suggest that the breakdown of part of the protein as it crosses the splanchnopleure is definite in the case of homologous albumin and even more so for the alpha and the beta globulins. This suggests that the process of destruction happens nonspecifically to any protein, including gamma globulin, when it is absorbed into the cellular vacuoles. In acute experiments, one finds that the breakdown of protein, whether albumin or gamma globulin, is virtually instantaneous, quite contemporary with the transport of protein to the circulation.

Dr. Park referred to the permeability of the basement membrane. One must accept the fact that it is permeable to protein, but can hardly be the location of the selective process, since the exclusion by this membrane of the protein which is broken down would lead to the extracellular accumulation of this protein in the tissues. It is difficult to believe that the proteolysis which disposes of this protein is extracellular.

REFERENCE

Villee, C. A. (ed.): The Placenta and Fetal Membranes, p. 141, Baltimore, Williams & Wilkins, 1960.

DR. McLAREN: I was interested in Dr. Coombs's reference to the passage of immunologically competent cells from the mother to the fetus. Normally, this must be kept at a low level indeed, because when such cells are transferred experimentally, the result is a graft-against-host reaction—runt disease often accompanied by stunting of growth and even by death. I believe that the passage of blood cells from the mother to the fetus has been shown to occur occasionally in clinical material. In mice, it normally occurs rarely, if at all—certainly in less than 1.0 per cent of pregnancies.

In inbred strains of mice, any selective pressure against passage of cells from the mother to the fetus would be relaxed. Mother and fetus being genetically identical, no harmful results would follow from passage of immunologically competent cells from the mother to the fetus. But if an inbred female mouse were mated with a male of a different strain, so that the embryos were F_1 hybrids, the passage of cells from the mother to the fetus would become harmful again at once. Curiously, although F_1 mice show hybrid vigor and tend to be better than their inbred parents, in many strain combinations their early growth is poor. I wonder whether this negative heterosis may be due to the passage of cells from the mother to the fetus. This may happen more readily in inbred than in outbred animals, owing to the relaxation of selective pressure.

MODERATOR FLEXNER: Is there evidence concerning the nature of the milk factor?

DR. McLAREN: The fact that it can be transmitted via the milk and for several generations shows that it is infective. I believe that it also can be seen under the electron microscope, so it is evidently an infective particle. When does an infective particle become a virus? What further experimental data would be required to enable an answer to this question?

DR. PARK: Dr. Russell asks: Is there any correlation between the amount of lung trophoblast and the degree of placental infarction? I could answer this question confidently only if I had been able to examine the whole of the placenta in all 220 patients whose lungs were examined. In the absence of this information, I would say that probably there is no correlation between the amounts of trophoblast and infarction. If there were, it would be in the negative sense, because infarcted dead tissue loses its trophoblast and thereafter would not be a source of supply to the lungs.

Dr. Ikle asks: Is it possible that lethal cases of so-called amniotic fluid embolism are caused by very massive syncytial cell embolism without amniotic fluid? There is virtually no possibility of confusion here. I have seen sections from 12 or 15 cases of amniotic fluid embolism; it is easy to demonstrate amniotic debris in the pulmonary vasculature, and in no case were there any more particles of trophoblast than one might see in any patient dying during pregnancy. In the literature, there are reports of 4 women who died from massive trophoblastic embolism causing acute right heart failure. I have seen sections from 3 of these cases. There was no doubt that the obstruction was due to trophoblast—there was no amniotic debris.

SESSION VII

Physiologic and Medical Problems

Moderator

LOUIS M. HELLMAN, M.D.

Department of Obstetrics and Gynecology, State University of New York, College of Medicine, Brooklyn, New York, U.S.A.

Homeostasis of the Fetus

DONALD H. BARRON, Ph.D.

Professor of Physiology, Yale University School of Medicine, New Haven, Connecticut, U.S.A.

Fetal Wastage Associated with Placental Insufficiency

DONALD G. McKAY, M.D.

Professor and Chairman, Pathology Department, Columbia University College of Physicians and Surgeons, New York, New York, U.S.A.

Anencephaly in Dundee

PROFESSOR JAMES WALKER, B.Sc., M.B., Ch.B., M.D.

Department of Midwifery and Gynæcology, University of St. Andrew's, Dundee, Scotland, United Kingdom

Congenital Anomalies in Modern Clinical Medicine

JAMES L. WILSON, M.D.

Department of Pediatrics and Communicable Diseases, University of Michigan Medical School, Ann Arbor, Michigan, U.S.A.

Homeostasis of the Fetus

DONALD H. BARRON, Ph.D.

The current view that the mammalian fetus enjoys but a small margin of safety with respect to its oxygen supply appears to have its genesis in studies made in the early '30's by Eastman[10] in the United States, by Anselmino and Hoffman[1] in Germany, and by Barcroft[2] in England. The high hemoglobin content and the low oxygen saturation of the cord bloods he sampled from infants at delivery led Eastman to infer that the blood of the babe in utero is exposed during arterialization in the placenta to a low oxygen pressure, as is the blood in the lungs of the mountaineer. And in seeking the genesis of icterus neonatorum, Anselmino and Hoffman[1] saw in the changes in the blood of the infant at birth a similarity to those which occur in the acclimatized mountaineer when he returns to sea level. The high hemoglobin content of the blood is reduced rapidly in both the babe and the mountaineer—apparently as the result of exposure to the high oxygen tension in the atmosphere at sea level. It was this rapid change in the hemoglobin content of the blood of the neonate that led Anselmino and Hoffman to consider the possibility that the fetal blood in utero was exposed during arterialization to oxygen at a low tension and to seek further evidence in support of this theory.

As no estimates of the actual oxygen tension in the fetal blood were available at that time, Anselmino and Hoffman looked for other parallels between the dynamics of the cardiovascular-respiratory mechanisms of the fetus in utero and those then thought to characterize individuals or animals acclimatized to life at high altitudes. In their study they drew attention, apparently for the first time, though Haselhorst and Stromberger[12] made the same observation shortly thereafter, that the blood of the human fetus has a higher affinity for oxygen than the blood of the adult. This feature, they urged, represented an adaptation to the low oxygen pressure to which the fetal blood was exposed in the placental capillaries (that the oxygen dissociation curve of the adult shifted "to the left" in the acclimatized mountaineer had been suggested earlier). In the case of the mountaineer, the low oxygen tension in the arterial blood was due to the low tension in the source—the atmosphere. In the case of the fetus, the tension in the source—the maternal arterial blood—clearly was not low. Accordingly, Anselmino and Hoffman ascribed the low tension in the fetal blood to: (1) the relative impermeability of the tissues of the placental barrier and (2) to their oxygen consumption.

In the years that followed much of the relevant data accumulated served to strengthen the analogy drawn by Eastman[10] and by Anselmino and Hoffman[1] with respect to the availability of oxygen in utero and at high altitude. The suggestion was clearly a fruitful one.

1. The oxygen dissociation curves of the fetal blood of each mammalian species studied has been found to be "to the left" of the maternal—to have a higher oxygen affinity (man,[12,16] goat,[3,13] sheep,[7,17] cow,[24] llama,[24] rabbit,[8]). In some species this characteristic feature appears to be due to

the properties of the fetal hemoglobin. In others, the genesis of the difference remains to be established.

2. Utilizing these oxygen dissociation curves of the fetal bloods, it has been possible, knowing the degree of oxygen saturation of the bloods in the umbilical vessels, to estimate the oxygen tension in the fetal placental capillaries. And in all species studied thus far, the tension has been found to be as low as Eastman and Anselmino and Hoffman suspected.

3. Estimations have been made—by relating the degree of oxygen saturation to the appropriate dissociation curve—of the oxygen tension in both the maternal and the fetal placental bloods (cow,[25]; sheep,[7]; rabbit,[8]; goat,[23]; man,[22]) and so of the transplacental oxygen tension gradient. And, in most of the species studied, the gradient is high compared with that across the pulmonary epithelium. Finally, an effort has been made to correlate the steepness of the transplacental oxygen gradient with the number of tissue layers in the placental barrier.[9]

These lines of evidence all pointed, albeit indirectly, to a low permeability of the placental barrier as the factor responsible for the low oxygen tension in the fetal blood and to the inference that the fetus is adapted to a condition which it cannot regulate.

The relationship of the fetus to its oxygen supply was made to appear even more unfavorable as a result of the studies of Barcroft and his associates[5] on the blood flow to the pregnant uterus of the rabbit. They observed that the blood flow to the uterus increased as pregnancy advanced and in proportion to the placental rather than to the fetal weight. Both blood flow and placental weight reached their maximum about the 25th day of gestation, though the fetus doubles its weight in the 5 days thereafter. As the oxygen requirements of the fetus continue to increase after the 25th day when the supply reaches its maximum, the oxygen tension in the uterine venous blood

falls steadily until term. At birth, the oxygen requirements of the fetus already are approaching the limit of its supply, and if parturition is delayed by the administration of hormones, the fetus dies in utero, apparently from anoxia.[6] In this case at least, the blood flow to the uterus in the rabbit and so its oxygen supply do not appear to be regulated in terms of the oxygen requirements of its contents; the control exercised by the tissues in the uterus over their source of supply—the maternal blood—appears to contrast sharply with that of the other maternal tissue.

But there are other lines of evidence indicating that the fetus and its placental membranes are not impotent victims of their uterine environment; that, on the contrary, they exercise some degree of regulatory control over the rate of blood flow and so the oxygen transport to the uterus and the rate at which oxygen diffuses from the maternal to the fetal blood across the placental barrier, though the mechanisms through which these regulations are operated remain to be described.

One of the earliest suggestions that a component of the placenta could influence the availability of oxygen to the embryo by affecting the rate of blood flow to the uterus came from a study of the late Sir Joseph Barcroft[4] in which Dr. L. B. Flexner had a prominent role. Barcroft and his collaborators were studying the oxygen utilization of the rabbit uterus at selected stages in gestation. As a part of their procedure, Barcroft removed one ovary from each doe studied some days before they were mated. As a result of the unilateral ovariectomy, the fetuses were confined to one horn, and the investigators were able to compare the oxygen content of the blood leaving the nonpregnant with that emerging from the veins of the pregnant horn.

Important for our purposes are the observations of the early part of the gestation period —before the 20th day. On the pregnant side, with but one exception, blood samples drawn from the uterine vein draining the nonpregnant horn were not more than 65 per cent saturated, whereas the saturation in the samples drawn from the veins of the pregnant horn were all 65 per cent and higher. As the blood reaching the two horns was oxygenated to the same degree, it is clear that prior to the 18th day of gestation the coefficient of oxygen utilization ($\frac{A-V}{A} \times 100$) was greater in the nonpregnant horn than it was in the pregnant. That is to say, the blood flow-rate relative to the oxygen consumption of the tissues in the pregnant horn was higher than the flow-rate in the nonpregnant.

As both uterine horns were under the same systemic influences, the greater relative blood flow on the pregnant side appears to be due to some influence wrought locally by the placenta on the vascular net, perhaps through hormonal action. Their suggestion gains support from the recent demonstration by Fukushima[11] that the application of a trophoblast hormone to the vessels in the uterine ligament of the mouse results in a local vasodilatation which begins about 3 to 4 hours after administration.

In the early stages of gestation in the sheep and the goat, the uterine blood flow is high relative to the oxygen consumption of the organ and its contents[19] as it is in the rabbit for the coefficient of oxygen utilization of the uterus in these animals also is quite low until about the 60th day after insemination (full term 145 to 147 days). Whether this hyperemia is the result of fetal influences rather than maternal remains to be decided. In the period between the 60th day and term, the uterine blood flow in the sheep and the goat increases with the increased weight of the uterus and its contents and their metabolic requirements[20] i.e., the increase in flow tends to parallel the increase in oxygen consumption, though not slavishly, for the oxygen capacity of the maternal blood increases in many individuals in the final one third of the gestation period.[19]

This correlation between blood flow and metabolic rate in the later stages of gestation suggests that the two factors might be causally related as they are in the heart and the brain, and in a search for the link we have estimated the oxygen and the carbon dioxide tensions in uterine blood samples via indwelling plastic catheters in unanesthetized unstressed ewes for the patency of the small vessels—arterioles and capillaries—that might be expected to be determined by the concentrations of oxygen and carbon dioxide in the interstial fluids that bathe them, and the tensions of O_2 and CO_2 in the venous blood are accepted indices of their concentration in the interstitial fluids. The results offer little support for the view that the flow is regulated in terms of the oxygen tension of the maternal placental and uterine capillaries, but the narrow range through which the carbon dioxide tension varied was at least suggestive.

Accordingly, we attemped to vary the uterine blood flow acutely in unanesthetized ewes in the final one third of the gestation period by changing the composition of the inspired air and so the carbon dioxide and oxygen tensions in the blood reaching the uterus. The uterine blood flow was estimated by the Fick principle, using 4-amino-antipyrine as the test substance. The material was injected, and the arterial and the uterine venous blood samples were drawn via plastic catheters introduced at least 24 hours prior to the experiment in every case. In most cases, 2, and in some, 3 venous samples were drawn and compared.

Our efforts to change the uterine blood flow by these means have been unsuccessful thus far. We have not been able to effect a significant change in uterine blood flow by alterations in the carbon dioxide and the oxygen tension of the maternal blood of 20 minutes to 3 hours in duration. Yet, we have observed the uterine blood flow per unit weight of tissue to be significantly increased in ewes indigenous to high altitudes (14,000 to 15,000 ft.) and so chronically exposed to a low oxygen tension as compared with values which we obtained in a series of ewes at sea level. The oxygen and the carbon dioxide tensions in the arterial blood of our sea level series varied around 90 and 35 mm./Hg, respectively. At altitude, the oxygen tension in the maternal arterial blood varied between 43 to 47 mm./Hg; the carbon dioxide tension, from 22 to 26 mm./Hg. At altitudes, as at sea level, the total blood flow to the uterus increased during pregnancy at about the same rate as the uterine mass along a rising exponential curve to a maximum at the end of gestation. But the rate per unit mass of tissue was higher than it was in the animals at sea level. The mean rate at all stages in gestation was 303 cc./kg./min. in the sea level series as compared with 373 at altitude.[14]

In summary, such evidence as we have suggests that the blood flow to the uterus does increase as gestation advances in parallel with the tissue mass and less closely with the oxygen requirements because of the tendency for the oxygen capacity of the blood to increase in the last trimester of pregnancy. The mechanisms by which this parallelism is achieved probably involve growth-regulating hormones of placental origin, for acute changes in the concentrations of the respiratory gases in the maternal blood do not appear to affect flow-rate on the maternal side of the placenta, though a chronic change in their levels does, and probably by acting on growth processes.

Though the rate at which oxygen reaches the maternal side of the placenta does not appear to be regulated to maintain the tension of that gas in the maternal placental capillaries at or about a specific level, there is evidence to indicate that the perfusion of the fetal side of the placenta is so regulated.[21] That is to say, the oxygen tension in the fetal blood tends to remain fairly constant despite wide variations in the oxygen tension in the blood perfusing the maternal placental capillaries, the immediate source of supply. Put in still another way, it appears that the transplacental oxygen tension gradient is not fixed or determined by anatomic features of the placental barrier; rather, it appears to be functionally determined and regulated.

The evidence that suggests that the trans-

placental gradient of oxygen tension is regulated comes in part from a comparative study of the gradients as estimated at selected stages in gestation between the 90th day and full term—145 days in a series of pregnant ewes at sea level and another series at high altitude (15,000 ft.). A single comparison of conditions at 113 days will illustrate the results obtained. In the ewe at sea level, the oxygen tension in the blood of the uterine artery was 91.0 mm./Hg, in the uterine vein 49.3; the mean oxygen tension in capillary $(V_{pO_2} + \dfrac{A_{pO_2} - V_{pO_2}}{3})$ was 63.2 mm./Hg. The oxygen tensions in the umbilical vein and artery were respectively 19.5 and 13.5 mm./Hg; the mean tension was estimated to be 15.5 mm./Hg. The transplacental gradient or the difference in the mean oxygen pressures in the maternal and the fetal bloods was 47.7 mm./Hg. In the ewe that had lived her life at high altitude, the arterial oxygen tension was 47.0 mm./Hg when sampled at 15,000 feet; the oxygen tension in her uterine venous blood was 43 mm./Hg. The mean oxygen tension in the maternal placental capillaries as estimated was 44.3 mm./Hg, i.e., about 20 mm./Hg lower than the estimated mean in the maternal placental capillaries at sea level. By contrast, the oxygen tensions in the umbilical vein and the umbilical artery of the fetus carried by the ewe at high altitude were 18.0 and 14.5 mm./Hg respectively. That is to say, they were not significantly different from the oxygen tension in the umbilical vessels of the fetus whose mother was at sea level. Taking the mean oxygen tension in the fetal placental capillaries to be 15.6 mm./Hg, the difference in the mean tensions on the two sides of the placenta is 28.7 mm./Hg (44.3 to 15.6), or approximately 20 mm./Hg less than the difference at sea level.

The results of a study by Kaiser *et al.*[15] of pregnant ewes that had conceived and remained at or about sea level until about the 95th day of gestation showed that the lower transplacental oxygen gradient in the ewes indigenous to altitude was not the result of a species characteristic; nor was it due to chronic exposure to a low oxygen pressure prior to conception and throughout gestation rather than to the operation of regulatory mechanisms shared by individuals in the sea level series. At that stage, the ewes were transferred to low-pressure chambers and kept for 10 days at a pressure of 385 mm./Hg. At the end of the 10-day exposure, the oxygen tension of the fetal bloods, as judged from their oxygen saturation and pH levels, was not significantly different from sea level controls.

These observations suggest that the oxygen tension in the fetal blood is held fairly constant and at a low level; a level which appears to be quite similar in all mammalian fetuses that have been studied thus far. And the magnitude of transplacental oxygen pressure gradient thus appears to vary directly with mean oxygen pressure in the maternal placental capillaries. We are confronted by evidence indicating that the fetus maintains the oxygen tension in its blood at a low level; that it is not a victim of its environment, as the analogy between life at altitude and in utero would suggest. Why the fetus elects, as it appears to do, to develop in a low oxygen tension rather than the higher level characteristic of its adult life provides ample scope for speculation and investigation.

REFERENCES

1. Anselmino, K. J., and Hoffman, F.: Die Ursachen des Icterus neonatorum, Arch. Gynäk. **143**:477-499, 1930.
2. Barcroft, J.: The conditions of fetal respiration, Lancet 1933.
3. Barcroft, J., Elliott, R. H. E., Flexner, L. B., Hall, F. G., Herkel, W., McCarthy, E. F., McClurkin, T., and Talaat, M.: Conditions of foetal respiration in the goat, J. Physiol. **83**:192-214, 1934.
4. Barcroft, J., Flexner, L. B., Herkel, W., McCarthy, E. F., and McClurkin, T.: The utilization of oxygen by the uterus in the rabbit, J. Physiol. **83**:215-221, 1934.
5. Barcroft, J., Herkel, W., and Hill, S.: The rate of blood flow and gaseous metabolism of the uterus during pregnancy, J. Physiol. **77**:194-206, 1933.

6. Barcroft, J., and Young, I. M.: Internal oxygen environment of brains of postmature rabbit embryos, J. Exper. Biol. **21**:70-76, 1945.
7. Barron, D. H.: Some aspects of the transfer of oxygen across the syndesmochorial placenta of the sheep, Yale J. Biol. Med. **24**:169-190, 1951.
8. Barron, D. H., and Battaglia, F.: The oxygen concentration gradient between the plasmas in the maternal and fetal capillaries of the placenta of the rabbit, Yale J. Biol. Med. **28**:197-207, 1955.
9. Barron, D. H., and Meschia, G.: A comparative study of the exchange of the respiratory gases across the placenta, Symposia Quant. Biol. **19**:93-101, 1954.
10. Eastman, N. J.: Foetal Blood Studies. I. The oxygen relationships of umbilical cord blood at birth, Bull. Johns Hopkins Hosp. **47**:221-230, 1930.
11. Fukushima, Toshiaki: Studies on the trophoblastic hormones upon blood vessels in the side ligament of uterus of mice by biomicroscopy, Shikoku Acta Medica **15**: 86-93, 1959.
12. Haselhorst, G., and Stromberger, K.: Über den Gasgehalt des Nabelschnurblutes vor und nach der Geburt des Kindes und über den Gasaustauch in der Plazenta, Ztschr. Geburtsh. u. Gynäk. **100**:48-70, 1931.
13. Hellegers, A. E., Meschia, G., Prystowsky, H., Wolkoff, A. S., and Barron, D. H.: A comparison of the oxygen dissociation curves of the bloods of maternal and fetal goats at various pHs, Quart. J. Exp. Physiol. **44**:216-221, 1959.
14. Huckabee, W., Metcalfe, J., Prystowsky, H., Hellegers, A., Meschia, G., and Barron, D. H.: Uterine blood flow and metabolism in pregnant sheep at high altitude, Fed. Proc. **18**:72, 1959.
15. Kaiser, I. H., Cummings, J. N., Reynolds, S. R. M., and Marbarger, J. P.: Acclimatization response of the pregnant ewe and fetal lamb to diminished ambient pressure, J. Appl. Physiol. **13**:171-178, 1958.
16. Leibson, R. G., Likhnitsky, I. I., and Sax, M. G.: Oxygen transport of the foetal and maternal blood during pregnancy, J. Physiol. **87**:97-112, 1936.
17. Meschia, G., Hellegers, A., Blechner, J., Wolkoff, S., and Barron, D. H.: Oxygen dissociation curves of the bloods of pregnant sheep, fetal and newborn lambs at various pH's, Fed. Proc. **19**:379, 1960.

18. Meschia, G., Prystowsky, H., Hellegers, A., Huckabee, W., Metcalfe, J., and Barron, D. H.: Observations of the oxygen supply to the fetal llama, Quart. J. Exp. Physiol. (in press)

19. Meschia, G., Wolkoff, A. S., and Barron, D. H.: The oxygen, carbon dioxide and hydrogen-ion concentrations in the arterial and uterine venous bloods of pregnant sheep, Quart. J. Exp. Physiol. 44:333-342, 1959.

20. Metcalfe, J., Huckabee, W. E., Prystowsky, H., Hellegers, A., Meschia, G., and Barron, D. H.: Uterine blood flow in unanesthetized pregnant sheep, Fed. Proc. 17:111, 1958.

21. Metcalfe, J., Meschia, G., Hellegers, A. E., Prystowsky, H., Huckabee, W., and Barron, D. H.: Transfer of oxygen across the sheep placenta at high altitude, Fed. Proc. 18:104, 1959.

22. Prystowsky, H.: Fetal blood studies. VII. The oxygen pressure gradient between the maternal and fetal bloods of the human in normal and abnormal pregnancy, Bull. Johns Hopkins Hosp. 101:48-56, 1957.

23. Prystowsky, H., Meschia, G., and Barron, D. H.: The oxygen tension in the placental bloods of goats, Yale J. Biol. Med. 1960. (in press)

24. Roos, J., and Romijn, C.: Some conditions of foetal respiration in the cow, J. Physiol. 92:249-267, 1938.

25. ———: Problems of foetal respiration in the cow. II. The oxygen and the carbon dioxide content of maternal and foetal blood, Proc. Kon. Ned. Akad., Wet 43, 1940.

Fetal Wastage Associated With Placental Insufficiency

DONALD G. McKAY,* M.D., and ARTHUR T. HERTIG, M.D.

Fetal death early in gestation has been reported for several species. In litter-bearing animals, the total ovular loss may be due to death of whole litters as well as to death of individual fetuses in a surviving litter. Brambell[1] and Frazer[4] have reported the total loss of whole litters and loss of individuals in wild rabbits and in rats. Brambell[1] estimated the total loss of ova after ovulation (excluding that at parturition) as 43.3 per cent, of which 10.2 per cent are lost before implantation and most of the remainder before midterm with mortality reaching a maximum by the 12th postcoital day. Of this 43.3 per cent, the loss of ova in litters that do not survive is 35.7 per cent, and that in litters that do survive is 7.6 per cent. Thus, 82.1 per cent of ovular loss in wild rabbits is accounted for on the basis of total litter loss, whereas only 17.5 per cent ovular loss is due to the death of one or more of the embryos in litters that survive.

Frazer[4] examined the uteri of rats on the 9th postcoital day and counted the number of implantation sites and conceptuses. These rats were killed at term, and the numbers of fetuses noted. Of the mated females in strain C, 85.3 per cent were pregnant at the time of implantation (day 7); 72.9 per cent were pregnant on the 9th day. Between the 9th day and term (21 to 22 days) there was a 20 per cent loss of implanted ova (9% as whole litters, and 11% as individual fetuses). By studying the resorption of the placentas involved in this loss, Frazer estimated that 89 per cent of the fetal deaths occurred between the 9th and the 11th days of pregnancy.

Perry and Corner[2,9] reported embryonic mortality in the domestic pig from studies of the loss in surviving litters. Perry reported the total loss to be 40 per cent before parturition, with 85 per cent of this loss incurred in the first half of the gestation period, and 75 per cent of it incurred before the 25th day. Most of the loss probably occurred at or about the time of implantation, between the 10th and the 20th days.

The results of the study by Corner[2] of pathologic changes in the embryonic pig in litters which survive show a 30 per cent ovular loss by term. One third of this loss is due to ova which do not segment; one third is due to ova which develop into blastocysts and then degenerate; and one third due to ova which become abnormal during the subsequent course of pregnancy. The proportion of normal to abnormal ova increases towards term. This relative decrease in abnormal fetuses is due to the resorption and the subsequent disappearance of fetuses that die in early stages. The ovular loss in early stages of gestation in each species has been discussed by these authors on the basis of factors associated with genetic or maternal variations.

Studies of the macaque embryo, by Lewis and Hartman,[7] by Heuser and Streeter,[6] and by Corner and Bartelmez[3] have indicated the high rate of ovular loss in this primate.

The only study in the human of the first 2 weeks of development is that of Hertig et al.[5] This study, covering a period of nearly 17 years, concerns the search for human pregnancies of the first 2 weeks of development in a series of 210 known fertile women coming to therapeutic hysterectomy at the Free Hospital for Women. Although all of the 210 patients

---

* Present Address: Dept. Pathology, Columbia University College of Physicians and Surgeons, New York, U. S. A.

253

had had from 1 to 14 children and were by and large under the age of 40, menstruating regularly, and had reported 1 or more coital dates at about the time of estimated ovulation, only 107 were found to be optimal with respect to the probability of finding an early conceptus at hysterectomy. These optimal conditions consisted of: (1) demonstrated ovulation; (2) recorded coital dates within the 24 hours before or after ovulation (as judged from the endometrial morphology); and (3) the absence of pathologic conditions in the tubes, the ovaries or the uterus that would interfere with conception.

Of these 107 patients with optimal probability of finding an early conceptus at hysterectomy, 34 were found to have fertilized ova ranging from a 2-cell tubal ovum to a 17-day villous ovum implanted in early decidua. Of these ova, 24 were normal and 10 obviously were abnormal. The factors potentially responsible for the failure to find conceptuses in the 73 remaining patients in the "optimal" group are as follows: (1) error in technic; (2) ease or difficulty of finding a specimen in any given stage of development; (3) abnormality of the zygote with subsequent degeneration and/or failure of implantation; and, (4) failure of the ovum to become fertilized. Of 9 specimens searched for in the tube, only 1 was found. In contrast, the 15 patients who should have harbored segmenting intrauterine stages yielded 7 morulae or blastulae, 4 being abnormal and 3 normal. At first glance, it would seem that to find a tiny 200-micra object in a cavity the size of that of the uterus would be more difficult than finding an ovum in a tube. Actually, the technic is relatively easy, since the uterus is opened under saline; the heavy though invisible ovum sinks and is easily but blindly pipetted out into a dish. Finding the ovum is easy once the fluid containing it is examined under a binocular microscope at a magnification of 10 to 20 diameters. The implanting stage of the blastocyst apparently is difficult to find, since in 5 attempts none was found. Moreover, the recently implanted blastocyst is little easier to

discover as shown by the fact that in 25 attempts only 2 specimens were recovered. The stage of the implanted but covered and non-expanded blastocyst (days 23 to 24, when the ovum is in the 10th and the 11th days of development) also is difficult to find as shown by the fact that of 17 attempts only 3 ova were found.

In contrast, after day 25 in the menstrual cycle (day 12 in the development of the ovum) the ovum is easy to find, provided that the endometrial surface is not traumatized and is searched with care before and after fixation. Thus, of 36 specimens so examined, 21 ova were found, 15 of which were normal, and 6 abnormal. This period of the menstrual cycle in these specimens gives us the best opportunity to deduce the fertility rate of the patients who are known to be fertile, or to have had coitus at or about the time of ovulation and who are free of pathologic changes in the pelvis. Moreover, the proportion of abnormal to normal ova and the type of abnormality gives us some clue as to what must have happened to ova after ovulation and before the stage of implantation when the ovum is easy to find.

With respect to the patient's age, number of labors, number of abortions, and proportion of labors to abortions, the smaller series of 36 patients (derived from the 107) is quite comparable with the 73 patients who apparently failed to produce a fertilized ovum. Their failure lies in the failure of the ovum to become fertilized or in the disintegration of an ovum once fertilized. The 36 patients with a perfect coital history and no pathologic pelvic changes in whom 15 normal ova were found implanted on endometria 25 days or older show that the maximal normal fertility rate is 42 per cent at or about the time of the first missed menstrual period. The finding of 6 abnormal implanted specimens in this period advances the maximum total fertility rate to 58 per cent at implantation, since these specimens were able to implant even though abnormal. These are destined to abort at some time either at or after the first missed menstrual period.

It is impossible to say what proportion of abnormal fertilized ova will disintegrate and what number will implant. However, judging from the fact that one half of all the segmenting ova found were bad and about one third of the implanted ones after day 25 were bad, perhaps one half the bad ones might implant but would disintegrate subsequently. No one knows exactly what the gross fertility rate in any one stage of gestation is for 100 ova after ovulation and exposure to spermatozoa. However, from our data its maximum is 58 per cent, provided that all fertilized ova implant. In all probability, the gross fertility rate lies between 80 and 90 per cent. This supposition is in keeping with the finding of Corner that approximately 10 per cent of sow's ova fail to become fertilized, 10 per cent segmented but failed to implant, 10 per cent implanted but aborted, and 70 per cent went to term as viable, living fetuses. The fate of fertilized ova is roughly comparable in man and other mammals.

The cause or mechanism of these abnormal pregnancies remains unknown. From the standpoint of history and histology there was no evidence of an abnormal local or endocrine environment. Admittedly, these are gross methods of examination. Whatever the biochemical, immunologic or other possible mechanisms of damage either intrinsic in the nuclear material or extrinsic in the embryonic environment are, it is clear that a certain number of these eggs are associated with placental or trophoblastic insufficiency. The earliest evidence of an inadequate trophoblast comes from some of the youngest known ova thus far seen in the group studied by Hertig and Rock.[5] Four abnormal segmenting human ova have been found free in the uterine cavity. They were characterized by varying degrees of abnormality which was manifest by the presence of multiple nuclei, pyknotic nuclei, necrosis of cells and atypical size of the entire ovum. The specimens of the first

stages of implantation contain representatives which show trophoblastic anomalies. One of these (Carnegie No. 8329) was characterized by a defective trophoblastic shell with absence of the cytotrophoblast in addition to absence of the embryo in the chorionic cavity. Whether the ovum was better organized and had more of its normal component parts at some previous stage of development is impossible to say. However, it seems unlikely that in the segmenting stage any cavity or embryonic cells had been present. It has been shown by Heuser and Streeter[6] that the syncytiotrophoblast is the first definitive type of trophoblast to form at the embryonic pole after the monkey blastocyst implants on the endometrium; it forms from indifferent polar trophoblast nearest the maternal endometrium. Whatever the factor responsible, syncytiotrophoblast is the first recognizably differentiated form of trophoblast seen at the implantation pole of the ovum. The lack of cytotrophoblast or embryo and, more particularly, a chorionic cavity would tend to indicate that the preimplantation form of this ovum consisted of merely a few primitive trophoblastic cells that had the potential for forming syncytiotrophoblast. Whether this pregnancy would have caused the patient to miss her next menstrual period is impossible to say; but, the probable resulting lack of chorionic gonadotrophic hormone stemming from lack of cytotrophoblast makes it unlikely that this patient would have missed her next expected period. In all probability, the patient would have had a profuse, albeit somewhat delayed, period but no clinical evidence of pregnancy.

Hypoplasia of the chorion in later stages of implantation is another example of placental insufficiency detectable by anatomic examination. Carnegie ovum No. 7800 is an example of this condition. The trophoblast is extremely defective and consists of only a small but variable amount of syncytiotrophoblast. At this stage of development, 15 days, the chorion should have well-developed branching villi on the surface. Since the villi are derived from cytotrophoblastic growth and stimulation, this is another example of insufficiency of the cytotrophoblast. The embryo is essentially normal and possesses a bilaminar germ disk, yolk-sac and amnion. The type of implantation is normal for this stage of development and shows maternal hemorrhage exuding from the defect in the overlying decidua capsularis. The endometrium is normal for this stage of pregnancy and shows early decidual reaction around the ovum as well as elsewhere. The massive hemorrhage within the gland beneath the ovum is normal and is analogous to that which exudes from the surface of the implantation site (Hartman's sign). The clinical counterpart of this pregnancy has been observed in the Pathology Laboratory of the Boston Lying-in Hospital. Such specimens show a hypoplasia of chorionic development with subsequent bald areas where no villi have developed. This results in insufficient placental tissue to nourish an otherwise normal embryo. The latter then dies, becomes macerated, and the ovum aborts toward the end of the 1st trimester of pregnancy.

Evidence of an inadequate trophoblast or insufficiency of the placenta can be observed in a variety of abnormal processes throughout the entire 9 months of gestation.[8] In evaluating these disease processes, it is apparent that the majority are associated with death of the embryo or the fetus rather than with congenital malformations of the embryo. The abnormalities of the placenta in the early stages of human pregnancy represent congenital malformation of the trophoblast. From the clinical and the histologic standpoints, these are more likely to be due to alterations in nuclear components of the cells than to maternal environmental factors.

REFERENCES

1. Brambell, F. W. R.: Prenatal mortality in mammals, Biol. Rev. **23**:370, 1948.
2. Corner, G. W.: The problem of embryonic pathology in mammals, with observations upon intra-uterine mortality in the pig, Am. J. Anat. **31**:523, 1923.
3. Corner, G. W., and Bartelmez, G. W.: Early abnormal embryos of the Rhesus monkey, Contrib. Embryol. **35**:1, 1954.
4. Frazer, J. F. D.: Foetal death in the rat, J. Embryol. Exp. Morph. **3**:13, 1955.
5. Hertig, A. T., Rock, J., Adams, E. C., and Menkin, M. C.: Thirty-four fertilized human ova, good, bad, and indifferent, recovered from 210 women of known fertility. A study of biologic wastage in early human pregnancy, Pediatrics **23**: 202, 1959.
6. Heuser, C. H., and Streeter, G. L.: Development of the macaque embryo, Contrib. Embryol. **29**:15, 1941.
7. Lewis, W. N., and Hartman, C. G.: Tubal ova of the Rhesus monkey, Contrib. Embryol. **29**:15, 1941.
8. McKay, D. G., and Hertig, A. T.: Placental insufficiency, Bull. Margaret Hague Maternity Hosp. **10**:3, 1957.
9. Perry, J. S.: Fecundity and embryonic mortality in pigs, J. Embryol. Exp. Morph. **2**:308, 1954.

Anencephaly in Dundee, 1950-1959

PROF. JAMES WALKER, B.Sc., M.B., Ch.B., MD. and ALWYN SMITH

The obstetrician is concerned with fetal malformation for several reasons. As a clinician, he may have special problems in the management of pregnancy or delivery. He must consider not only the immediate psychologic trauma to the mother but also its effect on her attitude to future reproduction. Since his professional responsibility is the management of the later stages of reproduction, he is impressed by the frequency with which congenital malformation accounts for reproductive failure in the form of inviable or stillborn infants. But he is impressed also by the evidence that many malformations may have their origins in abnormal environmental conditions, either for the fetus within the uterus or for the mother in her social or physical surroundings. Thus, the obstetrician who supervises the early stages of pregnancy is in a position to make observations of possible etiologic significance and possibly in the future may be equipped to intervene so as to prevent fetal malformation from developing.

However, it often seems to the obstetrician that many of the observations used in epidemiologic studies of fetal malformation might be improved considerably if they were recorded by obstetricians aware of the uses to which they might be put subsequently. Accordingly, in Dundee, we are seeking to exploit the advantages of obstetric and epidemiologic approaches by instituting a combined study of fetal malformation of the central nervous system. In this paper we communicate some preliminary results respecting anencephaly.

MATERIAL AND RESULTS

The data refer to anencephalic infants born to women domiciled within the city of Dundee during the 10 years from 1950 to 1959. Anencephalic infants resulted from 111 pregnancies during this period, one pregnancy giving rise to concordantly affected male twins so that the total number of affected infants was 112. During the period, the total number of registered births was 33,596, so that the incidence of anencephaly at birth was 3.3 per 1,000 births. Of the 112 affected, 105 were registered as stillborn, 6 as neonatal deaths, and 1 was not registered (being born dead after a gestation period of less than 28 weeks). Thus, the stillbirth rate from anencephaly was 3.1 per 1,000 total births, and the neonatal death rate from anencephaly 0.18 per 1,000 live births. Anencephaly accounted for 12.7 per cent of the 825 stillbirths occurring in the period and for a little over 1 per cent of the neonatal deaths.

This incidence is a little higher than that reported for Scotland as a whole over a similar period. Although complete data for 1959 are not yet available, the incidence of legitimate anencephalic stillbirths in Scotland 1950 to 1958 was 2.9 per 1,000 births.

The Dundee data show a secular trend similar to that for Scotland in that incidence has increased over the period. If the decade of the Dundee inquiry is divided into the 2 5-year periods (1950 to 1954 and 1955 to 1958), incidences are 3.1 and 3.5 per 1,000, respectively. Similar figures for Scotland for 1950 to 1954 and 1955 to 1958 are 2.8 and 3.0. In the case of Scotland, the

257

latter figure is largely contributed to by the very high rate for 1958 (the most recent year available), when the incidence rose to 3.3 per 1,000. In Dundee, high incidences occurred in 1956 and in 1958.

Most authors have reported a high incidence in first-born. Edwards,[3] using data published by the Registrar General for Scotland, 1950 to 1956, showed that variation in the incidence among first-born was responsible for much of the secular variation in total incidence. In Dundee, there is no evidence of a raised incidence in first-born. Although we have been unable to obtain the maternal age- and parity-distribution for all Dundee births over the whole period of the inquiry, we have these data for 3,437 out of the 3,468 (99%) births in 1956. It is possible that there may have been secular variation in the maternal age- and parity-distribution of all births during the period 1950 to 1959 and the year 1956 may be unrepresentative. Although we have no reason to suppose that it is grossly unrepresentative, comparisons of the maternal age- and parity-distributions of affected births with all births for 1956 only must be treated with appropriate caution. Table 1 shows the distribution by maternal age and parity of affected and total 1956 births together with maternal age- and parity-specific incidences estimated from the distribution for

1956 births. This table suggests that there may be an association with primiparity at low maternal ages and an association with low maternal age at high parities. Standardization for maternal age reveals a regular association with increasing parity (Table 2),

TABLE 2. Observed and Expected* Distributions for Anencephalic Births According to Parity

Parity	Number Observed	Number Expected*	Difference
	(a)	(b)	(a) — (b)
1.............	33	35.3	—2.3
2.............	26	29.2	—3.2
3.............	13	19.3	—6.3
4.............	15	10.4	+4.6
5 +.........	24	16.9	+7.1
All parities....	111	111	—

*Number expected if the parity distribution of anencephalic births resembled that of the control group when the influence of maternal age is removed.

whereas standardization for parity reveals no regular association with maternal age (Table 3). The relative unimportance of maternal age is in accord with the findings of most authors who have been able to examine maternal age and parity separately. However, Coffey and Jessop[2] provide an exception, in that they regarded the association with maternal age as more important than that with parity.

What is more interesting in our data is

TABLE 1. Distribution of 111 Anencephalic and 3,437 Births by Maternal Age and Parity

		Maternal Age (Years)			
		Under 25	25 to 34	35 and Over	All Ages
Birth Order					
1	Cases........................	20	10	3	33
	Controls.....................	758	357	20	1,135
	Incidence per 1,000 births.........	2.7	2.8	15.2	2.9
2 + 3	Cases........................	13	20	6	39
	Controls.....................	485	945	127	1,557
	Incidence per 1,000 births.........	2.7	2.1	4.8	2.5
4 +	Cases........................	8	21	10	39
	Controls.....................	51	459	235	745
	Incidence per 1,000 births.........	15.9	4.6	4.3	5.3
Total	Cases........................	41	51	19	111
	Controls.....................	1,294	1,761	382	3,437
	Incidence per 1,000 births.........	3.2	2.9	5.0	3.3

TABLE 3. Observed and Expected Distribution of Anencephalic Births According to Maternal Age

Maternal Age (Years)	Number Observed	Number Expected*	Difference
	(a)	(b)	(a) — (b)
Under 19.....	8	5.9	+2.1
20 to 24.....	33	31.3	+1.7
25 to 29.....	26	33.4	−7.4
30 to 34.....	25	24.3	+0.7
35 and over...	19	16.2	+2.8
All ages......	111	111	—

*Number expected if the maternal age distribution of anencephalic births resembled that of the control group when the influence of parity is removed.

the evidence that there have been secular and seasonal changes in the association of incidence with parity. Although we are not in a position to compare secular changes in the parity distribution of affected births with any possible comparable changes in the related population of births, it is noteworthy that the proportion of first-born among affected births fell from 37.5 per cent in the period 1950 to 1954 to 25.0 per cent in the period 1955 to 1959. Data published by the Registrar General for Scotland for 1958 show that over-all incidence in this year was the highest yet recorded and that this was particularly true for births later than the first-born which showed the highest incidence on record. The incidence in first-born, although high, has been exceeded on several occasions. This association of a

relatively high proportion of later births with a high over-all incidence is shown in the seasonal distribution of our own series. Since anencephaly must be determined early in fetal life, we thought it more informative to examine the seasonal distribution of conceptions leading to anencephalic infants rather than the seasonal distribution of deliveries. In 106 cases, the menstrual data seemed sufficiently reliable to permit allocation of the date of the last menstrual period to a specific one quarter of the year. Table 4 shows these 106 cases distributed according to parity and to season and year of last menstrual period. Although numbers are small, it seems that the association of a high proportion of later-born children with a high total of anencephalics is fairly regular.

The change in the seasonal distribution of anencephaly in the more recent period deserves separate comment. Most of the increased incidence in the October to December quarter of the 2nd half of the decade is attributable to unusually high incidences in 1957 and 1958 conceptions. Insofar as 1957 is concerned, this is in accordance with the view of Coffey and Jessop[1] that influenza may be of etiologic importance, since there was an influenza epidemic at this time, but there was no undue prevalence of influenza during the last one quarter of 1958. It is interesting that data (unpublished) for Scotland in 1958 and 1959

TABLE 4. Season of Last Menstrual Period of 106 Pregnancies

Year of L.M.P.		Jan. to Mar.	Apr. to June	July to Sept.	Oct. to Dec.	All
1950 to 1953	1st born...............	3	5	5	2	15
	Later born.............	9	8	8	2	27
	Total.................	12	13	13	4	42
	Per cent 1st born........	25.0	38.5	38.5	50.0	35.7
1954 to 1958	1st born...............	6	0	5	5	16
	Later born.............	14	17	5	12	48
	Total.................	20	17	10	17	64
	Per cent 1st born........	30.0	0	50.0	29.4	25.0
All years 1950 to 1958	1st born...............	9	5	10	7	31
	Later born.............	23	25	13	14	75
	Total.................	32	30	23	21	106
	Per cent 1st born	28.1	16.7	43.4	33.3	29.3

TABLE 5. Distribution by Duration of Gestation and Parity of 99 Pregnancies Resulting in Anencephalic Fetuses

Duration of Gestation (Weeks)	Less Than 33	33 to 37	38 and Over	Total Known Duration
1st born	14	10	6	30
Later born	23	31	15	69
Total	37	41	21	99
Per cent 1st born	37.8	24.4	28.5	30.3

show an unusually high incidence of anencephaly during the summer months of both these years. This corresponds to a raised incidence in conceptions occurring in the last quarters of 1957, and of 1958. The only notifiable disease to show a higher than usual incidence in both these periods was mumps (infective parotitis), although the reported incidence was far from high.

Variation in the association of incidence with parity has been reported before, notably by Ingalls et al.[4] Using data from Rhode Island, they showed that there had been a secular change in the relative incidence in first-born and, also, that the raised incidence in first-born was limited largely to cases born after a short duration of gestation. The association of parity with duration of gestation also is shown by our series. In 99 cases, the menstrual data seemed to be recorded sufficiently reliably to enable duration of gestation to be stated to the nearest complete week. Table 5 shows the 99 cases by parity and by duration of gestation. The proportion of first-born is higher in cases born after a short gestation period.

Ingalls et al.[4] stated that secular variations in the association of incidence with parity suggested that the association was more likely to reflect features of the social and physical environment of the mother than physiologic or pathologic changes in the uterine environment associated with pregnancy order. But such a view offers little to explain the association of primiparity with duration of gestation. MacMahon and McKeown[5] showed that sex ratio was associated with duration of gestation, but that the association was limited to cases in which hydramnios was recorded. Therefore, it is of interest to inquire whether the association of parity with duration of gestation is restricted similarly. In our data, the proportion of first-born showing hydramnios was 90.9 per cent compared with 73.1 per cent in later-born. The difference (17.8%) is conveniently significant at the 5 per cent level. Table 6 shows the distribution of hydramnios by parity and duration of gestation. For both first-born and later-born the frequency of hydramnios is lowest in cases in which the pregnancy proceeded to a nearly normal duration, and the propor-

TABLE 6. Distribution by Duration of Gestation and Presence of Hydramnios of 111 Pregnancies Resulting in Anencephalic Fetuses

		Less Than 33	33 to 37	38 and Over	Gestation Not Known	Total
First-born	Hydramnios recorded	14	10	4	2	30
	Total	14	10	6	3	33
	Per cent with hydramnios	100.0	100.0	66.7	66.7	90.9
Later-born	Hydramnios recorded	17	26	7	7	57
	Total	23	31	15	9	78
	Per cent with hydramnios	73.9	83.9	46.7	77.7	73.1
Total	Hydramnios recorded	31	36	11	9	87
	Total	37	41	21	12	111
	Per cent with hydramnios	83.8	87.8	52.4	75.0	78.4

tion with hydramnios is lower for later-born than for first-born at all durations of gestation. However, there are no cases of first-born without hydramnios at the shorter gestations and only 2 at the longer gestations, so that it is difficult to decide whether the association of primiparity with duration of gestation is limited to cases with hydramnios. The data are consistent with such a view but do not support it. However, the data do support the finding of Mac-Mahon and McKeown[5] that association of sex ratio with duration of gestation is limited to cases with hydramnios (Table 7). The frequency of hydramnios is greater in affected females, but the difference is not statistically significant.

Therefore, it is possible that the associations of sex and parity with duration of gestation may be dependent on sex and parity differences in the frequency of hydramnios. Hydramnios leads to early termination of pregnancy either because the mechanical effect results in early onset of spontaneous labor or more frequently because hydramnios leads to a diagnosis of fetal abnormality and the pregnancy is terminated by the obstetrician. In the absence of hydramnios, pregnancy may proceed more often to term. It is possible that cases with hydramnios are etiologically different from cases without, and that the differences also are associated with sex and parity. In this context, it is of

interest to examine some special groups of cases.

For example, 6 cases in our series were born alive. These include 4 males and 2 females and are morphologically heterogenous in that 2 cases were described at postmortem examination as cases of cranium bifidum and not true anencephaly. If the 7 heaviest of the affected infants, for whom detailed postmortem findings are on record, are considered, we find the following:

1. Only 1 (the lightest) had hydramnios.
2. None had spinal rachischisis.
3. The 3 heaviest were examples of cranium bifidum.
4. The 3 lightest were true anencephalics.

These 7 consisted of 4 males and 3 females.

It is of some interest to note that Coffey and Jessop[1] showed that the sex ratio was nearly 50 per cent in cases born alive or recently dead and of approaching normal weight.

Our 111 pregnancies giving rise to anencephalic fetuses related to only 105 women, since 6 had each had 2 pregnancies leading to affected infants within the series. Two others had other anencephalic infants without the series. Of the 8 women who have had more than 1 anencephalic infant, 3 also have had infants with hydrocephaly. Of the remaining 97 mothers, 5 had infants with spina bifida, in other pregnancies. Thus, of 105 mothers of anencephalic in-

TABLE 7. Sex Ratio by Duration of Gestation With and Without Hydramnios
Duration of Gestation (Weeks)

		Less Than 33	33 to 37	38 and Over	Gestation Not Known	Total
Hydramnios recorded	Males..............	5	7	5	2	19
	Females............	26	29	6	7	68
	Total..............	31	36	11	9	87
	Per cent Males.......	16.1	19.4	45.5	22.2	21.8
Hydramnios not recorded	Males..............	2	3	3	1	9
	Females............	4	2	7	2	15
	Total..............	6	5	10	3	24
	Per cent Males.......	33.3	60.0	30.0	33.3	37.5
Total	Males..............	7	10	8	3	28
	Females............	30	31	13	9	83
	Total..............	37	41	21	12	111
	Per cent Males.......	18.9	24.4	38.1	25.0	25.2

fants, 13 have had other infants with central nervous system malformation.

Record and McKeown[6] reported that the incidence of central nervous system malformation in subsequent sibs of affected individuals was some 6 times the incidence expected when the associations of incidence with maternal age and parity and the secular variations in incidence were taken into account. Although our methods of ascertainment preclude similar calculation of recurrence rates, there can be little doubt that our data support the finding that there is an undue concentration of incidence in some fraternities.

Whether such a familial concentration provides support for a genetic causal hypothesis or whether it is interpreted as evidence that the environmental agencies tend to persist in their association with mothers of affected, there is little doubt that it confronts the obstetrician with a difficult problem when he is asked to advise about the prognosis for future reproduction in affected families. Therefore, we should like to consider the data from the point of view of the obstetrician facing this problem.

Thirty-three mothers had anencephalic infants at their first pregnancy. In 2 instances we have no further record; in 9 cases there have been no further pregnancies; since then 12 mothers have had normal infants. Ten have followed with abnormal pregnancies. Three have had early abortions; 2 have had stillbirths from other causes than CNS malformation; 5 had hydrocephaly, anencephaly or spina bifida in subsequent infants. Of these, 1 had an anencephalic at her 2nd pregnancy, 2 had hydrocephalics at the 2nd and anencephalics at the 3rd pregnancies, and 1 had a normal child at her 2nd pregnancy followed by an anencephalic at her 3rd.

Of 26 mothers who had had anencephalics at the 2nd pregnancy, 9 subsequently have had a normal reproductive history, 10 have had no further pregnancy to date, and 6 have had malformed infants including 4 anencephalics, a mongoloid defective and a case of cleft palate. One other mother's only subsequent pregnancy ended in abortion.

In mothers having an anencephalic infant at their 3rd pregnancy, this proved to be an isolated instance if previous pregnancies had been normal. In 10 cases where the 1st or the 2nd pregnancy had ended with an affected birth (meningocele, spina bifida, hydrocephaly or anencephaly), normal infants followed at the 4th or later pregnancies. In one case, recurrent deformity occurred at later pregnancy.

It is difficult to resist the following tentative conclusions:

1. Of those mothers who have an anencephalic infant in a 1st or a 2nd pregnancy, there is a small group who continue to have infants with CNS malformation, but in whom normal infants may occur in later pregnancies.

2. However, in 90 per cent of women, anencephaly is an isolated phenomenon which does not recur.

3. Several CNS malformations seem to be related to anencephaly in that they show a tendency to concentration in fraternities in which anencephaly has occurred.

4. Prognostically, anencephaly in primigravidae is serious. If the mother is elderly, she may be unable or unwilling to embark upon further pregnancy, and if she is young, there would seem to be a 15 to 20 per cent chance of producing a series of malformed infants.

In conclusion, we feel that there is evidence that secular variation in the incidence of anencephaly may be attributable to differences in the relative proportions of etiologically distinct varieties of the diseases which, however, resemble one another sufficiently to be commonly classified under one heading. These etiologically distinct varieties may exhibit different associations with sex, parity, seasons and hydramnios and may be in association with different intra-uterine survival.

There is some morphologic evidence in favor of this view; the familial concentration of central nervous system malformation is consistent with the view that not all varieties are familial.

We can find no consistent evidence of association of incidence with maternal influenza, but the possible etiologic importance of maternal infection certainly cannot be discounted.

From the point of view of the clinician, anencephaly, particularly in primigravidae, presents a difficult problem for prognostic counseling.

We acknowledge gratefully the help given to this investigation by many who have charge of mothers of the affected children and, in particular, that of Dr. Fulton and her staff in the Health Department of Dundee.

REFERENCES

1. Coffey, V. P., and Jessop, W. J.: A three years study of anencephaly in Dublin, Irish J. M. Sc. **393**:391, 1958.
2. ————: Maternal influenza and congenital deformities, Lancet **2**:935, 1959.
3. Edwards, J. H.: Congenital malformations of the central nervous system in Scotland, Brit. J. Prev. & Social Med. **12**:115, 1958.
4. Ingalls, T. H., Pugh, T. F., and MacMahon, B.: Incidence of anencephalus, spina bifida and hydrocephalus related to birth rank and maternal age, Brit. J. Prev. & Social Med. **8**:17-23, 1954.
5. MacMahon, B., and McKeown, T.: Note on the sex ratio in encephalus, Brit. J. Soc. Med. **6**:265, 1952.
6. Record, R. G., and McKeown, T.: Congenital malformations of the central nervous system. II. Maternal reproductive history and familial incidence, Brit. J. Social Med. **4**:(No. 1) 37, 1950.

Congenital Anomalies in Modern Clinical Medicine

JAMES L. WILSON, M.D.

It is fitting that the attention of this First International Conference on Congenital Malformations has been and will be largely directed toward the consideration of the scientific basis for the cause and the pathogenesis of these anomalies. The malformations with which we are concerned result from complex interactions of genetics and intra-uterine disease and only through a better understanding of these problems can prevention be effected. However, the practitioners of medicine have no opportunity to study, diagnose, or understand intra-uterine disease or the ability to control genetic factors.

The physician each day is faced with infants who, if they could, would complain like Shakespeare's King Richard, "Deformed, unfinished, sent before my time into this breathing world scarce half made up." Now we must ask, "What are we going to do?"

The problem of the care of these patients is immediate. Although effective attempts in prevention still may be found, this lies in the future, and it is right that this Conference should pay some attention to the present situation as it exists, give thought to the importance of the present incidence of children with congenital anomalies in ordinary practice, mention some of the things that can be accomplished at present to aid them and emphasize the problems that face us in their long-continued care.

Several things make the problem of care of these abnormal infants more frequent and burdensome in practice now than it was a few years ago. One is that with the well-publicized advances of medicine and the in-

crease in the public's sophistication, the people themselves are demanding more aid in their difficulties. Conditions which years ago were seen as simple acts of God to be accepted patiently are being looked upon as possibly remediable, and no physician can avoid the insistent appeal of parents for aid in any circumstance where abnormality results. This action of the public is inevitable and natural, and in my own country at least is increased enormously by the many medically oriented articles which appear in every popular magazine.

Another factor that makes the problems of the abnormally formed child more prominent than before is the decreased incidence of other disease. Mortality and morbidity from infectious and nutritional disease in infancy has been reduced greatly by public health methods and by the direct medical care of individuals. Except in the neonatal period, we can look with great satisfaction on reduction of disease, but this has changed the character of our practice. As an example, in the infants' ward of my own large teaching hospital, something like 90 per cent of all the patients referred in for care are sent because of congenital malformations. This is not a fair reflection of the hospital problems all over the country, because a teaching hospital receives a disproportion of difficult patients; but it gives some impression of the changing emphasis and demands for care. A few years ago the wards would have been filled with acute and chronic nutritional problems, septicemia, bronchopneumonia and mastoiditis. Those with bad congenital heart disease and hydrocephalus would not have been admitted except to die quickly.

Another and correlated factor is the longer life of these infants with handicapping abnormalities. Advances in effective medical treatment of infectious and nutritional diseases have resulted in a greatly increased survival of children with abnormalities who a few years ago would have been lost sight of under the burden of a great incidence of other serious diseases and soon would have died instead of surviving, as they do now, to compel our attention to their problems for a lifetime. Each successful step that we take to correct or ameliorate these conditions leads to a happy prolongation of life but also to a prolonged medical problem. Any attempts toward alleviating the condition that are less than immediately and completely successful will add to the burden of medical care for years to come.

A mere listing of the congenital malformations for which we now have some form of treatment would be of little value, nor would we have time to do it. We may mention in passing the common and old problems of cleft palate and harelip and clubfeet as examples of those that have been handled with satisfaction. It would be better to prevent them, but we can be happy with how successful and complete the care for them can be in early life. However, even here, we have some residual and long-continuing psychological problems, some training problems in speech, which add to the burden of their total medical care.

It is now almost 20 years since the first successful survival occurred in the repair of a child born with an esophageal stenosis or tracheo-esophageal fistula. Now, in many of our hospitals, these most difficult operations are taken in their stride, and a high percentage are treated successfully, although the utmost of medical and clinical skill is required. Often, painstaking and prolonged efforts are necessary, though ultimate success occurs in a very high percentage of these cases, and no permanent gross handicap results, unless it is the psychological one resulting from the trauma to which they have been subjected for so long. However, among this group still are those who require treatment over many months for dilatation of their esophagus or for septic complications of their operations. The burden of cost of this often is too much for the average citizen to bear without aid even in a wealthy country.

At present, a most astonishing and dramatic surgical success has occurred in the repair of congenital abnormalities of the heart and the great vessels. This work has been so greatly publicized that there is little need to expand upon it. The development of the necessary surgical procedures has been dependent upon our ability to sustain life by artificial circulation technics which will be useful for many other purposes, and the development of procedures for lowering the metabolism by hypopyrexia. Before surgery is carried out, we now are able to probe with a catheter into each chamber of the heart and to determine the oxygen saturation and the blood pressure there; by x-ray cineography we can trace a mass of radiopaque material through the great vessels and the heart; we can even insert microphones directly into the chambers of the heart to study the origin of sounds which we are used to studying with the classic stethoscope. It is possible now for time-consuming and elaborate "plumbing" rearrangements to be made within the heart itself and to accomplish this with a relatively low mortality. The development of artificial hypothermia, as well as the artificial heart, has expanded enormously the opportunities for a surgeon to make repairs with more leisure than before and therefore with nicer results. However, only the years are going to tell us how many of these children who have been improved by surgical manipulation of the structures of the heart will live through a normal duration of life. Obviously, the total amount of medical care expended upon these individuals will become greater because of their survival and longer life.

Some of the birth defects producing gruesome deformities are those of the central nervous system and its enclosures leading to meningoceles or meningo-encephaloceles and to hydrocephalus. Important steps in treatment have been made here, though it seems probable that we will look back on them soon as crude, even meddlesome medicine, because certainly they are of limited success as yet, and again a success which can be surely evaluated only as the years go by. Various shunting procedures have been developed to bring in balance the production and the absorption of spinal fluid and to arrest progressive hydrocephalus and prevent subsequent brain damage which is irreversible. The Holter valve with its modifications seems at the moment to be the most promising technic, but here great secondary problems arise not only from failure of the bypassing tube to remain open but also because of secondary infections. Perhaps the greatest problem of all is the determination when to use this rather radical, though technically simple, procedure. To use it early enough to prevent any possible brain damage brings us to the risk of doing it on some infants unnecessarily, and the fact that spontaneous arrest of early and mild hydrocephalus can occur must enforce caution. The use of these technics demands the greatest clinical skill in judgment in order that no harm should be done to many children in order to prevent harm to some. The diagnosis of early and presently progressing hydrocephalus requires skill and knowledge unfortunately often lacking in some of the enthusiastic attempts to institute early treatment.

The treatment of meningocele and meningomyelocele still is beset with a high percentage of failure in those in which the cord itself is, or can be, damaged, but the treatment of this condition as well as hydrocephalus is resulting in increasing success.

Here again, however, successful attempts to prevent death lead us to far greater problems to make that life useful and happy over the years. Paralysis of the legs, fecal and urinary incontinence, mental damage and cerebral palsy, all obviously present major problems that demand skillful and long-continuing care from many medical specialists.

Perhaps much more exciting and promising to many of us than the gross anatomic abnormalities are more subtle congenital chemical abnormalities, or, as some have called them, molecular diseases. These are exciting scientifically because as we begin to understand them, they bring us closer to knowledge of many new details of cellular physiology. As many as 50 varieties of diseases related to dysfunction in minute areas in the collecting tubules of the kidney are described, often associated with other abnormalities. The diseases are highly complicated, but we are all learning to give a little help.

Disturbances in the handling by the body of a single protein or of a single carbohydrate molecule, due probably to the congenital absence of a single enzyme, are being recognized. A simple enzyme defect can cause a distortion of sexual development, called pseudohermaphroditism, and consequent to this, a disturbance in water and salt balance that soon could be fatal. Early recognition can lead to very effective treatment. We can mention only the names of other such conditions as phenylketonuria, cystinosis, or dysfunction of glycogenesis, which are now well known. There are many disturbances of amino acid metabolism now being identified as the cause of mental disturbances of congenital origin. At the moment we must admit that although we can modify these diseases and can keep a child with glycogen storage disease from having constant hypoglycemic convulsions, can keep a child with tubular function defect from having a maximum degree of rickets or bone deformities from rachiticlike processes, we are a long way from being happy and satisfied with our success.

There are quite a few conditions which we can correct satisfactorily if early diagnosis is made and where early diagnosis is very simple to make. It looks as if by proper dietary programs, presently expensive but still practical, we could prevent brain damage from phenylketonuria, provided that we detect this very early in infancy by a simple urine test. Also, it is quite easy to prevent damage from such a disease as galactosuria where there is an abnormal handling of the sugar, galactose, if an early diagnosis is made, again quite simply by urinalysis.

We can prevent many cases of irreparable damage to the kidneys of a boy if we could detect early in his life that his urinary stream is weak, which would give us a lead to the fact that he has a partial urethral obstruction. Usually, we see these children only after they become very sick because of resulting renal destruction. Thus, these serious congenital malformations can be prevented from causing damage by a routine examination of a small baby's urine for sugar, or for phenylketones, or observations of the urinary stream, procedures which require only the simplest of observations. However, any procedure is difficult to carry out in all children regardless of its simplicity. The administrative problem of extending successfully these routine examinations to every infant is indeed a great one. Merely putting our hands on every infant of a community for any kind of examination is difficult. Though it is a matter for simple observation by a physician, an enormous public health organization is necessary to get these simple observations accepted by all parents and carried out routinely. Here we face the problem of routine and careful health surveys of all infants, carried out as a public health procedure. Theoretically, we would need 10,000 urine examinations, each of which might take as little as a minute to do, before one case of early phenylketonuria is discovered, but if we saved one brain, it would be worth it as the total cost would not be great.

Indiscriminate and wide extension of certain diagnostic steps routinely carried out without a parental report of clinical complaint costs a great deal and even carries with it some risk. Many investigative procedures are expensive and intrinsically dangerous, such as those that demand exposure to x-rays. There is another danger that exists always when we hunt for trouble without a complaint from our patient—that we will discover a variation from normal that in fact is not causing any trouble and will remain harmless, but which we are tempted to treat. An enormous amount of meddlesome surgery may easily be initiated by uncritical thoroughness.

In the rapid progress of ameliorative procedures, lifesaving in nature, we build up for ourselves other problems which we must clearly face, which are going to demand perhaps far greater total expense than the original problem. A life saved by early treatment may well be still a handicapped life. It cannot be overemphasized that the care of many patients in what is referred to so glibly as a multidisciplinary approach can be remarkably effective, but often the multidisciplinary approach fails because no one person continues to be the family doctor-adviser and follows the patient over the years while the specialists, the neurosurgeon, the thoracic surgeon, the neurologist, the physiotherapist, the metabolism expert, all are co-operating wisely and effectively in the emergency of early treatment. To treat a meningo-encephalocele successfully at the moment, but leaving the child with paralyzed legs, offers a lifetime problem for which someone must assume continuous medical responsibility. Not only must such individuals be protected from emotional disturbances, but they must be specially educated. The family must be prepared by very wise and thoughtful advice and guidance over many years. What can be an unhappier result than that of a persistent fecal incontinence found in a 12-year-old girl, whose life at birth was victoriously saved from the results of an imperforate anus, but whose anal sphincter, if it ever existed, was lost in the lifesaving operation. Who is the one to follow such an individual over the years after surgical procedures are exhausted, to aid the parents and the school teachers to allow that child to live a normal life and avoid the severe psychological harm that usually occurs. The handicapped child, life successfully saved, may well hate us in the future as it faces the competitions of life when the adolescent and the adult pressures begin to weigh upon it.

I am reminded of the problems we faced in acute poliomyelitis when, with the respirator, we began to save triumphantly the lives of those who had respiratory muscle paralysis, only to see some of the most tragic situations imaginable, grossly handicapped, yet living individuals, utterly dependent on others constantly for their existence. However, terrible as this problem was, we learned to do much to alleviate it even though complete success is far from us. This is true of many of the other types of conditions which face us and will continue to face us in increasing numbers as partial success, which is always our first accomplishment, occurs in the treatment of handicapping conditions. We can wonder with a little dread if in the future at some time we will succeed in preventing only some part of intra-uterine disease which would result ordinarily in fetal death, and whether we will be presented with an increasing number of individuals, "scarce half made up" for complete and independent life. A recent summary by Doctor Bronson Crothers in his book *The Natural History of Cerebral Palsy* where he relates his experiences with individuals over many, many years, contains shocking examples where early success in treatment, only to be followed by desperately unhappy lives as adults, because of the lack, perhaps sometimes inevitable, of thoughtful and effective continual medical follow-up care.

To summarize: the pediatrician and the general physician are faced more and more with children who in past years would not have survived but who do now with great handicaps which will require long-continued supervision in care, with the greatest of surgical, medical and psychological skills. In a civilization where active enthusiasm for, or even passive omission of, lifesaving procedures is considered abhorrent, as it is to me, the burdens of partial medical success must be expected to be expensive and distressing.

SESSION VII

Discussion

Moderator

LOUIS M. HELLMAN, M.D.

*Department of Obstetrics and Gynecology, State University of New York,
College of Medicine, Brooklyn, New York, U.S.A.*

Panel Members

EDITH L. POTTER, M.D.

*Department of Obstetrics and Gynecology, University of Chicago School
of Medicine, Chicago, Illinois, U.S.A.*

RICHARD L. MASLAND, M.D.

*Director, National Institute of Neurological Diseases and Blindness,
Bethesda, Maryland, U.S.A.*

PROFESSOR MARIJ AVČIN, M.D.

Professor of Pædiatrics, University of Ljubljana, Ljubljana, Yugoslavia

DONALD H. BARRON, Ph.D.

*Professor of Physiology, Yale University School of Medicine,
New Haven, Connecticut, U.S.A.*

PROFESSOR JAMES WALKER, M.D., F.R.C.O.G.

*Department of Midwifery and Gynecology, St. Andrew's University,
St. Andrew's Fife, Scotland, United Kingdom*

DONALD G. McKAY, M.D.

*Professor and Chairman, Pathology Department, Columbia University,
College of Physicians and Surgeons, New York, New York, U.S.A.*

DR. POTTER: I have been particularly interested in differences in the frequency of malformations in Chicago and in Scotland. The number of deliveries—approximately 3,500 per annum—is about the same in our own hospital as in Dundee. During the last 25 years, I have been able to examine all stillbirths and infant deaths in our hospital. Autopsies were performed in 95 per cent of them.

A chart of the frequency of malformations in relation to all causes of death during a 25-year period reveals that perinatal mortality from all causes fell from 40 (per thousand) to 19 in this period. There has been no significant change in the frequency of malformations. In the last 5 years, their incidence was 3.3 (per thousand), approximately the figure reported by Dr. Walker for anencephalus alone in Dundee.

Next, we listed causes of death in relation to maturity (assessed on the basis of weight): malformations rank first of all causes of death in births over 2,500 grams, and third in lighter weight births.

An analysis of the frequency of malformations showed that those of the central nervous system account for 40 per cent.

Subdivision of the central nervous system malformations indicated that of 133 affected in a 20-year period, 58 were anencephalics. This is approximately one quarter of the incidence reported by Dr. Walker. In our hospital, cases are quite unselected in relation to malformations.

Anencephalus and spinal rachischisis were found in one twin of a presumptively monozygotic pair in which the other was normal. A normal surviving child was found with an anencephalic twin; the vessels of the abnormal child arose from the vessels of the normal twin. An example of a single chorion, a single placenta, with 2 amnions is shown. One child of this pregnancy had multiple malformations, including renal agenesis and an absence of the terminal portion of the intestine. Hence, it is important to recognize that even when twins are de-

rived from the same egg, the arrangement of the chorionic tissue and of the placenta may result in differences in development during intra-uterine life. So, while we have no example of anencephalus in nonidentical twins, the malformation has occurred in 3 apparently monozygotic pairs with 1 normal and 1 abnormal child.

Differences between Dr. Walker's results and our own are not only in respect of frequency. He reported a higher incidence of recurrence in subsequent pregnancies. Probably, there is also a difference in frequency of associated malformations, which were present in only 15 per cent of our anencephalics.

There is more than one type of anencephalus. Those in which there is diffuse involvement of the spinal area as well as the brain show a much higher proportion of females than of males. Moreover, some of these children appear to be normal except for the abnormality of the central nervous system. Almost all anencephalics have extreme hypoplasia of the adrenal gland, but in 2 fetuses of about 14 and 16 weeks' gestation, the adrenal glands were entirely normal for that period of development. Indeed, they were heavier and better developed than the adrenal glands of the typical anencephalic fetus at the time of death.

MODERATOR HELLMAN: Is there any relation between the time of ovulation and fertilization in the menstrual cycle and the incidence of congenital malformations?

DR. POTTER: We have no means of establishing accurately the time of ovulation. There is experimental evidence that aging of the egg is responsible for a high frequency of early death and malformation and, possibly, it is related also to the increasing frequency of malformations born to older women (since the frequency of their sexual intercourse is relatively low).

DR. MASLAND: We need to know much more about the mother of the malformed child. Mortality before birth is high, and the question arises whether it is due primarily to the mother or to the fetus. Several lines of evidence point to the significance of the maternal environment.

1. Fetal growth is retarded in late pregnancy, and probably this is due to limitations of the resources of the uterus.

2. As reported by Raïha and others, prematurity is common when maternal heart size is small, particularly if the mother also has anemia.

3. The recurrence of malformations, especially of the central nervous system in children of the same mother, also is suggestive.

4. The fact that the twin of a defective child usually is normal indicates that the defect cannot be attributed solely to inheritance.

5. Record and McKeown showed that there was a raised incidence of abnormal pregnancy preceding the one which resulted in an anencephalic birth.

6. Stillbirth rates examined by Yerushalmy indicated that there is a favorable age period in respect to each parity.

REFERENCES

1. Raïha, C. E., Lind, J., Johanson-Unnerus, C. E., Kihlberg, J., and Vara, P.: Relationship of premature birth to heart volume and hemoglobin percent in pregnant women, Ann. Paediat. Fenniae 2:69-74, 1956.
2. Record, R. G., and McKeown, T.: Congenital malformations of the central nervous system. II. Maternal reproductive history and familial incidence, Brit. J. Social Med. 4:26-50, 1950.
3. Yerushalmy, J.: On the interval between successive births and its effect on survival of infant. I. An indirect method of study, Human Biol. 17:65-106, 1945.

DR. AVČIN: In view of the high incidence of congenital malformations, an extensive program of prevention and treatment has been introduced in Yugoslavia. The main features are:

1. Early registration of pregnant women.
2. Regular examination at antenatal clinics. Women are examined at least 3 times during pregnancy. In addition to full clinical investigation and care, particular attention is given to hygiene, nutrition, genetic counseling and health education. In our experience, legalized abortion has been of little value in the prevention of congenital abnormalities.

3. Care of handicapped children. The program includes: (A) diagnosis, classification and registration; (B) medical and surgical treatment; and (C) rehabilitation.

MODERATOR HELLMAN: I would provide evidence that fetal homeostasis exists in man as well as in the sheep.

Various stimuli affect fetal heart rates in the last trimester of normal pregnancy. These rates vary by 7 to 10 beats per minute. After inhalation of 12 per cent oxygen, the fetal heart rate increased, but there was a reduction of the beat-to-beat variation.

The maternal and the fetal heart rates of a woman frightened by threat of an anesthetic were studied. She had tachycardia with reduction of her own beat-to-beat variation. After a short interval, the same changes were observed in the fetus.

One mg. of atropine given intravenously to the mother over a period of about 2 minutes caused tachycardia in the mother with a reduction of beat-to-beat variation. Atropine also increases cardiac output and, presumably, uterine blood flow. There was slowing of the fetal heart; the fetus did not make use of the increased uterine blood flow. Fortunately, atropine does not lead to tachycardia in the fetus until about 20 minutes after its administration to the mother. This demonstrates the radical adjustment in the fetus to changes in the maternal circulation.

DR. BARRON: I am asked to comment on fetal homeostasis in relation to the teratogenic effect of reduced atmospheric pressures. Every biologic goal is achieved through the integrative action of a number of variables, any one of which may be limited. A variable in the maternal organism may be the circulating blood volume. Our problem is to determine these variables and their limits. It seems probable that these limits differ for the same variables in different animals. For example, some animals apparently do not reproduce at 15,000 feet, but the fertility of others (including man) seems to be unimpaired at this altitude.

PROFESSOR WALKER: Dr. Wildervanck suggests that anencephaly is merely part of a subsyndrome of status dysraphicus, which is a combination of a syndrome of deformities, congenital perceptive deafness, Klippel-Feil anomaly and abducens paralysis. He has observed this grouping in a number of cases of malformations of the central nervous system. All of the affected are females.

Although we are not familiar with this syndrome, we have observed that anencephalics (with the exception of the large ones with normal midbrains and spinal cords) commonly have malformations especially of the mid-line (e.g., omphalocele, cleft palate, high arched palate).

DR. POTTER: I have never seen the syndrome that Dr. Wildervanck has described. We have been interested in the gradation between the Klippel-Feil syndrome and iniencephaly, which is a condition of dis-

placement rather than lack of brain tissue. The spinal column is completely open, and the brain lies over the back of the child instead of in the normal position. There are all gradations from a small reduction in numbers of cervical vertebrae and a little shortening of the neck to a fatal malformation. Another example of a gradation is that between cebocephaly (in which there are fused cerebral hemispheres and 1 optic nerve but 2 eyes) and cyclopia. In our experience, anencephaly does not seem to be graded from a relatively minor anomaly compatible with survival to the lethal condition.

DR. MCKAY: Dr. Zwilling asks whether there is evidence in mammals which implicates the sperm as a cause of fetal wastage. In general, we have been referring to the zygote, which would contain nuclear material from both parents. However, I know of no experimental evidence which implicates the sperm. Dr. Stott asks: By what process are abnormal embryos eliminated? In the case of blastocysts and earlier embryos, the cells are destroyed by necrosis, and their contents are resorbed. When later implanted embryos die, there is hemorrhage and necrosis of the decidua, resulting in clinical abortion.

SESSION VIII

Perspectives

Chairman

PROFESSOR A. A. MONCRIEFF

Professor of Child Health, and Director of the Institute of Child Health,
The Hospital for Sick Children, Great Ormond Street, London, W.C. 1, United Kingdom

Genetic Control of the Stability of Development

PROFESSOR CONRAD H. WADDINGTON, C.B.E., Sc.D., D.Sc., F.R.S.

Institute of Animal Genetics, University of Edinburgh, West Mains Road,
Edinburgh, Scotland, United Kingdom

Some Molecular Aspects of Congenital Malformations

E. L. TATUM, Ph.D.

The Rockefeller Institute, New York 21, New York, U.S.A.

Future Possibilities in the Genetical Study of Congenital Malformations

PROFESSOR L. S. PENROSE, M.D., R.R.S.

Department of Eugenics, University College, London, W.C. 1, United Kingdom

Antibodies, Viruses and Embryos

JAMES D. EBERT, M.D.

Carnegie Institution of Washington, Baltimore, Maryland, U.S.A.

Medical Problems, Psychological and Social

PROFESSOR ROBERT DEBRÉ

Professor Emeritus, Faculty of Medicine, University of Paris,
Former President, Academy of Medicine, 5 rue de l'Université, Paris, France

Closing Remarks

SIR GEOFFREY MARSHALL, K.C.V.O., C.B.E., M.D., F.R.C.P.

President, Royal Society of Medicine, 1 Wimpole Street, London, W. 1, United Kingdom

Genetic Control of the Stability of Development

PROFESSOR CONRAD H. WADDINGTON, C.B.E., Sc.D., D.Sc., F.R.S.

One of the most striking features of the processes of embryonic development is their resistance to the action of agents which might tend to disturb the normal course of events. Even after gross injuries have been inflicted on the embryo, it has a strong tendency to get back to normal and to finish its development, looking as though nothing untoward had happened. The first experimental students of development, such as Driesch, were impressed enormously by this capacity of the developing animal to "regulate," as they said. In recent years, people often have spoken in this connection of the stability of development. To my mind, however, the word "stability" suggests something which does not change, whereas, of course, an embryo is altering continuously as time passes. Therefore, I prefer to speak of the "canalization of development," a phrase which implies that the developmental processes normally proceed along a certain path and tend to get back into this path if, for any reason, they are temporarily diverted out of it.[7,8]

In general, the early experimental embryologists who were impressed with the capacity of embryos to regulate did not bring this into any explicit relation with the hereditary constitution of the animal. However, as soon as one considers the matter from a genetic point of view, it is clear that the canalization of development is an expression of hereditary potentials and must have been brought into being by the processes of natural selection which control the evolution of all living things. In recent years, there has been an increasing interest in the nature of the buffering mechanisms, which tend to confine developing systems within definite pathways, and their relation to underlying genetic factors. Of course, congenital abnormalities are cases in which, for one reason or another, development fails to remain within its normal path but diverges so as to finish in some abnormal end-result. In the laboratory, we can produce similar aberrations of development either by the application of abnormal environments or by breeding animals which have unusual genetic constitutions. We can regard the canalization of the particular developmental system in question as opposing a certain resistance to such teratogenic agents. The hereditary constitution of the zygote may endow the developing system with a degree of buffering which renders it insensitive to a particular intensity of a certain environmental stress or agent. Again, the buffering which arises from the general genetic constitution of the animal may be such that the substitution of a particular mutant allele at a certain locus is ineffective in causing development to become abnormal.

Before discussing further the genetic control of canalization, it is necessary to consider briefly the types of instability which developing embryos exhibit. It is commonplace to remark that there are certain periods of maximum sensitivity to generalized teratogenic agents such as abnormal temperatures, ionizing radiation, etc. In general, these are periods for which our understanding of developmental processes would lead us to anticipate relatively unstable conditions, either because drastic physical changes are proceeding, or because important consequences are known to ensue, or for both of

275

these reasons. The period of gastrulation in vertebrate embryos is a good example. It involves the physical process of the invagination of the inner layers of the embryo and has as its consequences a whole set of inductive interactions. Now, the evidence suggests that the proper performance of such a morphogenetic chance as invagination is upset very easily by a large variety of agents. For instance, both in birds and amphibia high temperatures tend to cause an arrest of the gastrulation movements. Again, in the mouse embryo the turning movement by which the embryo becomes rolled up into a right-handed spiral often is disturbed by such agents as trypan blue.[9] In both cases, the physical abnormalities have profound later consequences, either by the derangement of the mutual relationships between inducing and reacting tissue or by the disturbance of the circulatory system and the general body conformation.

Periods which are physically unstable in this way are often also rather open to attack by chemical means. It is noteworthy that the teratogenic agents we have at our disposal rarely impinge directly on the intertissue reactions, such as induction, which play such an important part in embryogenesis. For instance, when gastrulation processes are attacked, such mesoderm as remains reasonably healthy seems to be able to induce corresponding neural tissue, although, of course, the nervous system which results is likely to be highly defective if the inducing material has been damaged or impeded from moving into its normal location. But chemical sensitivity seems to be more marked in connection with intracellular processes rather than with intercellular ones. In the chick embryo, for instance, the cells which are in process of being invaginated through the streak are attacked by a wide variety of agents, such as amino-acid and purine analogues, nitrogen mustards, triazines and other cytotoxic compounds.

I have referred to these stages of development, which are both especially sensitive and also have particularly important consequences, as "epigenetic crises." The point I want to make here is that they commonly have two aspects: a physical and a chemical. The physical movements which produce rearrangements of the tissues may be disturbed, with profound later consequences, even when the cells remain quite healthy. On the other hand, if the cells are damaged chemically, this damage usually affects processes going on within the cells. This often results in an inhibition of their movements, and this may lead to induction occurring in too restricted an area. But the actual chemical interaction between tissues by way of induction or some similar process seems to be rather resistant to disturbance.

It is when embryos are not undergoing any general epigenetic crisis that one can expect to obtain relatively specific inhibitions of particular tissues. In general, it seems that each type of tissue is inhibited most easily in the first stages of its differentiation, and we know of a number of agents which have a particularly strong effect on certain definite tissues at such times. In the early vertebrate embryo, several major types of tissue begin to differentiate almost immediately after the epigenetic crisis of gastrulation. Insofar as we find specific differences in the action of teratogens applied to these stages, it is, I think, usually a question of the first stages of cytodifferentiation rather than of different types of influence on gastrulation itself. Some evidence of this may be seen if we compare the effects of substances that are expected to affect general protein metabolism, such as amino-acid and purine analogues, with certain cytotoxic alkylating agents. In the early chick embryo, for instance, the abnormalities produced by amino-acid analogues are very similar to those resulting from purine analogues.[10] Both strike at roughly the same group of tissues. In particular, they hit the mesoderm which is being produced from the primitive streak, and the developing neural groove, particularly its anterior end. Perhaps, there are some slight differences between the amino-acid and the purine effects, but even if these are real, which is not entirely certain, they are, at best, slight modalities in a response which is, in general, very similar in the two cases. On the cytologic level, however, the 2 types of agents do appear to operate in different ways. Purine analogues such as azoguanine, which might be expected to interfere with nucleic acid metabolism, cause chick embryonic cells to become arrested during the course of mitosis. With amino-acid analogues there does not appear to be any particular sensitivity of the dividing cells, and one sees the appearance of large basophilic lumps in the cytoplasm, probably of RNA.

Presumably both of these types of agents strike at regions of the embryo in which the metabolism of proteins, linked with that of nucleic acids, is proceeding at the fastest rate. However, certain alkylating agents are more specific in their effects if used in sufficiently low dose—of course, at higher doses they damage all cells. For instance, triethylomelamine in low doses produces a very characteristic type of effect, the disappearance of the central core of the somites and, eventually, a great enlargement of the myocoele so that the somites become quite hollow. Also there is a tendency for the production of giant cells, perhaps by the inhibition of cell division; this also is found with several other cytotoxic agents.

Another group of cytotoxic substances, namely the aminophenyl derivatives of nitrogen mustard, which were examined by Dr. A. Jurand in our Institute, proved to be specific against the developing nervous system in chick embryo, if applied in the form of acetyl or particularly fluorineacetyl derivatives.[2] Their parent compound, i.e., the aminophenyl derivative of nitrogen mustard itself, also has a cytotoxic activity but of a general nature directed against all embryonic tissues simultaneously. With the acetyl and the fluorineacetyl derivatives, the chick embryos show a marked abnormality of the neural tube, which remains unclosed as a flat neural plate; after higher doses there is an almost complete destruction of the nervous tissue due to pyknotic breakdown of its cells, whereas all other tissues in the neighborhood, deriving from other germ layers, remain compartively normal. This specific activity might be due to some enzymes (e.g., peptidazes) localized in the presumptive neural tube cells, which sets free the parent aminophenyl derivative of the nitrogen mustard and thus produces its local activity. This chemical sensitivity of differentiating tissues must be an expression of the particular constellation of genes which are becoming active in the cells. If one compares widely different species, one can find evidence of differences in such specific sensitivities. For instance triethylomelamine, which, as just pointed out, affects particularly the somites in the chick embryo, has a rather localized action against the neural tube in the amphibia. However, this type of genetic control of specific tissue sensitivity, although of some theoretic interest, does not seem likely to be of much relevance to human congenital abnormalities. The majority of these do not exhibit any great specificity in the tissue primarily affected but usually involve the morphogensis of an organ or an organ-system. That is to say, they remind one rather of the effects of interfering with the physical aspect of an epigenetic crisis; of course, in those that survive to term it is usually, though not always, a rather minor crisis, arising late in development. Processes of this kind can be disturbed by a variety of fairly slight deviations from normal conditions, and it is against hazards of this kind that one may expect natural selection to have built up a measure of developmental canalization. It is not so easy to see why it should have done so against unusual chemicals which have a tissue-specific action, and the genetic differences of this kind which we find between widely divergent groups of vertebrates probably are chance results of genotypes which have been selected on quite some other basis.

When we examine the effects of generally acting deleterious conditions, which produce disturbances of epigenetic crises, we immediately come across evidence of genetically controlled differences in reaction. For instance, one may mention Landauer's well-known work on the teratogenic effects in the chick of such substances as insulin, boric acid and a number of others, which provoke malformations particularly of the rump, the limbs or the beak. He found that different strains of fowl react differently, both in the over-all number of malformations produced and to some extent in the proportion of the different types. Also, there were individual differences within a breed, and these responded to selection. Again, to mention another example, trypan blue administered to the mother provokes malformations of the fetus in mice. The effect in this animal seems to be largely, though not wholly, due to disturbances of the fluid balance and the circulatory system, leading to the appearance of subepidermal blebs and a derangement of the turning movement of the embryo which was mentioned previously. One aspect of the syndrome is the failure of proper closure of the neural tube, and this may lead to pseudencephaly. Newborn mice showing this malformation were seen in experiments performed by Hamburgh[1] on the Bagg Albino strain but did not appear in work by Carter and myself on an inbred CBA strain. I have quoted this case in order to bring out the difficulties of interpretation with which one is often faced in this field. We could suppose that the CBA strain is better buffered against pseudencephaly than the Bagg Albino strain. And one can see many phases at which this buffering might occur: it might be against the primary effect on neural tube closure, or against a number of secondary processes, such as the breakdown in later life of an imperfect closure. But it also might be that the deficiency in the CBA's of mice born with pseudencephaly does not indicate a lower effectiveness of trypan blue in producing the condition, but simply that, in this strain, fetuses with this condition do not survive so often to birth.

Both because of the labor involved in following exactly what happens to mammalian embryos treated with a teratogen, and because of its comparatively slow rate of breeding, it has not been possible to proceed very far with an analysis of the genetic control of developmental canalization in mice or any other animal closely comparable with man. Our studies in this field have been carried out with *Drosophila melanogaster*. Of course, this animal is zoologically very far removed from the mammals, but there is no reason to doubt that the genetic principles derived from it can be applied to them also. Like the embryos of vertebrates, the developing Drosophila passes through a number of epigenetic crises. In fact, this expression was first used in connection with one of them, a contraction by which the pupal insect, which at an earlier phase becomes highly inflated with hemolymph, returns to its normal size and shape. This is one of the relatively rare examples of a late-occurring epigenetic crisis which affects the whole body of the animal, even though by that time this body has become considerably differentiated into different regions.

One particular phase of the contraction occurs in the wings and is the period during which the wing veins of the adult appear in their definitive form. If a high temperature is applied for a short period, at or just before this contraction, various abnormalities in the wing venation may result. Such abnormalities usually occur in only a proportion of the flies subjected to the temperature shock. If one selects for further breeding only those animals in which wing abnormalities have been produced, the frequency of the abnormalities will be increased in the next generation. By continuing such selection, one can produce strains which are highly sensitive to this type of teratogenic disturbance, and similarly by breeding in every generation those animals in which the temperature treatment fails to produce any effect, one can build up highly resistant strains. This shows conclusively that the buffering of development against the effects of temperature is under genetic control and responds to selection like any other character controlled by the genetic constitution.[5]

It is noteworthy that this control is rather highly specific as regards the type of effect which the teratogenic agent produces. If one starts with a normal heterogenous population of Drosophila, which would be expected to contain much genetic variation in it, one can select out of it a series of strains each of which responds to the temperature treatment in a particular manner, for instance, by the lack of a particular vein, or the addition of an extra vein at some specific place in the wing. It is not merely the case that some strains are more sensitive and others less so. Strains differ not only in the degree of sensitivity but also in the type of response which they show. When such strains are kept under normal conditions, without being subjected to any particular teratogenic stimulus, some abnormal individuals nevertheless will appear in them. Indeed, if selection has gone far enough, the previously abnormal phenotype may appear in a very high proportion of cases—a phenomenon which I have spoken of as genetic assimilation, which I have discussed in relation to evolutionary processes in another place.[8] In the present context, it is more relevant to notice that even when selection has not proceeded very far, a proportion, which may be quite small, of deviant individuals will occur in the population. In many ways, these are quite comparable with congenital abnormalities in human populations. The point to notice is that the particular type of abnormality which occurs spontaneously in a population corresponds to the type for which that population has been selected. Thus, different populations containing different gene pools will tend to throw up different types of congenital abnormality.

Some authors, particularly Lerner,[3] have attributed great importance to heterozygosity in controlling the appearance of spontaneous abnormalities. He suggests that a genotype in which many genes are present in heterozygous form will determine a course of development which is well buffered and unlikely to produce an abnormal end-result. Spontaneous congenital abnormalities, not attributable to particular teratogenic agents in the environment, will tend to be produced in those individuals in the population in which the level of heterozygosity is particularly low. In some ways, this is an attractive hypothesis, and there is little doubt that many heterozygous genotypes do produce well-canalized courses of development. However, this certainly is not the whole story. I have attempted recently by selection to improve the canalization of a particular phenotype, that is to say, to reduce its sensitivity to environmental agents which might tend to alter it.[7] The phenotype in question was that of the Bar eye in Drosophila. The dominant mutant gene Bar produces a considerable reduction in the size of the eye and in the number of facets out of which it is composed. It was well known that the phenotype is environmentally sensitive, the eyes being larger at a low temperature and smaller at a high one. The experiment consisted in setting up a number of brother-sister matings, separating the progeny into two lots, one of which was reared at 18° C. and the other at 25° C., and then collecting for further breeding those families in which the differences between the 18° C. and the 25° C. populations were the least. After 6 generations of such selection, the temperature sensitivity was very greatly reduced, that is to say, the development had become very much better buffered against the effects of temperature. This had been achieved in spite of the 6 generations of brother-sister mating that had taken place, which must certainly have resulted in a very considerable reduction in the level of heterozygosity.

Again, some years ago, Sang and MacDonald in our laboratory studied the effect of a teratogenic agent on Drosophila, sodium metaborate, which causes a reduction in the size of the eyes.[4] They investigated its effect on normal wild-type strains and also on strains which were heterozygous for a gene which also affects the eyes in a rather similar way, namely eyeless. It emerged very clearly that the heterozygous eyeless flies were more sensitive to this teratogen than were the homozygous wild-type. Here we have a clear example in which heterozygosity for a particular gene reduces canalization. There is no reason to suppose that such situations are rare, and they may occur even when the genes concerned are such that the homozygote, reared in normal environments, rarely if ever shows any harmful effects.

Such facts, and also the possibility of genetic control of the type of response, show that we are dealing with genetic systems which are much more specific than mere heterozygosity as such. Although this was perhaps only to be expected, it is unfortunate in that it becomes very difficult to see a practical method of improving the human hereditary situation in respect of congenital abnormalities. So far the only means we know to improve the canalization of development is to exercise selection against the effects of some definite external stress, and such a procedure certainly could not be applied to mankind.

REFERENCES

1. Hamburgh, M.: Malformations in mouse embryos induced by trypan blue, Nature (Lond) 67:28, 1952.
2. Jurand, A.: Comparative investigations of the action of the nitrogen mustard derivatives on the early stages of development of chick embryos, J. Embryol. Exp. Morph. 8:60, 1960.
3. Lerner, I. M.: Genetic Homeostasis, Edinburgh, Oliver & Boyd, 1954.
4. Sang, J. H., and MacDonald, J. M.: The production of phenocopies in Drosophila using salts, particularly sodium metaborate, J. Genet. 52:392, 1954.
5. Waddington, C. H.: Organizers and Genes, London, Cambridge Univ. Press, 1940.
6. ————: The Strategy of the Genes, London, Allen & Unwin, 1957.
7. ————: Experiments on canalising selection, Genet. Res. 1:140, 1960.
8. ————: Genetic assimilation, Adv. Genet. 1961 (in press).
9. Waddington, C. H., and Carter, T. C.: A note on abnormalities induced in mouse embryos by trypan blue, J. Embryol. Exp. Morph. 1:167, 1953.
10. Waddington, C. H., and Perry, M.: Effect of some amino-acid and purine antagonists on chick embryos, J. Embryol. Exp. Morph. 6:365, 1958.

Some Molecular Aspects of Congenital Malformations

E. L. TATUM, Ph.D.

In this discussion of congenital malformations from the viewpoint of molecular biology, we have the opportunity or even the obligation of taking a broad view of the area in attempting to define future possibilities of research and understanding. Therefore, it seems necessary to avoid a rigid definition of congenital malformations, and to include not only anatomic abnormalities present in man at birth but also, and especially, molecular abnormalities detected in any organism, from virus to man.

It seems worthwhile to base our examination on several premises: (1) that the intrinsic genetic complement of every organism is the ultimate determiner of its every character, from biochemical to morphologic, subcellular to organismic; (2) that development and differentiation involve an orderly, sequential expression of the genetically established potentialities; (3) that this orderly chronologic expression is the consequence of interplay between the genome and the cellular or extracellular environment; and (4) that the individual members of the genetic complement involved in development and differentiation are not acting differently qualitatively from other genes, but that all genes exert their directive control of a cell or an organism at a primary molecular level, that is, by controlling the synthesis of enzymes and other proteins.

When one views the long, many-stepped interrelated pathway leading from DNA (deoxyribonucleic acid) of the gene in a chromosome in the nucleus through RNA (ribonucleic acid) to the protein synthesizing ribosomes in the cytoplasm, to the protein itself and its enzymatic or other function in the cell, eventually to characters such as the shape or the size of a limb, it is not surprising that we as yet are unable to pinpoint the primary molecular site of action of most genes controlling differentiation and development. However, there seems to be little question, that defective or abnormal development, either metabolic or morphologic, represents failure of particular genes to express themselves at the proper time, place and/or to the proper extent. However, in spite of the complexity of the problem, there are several approaches, already discussed thoroughly in this Conference. These include: the examination of cellular or tissue enzyme complements, and the correlation of their appearance with developmental stages; the analysis of environmental effects on cell or tissue differentiation through transplantation and related experiments; and the examination of the interruption of the normal course of development as a consequence either of genetic change or of the use of teratogenic agents, either chemical or physical. These various approaches can be viewed most simply and satisfactorily as attacking the chain of events leading from gene to character at various levels of organization.

However, it would seem to be profitable in our consideration to limit this discussion largely to the molecular level of events, summarizing the state of our knowledge (1) of gene function in relation to enzyme synthesis and metabolism, and (2) of the regulation and the integration of the metabolic functioning of the primary gene products, the enzymes. In this summary, we shall be asking ourselves what broad, general principles can be formulated, and to what extent they have been or can be applied to the problems of human genetics and development.

First, however, I wish to refer briefly to some of the evidence supporting the basic concept that the genetic material undergoes changes in activity in relation to development and differentiation.[15] At the cytologic level, this is indicated by the appearance of puffs and loops in the so-called "lamp-brush" chromosomes of the vertebrate oocyte, perhaps analogous to the Balbiani rings and puffs in the dipteran giant salivary chromosomes. These have been interpreted as representing regions of differential metabolic activity involving the production of RNA. At the functional level, the differentiation of the nuclei of the amphibian embryo, shown by King and Briggs[22] by nuclear transplantation technics, strongly suggests differential and, in part, irreversible gene activity related to the stage of differentiation. At the molecular level, perhaps the most convincing model yet available is the change from the production of fetal to adult hemoglobin in man, in which the gamma-chain dimer component typical of the fetal hemoglobin, and controlled by one gene, is largely replaced shortly after birth by the adult beta-chain dimer, controlled by another, nonallelic gene. The simplest explanation for this phenomenon is that of differential gene activity.[21]

Let us now examine the central hypothesis—that genes act in a primary way by determining protein specificity. I need only remind you that in molecular terms, the most widely accepted view is that there is a 1:1 relationship between specific base pair sequences in the DNA molecule and amino acid sequence in a specific protein. According to this view, mutation may be as simple as replacement of one base pair by another and may result in the production of a mutant protein with only one amino acid changed. Other gene mutations may result in a "nonsense" sequence and hence fail to permit completion of synthesis of the par-

ticular protein, or lead only to the synthesis of an inactive altered protein. If an active protein is formed, depending on how critical is the role of the particular amino acid in the subsequent coiling of the protein and, hence, in the metabolic functioning and stability of the protein, one might expect the protein to be changed in enzymatic activity either quantitatively or qualitatively, or to differ in physical characteristics such as pH dependency or heat stability.

Examples of these various possibilities as a consequence of genetic change are now well established among the more than 50 instances studied in micro-organisms and in man.[13] The most striking support for the basic hypothesis is, or course, the change in only one amino acid in sickle-cell hemoglobin in man.[22] Unfortunately, because of the lack of technics for separating an individual DNA molecular species, or of adequate methods of establishing their base sequence, in no instance as yet has it been possible to correlate this sequence with protein amino acid sequence. The closest approach is via the functional and recombinational analysis of the fine structure of genetic loci, particularly in bacterial viruses[3] and in micro-organisms,[5,9] in which the smallest definable genetic unit of DNA is apparently of the order of a few base pairs.

Nevertheless, we can illustrate some of the various classes of effects of gene mutation on proteins with examples in man.[2,6,18] Some instances of essentially complete absence or drastically lowered levels of specific enzymes or other proteins include: branching enzymes in glycogen storage disease, tyrosinase in albinism, catalase in acatalasemia, gamma globulin in agammaglobulinemia, serum albumin in analbuminemia, the blood-clotting factor V and antihemophilic globulin in hemophilia, and the specific transferase in galactosemia. Lowered enzyme levels also are illustrated in the case of alkaline phosphatase and glucose 6-phosphate dehydrogenase.[1] In all these cases, as in micro-organisms, the absence of the specific protein is associated with a single recessive gene, and in some instances the heterozygous condition is intermediate. So far, the deficiencies of only the plasma proteins can be compensated for by direct replacement.

Alteration of protein structure associated with genetic change is illustrated by abnormal serum cholinesterase, in which the alteration is so far definable only as a change in substrate affinity and by hemoglobins S, C and G, in which single amino acid changes from the normal hemoglobin A have been demonstrated,[19,21] apparently as the consequence of mutation at two distinguishable genetic loci. The difficulty of reconciling the control of adjacent amino acids in hemoglobins C and G by two apparently nonallelic genes with the proposed 1:1 relationship of gene and protein structure may be more apparent than real. More information on the biosynthesis of the final hemoglobin molecule is needed, since the two loci may be concerned in a manner analogous to that of the two separate loci governing the adult and the fetal hemoglobins, or analogous to that of the two loci controlling tryptophane synthetase in bacteria.[37] The co-operation of two different allelic genes located in different haploid nuclei in *Neurospora* in the synthesis of a single protein as in the recently discovered phenomenon of complementation[5] also may serve as a valuable model.

One of the main problems in appraising the presumed role of all genes in protein synthesis, particularly in reference to developmental processes, is that of distinguishing between primary, secondary, or higher gene functions. To a considerable extent this difficulty stems from the complexity of developmental processes, and from the necessary involvement of morphologic, topographic and cytologic relationships and structures in developmental processes. However, it does not seem unrealistic to expect the eventual identification of the critical primary defect in many cases to be

enzymatic. For example, many apparently unrelated abnormalities in skeletal development may be attributed to a drastically lowered serum phosphatase level in hereditary hypophosphatasia. Much more will have to be known than is known at present about the functioning of enzymatic processes in development, particularly in relation to structure, before a critical evaluation of the basic premises can be made.

It might be emphasized at this point that tissue culture of single cell lines of mammalian cells[11,31] provides a powerful tool for comparing normal and mutant cells and, therefore, potentially for determining the primary defective gene product or reaction responsible for hereditary developmental abnormalities. This technic also should prove to be extremely useful in detecting otherwise hidden recessive genes, especially when supplemented with methods of applying stress conditions to the cells, such as provision of excess of substrate as in galactosemia or phenylketonuria, exposure to primaquine as in glucose-6-phosphate dehydrogenase deficiency, or exposure to dibucaine in pseudocholinesterase abnormality. Also, there seem to be good grounds for optimism for the future, for example, in connection with the recent discoveries relating chromosome number and balance to development in man. It seems reasonable that insofar as the appropriate balance of sex chromosomes in man determines the course of development of normal sexual characteristics, it does so through the activities of genes located in these chromosomes, perhaps in a manner analogous to classic genetic "position effects." A comparative study of the enzymatic and metabolic activities of normal XX and XY and abnormal XO (Turner's syndrome) and XXY (Klinefelter's syndrome) cells in tissue culture might lead to the identification of the biochemical factors involved in this phase of development. Similar biochemical studies on the effects of chromosome imbalance as in mongolism, due to a single extra small chromosome should also prove most rewarding.

Another molecular aspect of the relation of gene to protein which deserves at least mention at this time, pending a fuller discussion by Dr. Ebert, is that of the probable intermediary role played by RNA or RNP (ribonucleoprotein). In the light of current ideas regarding the specific roles of organized RNA in ribosomes and soluble RNA in bringing about the lining up of activated amino acids and their sequential ordering in protein, it would seem reasonable that RNA should possess a specificity homologous to that of DNA. In confirmation of this point, we need only to cite the evidence that purified RNA carries the genetic information of many viruses, including TMV, and that presumed molecular alterations in TMV nucleic acid, as in nitrous acid-induced mutations, may result in changes in amino acid sequence in the virus protein.[32,35]

That RNA, by virtue of these properties and functions, and the probable relationship of RNA to DNA, might be concerned in gene activity as expressed in development and differentiation, also seems to be reasonable. In this regard the recent results of Ebert[12] and Niu[29] may be cited, indicating that RNP or RNA is indeed specifically involved in embryologic differentiation.

Now, let us consider briefly some of the ways in which gene activity might be controlled selectively or regulated during differentiation either primarily in enzyme synthesis or secondarily in enzyme activity. As the result of considerable work during the past decade, particularly with micro-organisms, several classes of regulatory systems are now well known, which may serve as extremely useful models in considering vertebrate differentiation. In essence they may be considered as responsive systems, in which particular molecules of either substrate or product are concerned as stimuli, or put alternatively, in which the interaction of a biologic machine and its environment

is concerned in the regulation of the machine's activities.

One such system is enzyme adaptation, or induced enzyme biosynthesis.[28] In this, the contact of a cell with a suitable inducing substance, usually, but not necessarily, a substrate for a given enzyme, specifically induces the synthesis of that enzyme. The substrate molecule is attacked by the enzyme, and the new product in turn may in a similar manner induce the synthesis of a second enzyme which attacks it, and so on. The possible involvement in differentiation of this type of "sequential induction"[33] is obvious. With the further introduction of a system of control of the accumulation of substrate within the target cell, as with the specific "permeases" of bacteria, the production of which inside the cell apparently is also induced by a given substrate, one has a model of a system in which no enzyme is produced until a certain threshold concentration of substrate is reached. After the production of the permease is triggered, substrate is concentrated inside the cell, and enzyme synthesis is maintained thereafter even in the presence of low concentrations of substrate.[7] Such a model system combines the elements of specificity and irreversibility apparently demanded by differentiation.

Additional flexibility of control of enzyme synthesis can be provided by a negative feed-back system known as enzyme repression. In this the presence of an enzyme product in amounts in excess of need, in certain instances in bacteria, is able to repress synthesis of the enzyme or enzymes necessary for the synthesis of that product.[36]

There is some reason to believe that enzyme induction and repression may not be as different as might appear, but that an inducer molecule may act by displacing the repressor molecule normally in combination with the enzyme-forming system.[16,30] Since in bacteria a gene mutation may convert an inducible enzyme system to a constitutive one, it would appear that the principles of control of synthesis of all enzymes are similar. An attractive hypothesis is that RNA, which may transfer information from DNA in the nucleus to the enzyme-forming system in the cytoplasm, may itself be the repressor molecule.

The most completely investigated inducible enzyme in mammalian systems is tryptophane peroxidase.[23] Induction of the synthesis of increased amounts of this enzyme can be effected in the intact animal by the specific inducer, tryptophane, or by the less specific molecule, hydrocortisone, which also "induces" other enzymes such as tyrosine transaminase. Both these enzymes undergo very significant increases in concentration shortly after birth. Although it is possible that the effects of hydrocortisone may be on uptake of specific inducer substrate molecules, it is also possible that it may act by relieving a repression. A similar situation may be involved in the effect of thyroxine in amphibian metamorphosis, during which enzymes involved in nitrogen metabolism and excretion undergo changes in concentration.[4]

Over and above the regulation of enzyme synthesis, development may involve regulation of enzyme activity. The simplest theoretic model for this regulation is one involving mass-action equilibria in which availability of substrate and removal of product are important factors. Obviously, intracellular structure and organization must be considered in this record. Regulation also may be achieved at a somewhat more complex level involving the concentration or the activity of co-factors of the enzymatic reaction, such as TPN and DPN the state of oxidation of which may be important in steroid hormone activity.[34] Hormones also may directly affect enzyme activity.[27] At another level, enzyme activity also may be regulated by product feed-back systems. The inhibition of the action of enzymes, involved in early, critical steps in biosynthetic sequences, by the final end-product of the sequence has been demonstrated in bacteria.[25] This is termed "negative feed-back inhibition," and it cannot be explained by simple mass-action phenomena.

From the standpoint of development and differentiation, both cellular and organismic, any of these regulator systems may be involved in the ultimate expression of the genic potentialities of an organism. Actually, the requisite flexibility and delicacy of control needed may demand the simultaneous and interwoven involvement of all these systems and probably of others yet to be discovered. For example, the accumulation of an intermediate substrate as the result of mutational change may lead by sequential "auto-induction" to the synthesis of an entire set of new enzymes involved in the metabolism of that substrate.[17] A similar consequence might follow any type of feed-back regulation as has been discussed already.

Other models which should be kept in mind in future work relate to the integration of structure and biochemical function. Compartmentalization of cell function into subcellular structures, as typified by the association of oxidative systems in mitochondria, and as suggested by nonequilibration of certain labeled metabolites and by the different metabolic fates of endogenous and exogenous substances, obviously may affect enzyme synthesis and activity via any or all of the regulatory mechanisms just outlined. Structure and metabolism also may be interrelated by a mechanism in which the synthesis of a high polymer compound, such as starch or nucleic acid, is dependent on a primer molecule of that substance.

Now we should consider briefly the effects of particular molecules which may accumulate in a cell or an organism as the result of metabolic interference. These molecules per se appear to affect metabolism and development probably via feed-back and other regulatory mechanisms. In hereditary galactosemia, for example, the accumulation of galactose and galactose-1-phosphate appears to be at least partially responsible for the variety of developmental consequences typical of this condition. In hereditary phenylpyruvic oligophrenia, phenylpyruvic acid, which is accumulated in abnormal concentrations, itself appears similarly to be responsible for the pleiotrophic developmental effects observed. In both instances, some alleviation of the typical symptoms apparently can be achieved by removing or drastically lowering the dietary intake of the precursor molecule, either phenylalanine or lactose. It seems probable that with increasing knowledge of the primary metabolic defect in other conditions, some will prove to be susceptible to similar therapy.

Another promising theoretic possibility would be to make use of the cells' own regulatory feed-back mechanism to decrease the production and the accumulation of an undesirable product. This approach has been followed already in the treatment of magaloblastic anemia, in which orotic acid accumulates in large quantities. Hugeley et al.[20] fed large amounts of the end-products of orotic acid in the form of yeast nucleic acid, with a remarkable decrease in orotic acid production and some beneficial therapeutic results.

We have explored some of the molecular aspects of gene activity as expressed during development and differentiation and have pointed out some ways in which, in the near future, with increasing knowledge of the involved molecular chain of events, an abnormal or potentially abnormal organism may be restored to normality. The most immediately available therapeutic measures essentially consist of compensating for the defect in the genetic material or its metabolic consequences by replacement of an essential missing material, either a particular metabolic product or a protein, or by preventing the overproduction of an undesirable compound by one means or another.

However, looking still further into the future, we may speculate on the inherently more satisfactory possibilities of replacing defective genetic material. If the immunologic difficulties now preventing it can be overcome, cell or tissue transplantation may be possible as a means of introducing nor-

mally functioning genetic material into an organism. Another alternative, admittedly even more speculative, would be to replace, in an individual's own cells, perhaps in tissue culture, the defective gene by another, followed by reimplantation. This replacement might be by mechanisms anologous to transformation, somatic recombination, or transduction, processes by which DNA now can be transferred successfully from one individual cell to another in micro-organisms.

With increased knowledge of DNA structure and of the mechanism of gene mutation, it may prove possible predictably to alter and improve genes within a living cell by a process of controlled or directed mutation. Beginnings have already been made in this direction by the use of nucleic acid base analogues as mutagens[14] and by the conversion of one base to another as proposed for the mutagenic action of nitrous acid on tobacco mosaic virus.[35]

With detailed knowledge of the properties of nucleic acid, it may be possible to reconstitute better genes from mixtures of dissociated single-stranded DNA as in the recent experiments of Doty et al. with bacterial DNA.[10,26] It even may be possible to synthesize DNA in vitro by enzymatic procedures such as those of Kornberg[24] and then to incorporate them into cells as desired.

Finally, with increased knowledge of the finer details of DNA and protein structure and of the code relating one to the other,[8] eventually it may be possible to synthesize better DNA, genes and, hence, proteins and other enzymes to order. This would be the ultimate in "biologic engineering."

REFERENCES

1. Allison, A. C.: Glucose-6-phosphate dehydrogenase deficiency in red blood cells of East Africans, Nature (Lond) 186:531, 1960.
2. Bearn, A. C.: Hereditary variation in synthesis of serum proteins in health and disease, Metabolism 9:208, 1960.
3. Benzer, S.: On the topology of the genetic

fine structure, Proc. Nat. Acad. Sc. USA **45**:1607, 1959.

4. Brown, G. W. Jr., and Cohen, P. P.: *in* McElroy, W. D. and Glass, B. (eds.): The Chemical Basis of Development, p. 495, Baltimore, Johns Hopkins Press, 1958.

5. Case, M., and Giles, N. H.: Comparative complementation and genetic maps of the pan-2 locus in *N. crassa,* Proc. Nat. Acad. Sc. USA **46**:659, 1960.

6. Ciba Foundation Symposium: Wolstenholme, G. E. W., and O'Connor, C. M. (eds.): Biochemistry of Human Genetics, Boston, Little, 1959.

7. Cohn, M., and Horibata, K.: Inhibition by glucose of the induced synthesis of the beta-galactoside-enzyme system of *E. coli.* Analysis of maintenance, J. Bact. **78**:601, 603, 624, 1959.

8. Crick, F. H. C., Griffith, J. S., and Orgel, L. E.: Codes without commas, Proc. Nat. Acad. Sc. USA **43**:416, 1957.

9. Demerec, M., and Hartman, P. S.: Complex loci in micro-organisms, Ann. Rev. Microbiol. **13**:377, 1959.

10. Doty, P., Marmur, J., Eigner, J., and Schildkraut, C.: Strand separation and specific recombination in deoxyribonucleic acids: physical chemical studies, Proc. Nat. Acad. Sc. USA **46**:461, 1960.

11. Eagle, H.: Animal cells and microbiology, Bact. Rev. **22**:217, 1958.

12. Ebert, J.: Viruses as Tools in Studying Embryonic Development, p. 406, Carnegie Institution of Washington, 1958-59.

13. Fincham, J. R. S.: The biochemistry of genetic factors, Ann. Rev. Biochem. **28**: 343, 1959.

14. Freese, E.: The difference between spontaneous and base-analogue induced mutations of phage T4, Proc. Nat. Acad. Sc. USA **45**:622, 1959.

15. Gall, J. G.: Chromosomal differentiation *in* McElroy, W. D. and Glass, B. (eds.): The Chemical Basis of Development, p. 103, Baltimore, Johns Hopkins Press, 1958.

16. Gorini, L.: Antagonism between substrate and repressor in controlling the formation of a biosynthetic enzyme, Proc. Nat. Acad. Sc. USA **46**:682, 1960.

17. Gross, S. R.: Enzymatic autoinduction and the hypothesis of intracellular permeability barriers in Neurospora, Tr. New York Acad. Sc. **22**:44, 1959.

18. Harris, H.: Human Biochemical Genetics, London, Cambridge Univ. Press, 1959.

19. Hill, R. L., and Schwartz, H. C.: A chemical abnormality in haemoglobin G, Nature (Lond) **184**:641, 1959.

20. Hugeley, C. M., Jr., Bain, J. A., Rivers, S. L., and Scoggins, R. B.: Refractory metaloblastic anemia associated with excretion of orotic acid, Blood **14**:615, 1959.

21. Hunt, J. A., and Ingram, V. M.: Biochemistry of human genetics *in* Wolstenholme, G. E. W., and O'Connor, C. M. (eds.): Ciba Foundation Symposium on Human Biochemical Genetics in Relation to the Problem of Gene Action, p. 114, Boston, Little, 1959.

22. King, T. J., and Briggs, R.: Changes in the nuclei of differentiating gastrula cells, as demonstrated by nuclear transplantation, Proc. Nat. Acad. Sc. USA **41**:321, 1955.

23. Knox, W. E.: *in* Physiological Adaptation, p. 107, Am. Physiol. Soc., 1958.

24. Kornberg, A.: Enzymatic synthesis of DNA acid, Harvey Soc. Series **53**:83, 1957-58.

25. Magasanik, B., Magasanik, A. K., and Neidhart, F. C.: Regulation of cell metabolism *in* Wolstenholme, G. E. W., and O'Connor, C. M. (eds.): Ciba Foundation Symposium on Human Biochemical Genetics in Relation to the Problem of Gene Action, p. 334, Boston, Little, 1959.

26. Marmur, J., and Lane, D.: Strand separation and specific recombination in deoxyribonucleic acids: biological studies, Proc. Nat. Acad. Sc. USA **46**:453, 1960.

27. Marks, P. A., and Banks, J.: Inhibition of mammalian glucose-6-phosphate dehydrogenase by steroids, Proc. Nat. Acad. Sc. USA **46**:447, 1960.

28. Monod, J.: Enzymatic adaptation and its bearing on problems of cell physiology, genetics and differentiation, Growth Symposium: 223, 1947.

29. Niu, M. C.: *in* Bass, (ed.): Evolution of Nervous Control, p. 7, Amer. A. Adv. Sc. Symposium, 1959.

30. Pardee, A. B., Jacob, F., and Monod, J.: The genetic control and cytoplasmic expression of inducibility in the synthesis of betagalactosidase by *E. coli,* J. Mol. Biol. **1**:165, 1959.

31. Puck, T. T.: The mammalian cell as an independent organism *in* Cellular biology, nucleic acids, and viruses, Trans. New York Acad. Sc. (spec. publ.) **5**:291, 1957.

32. Schuster, H., and Schramm, G.: Bestimmung der biologisch wirksamen Einheit

in der Ribosenucleinsaure des Tabak-mosaikvirus auf chemischem Wege, Z. Naturforsch. **13b:**697, 1958.

33. Stanier, R. Y.: Enzymatic adaptation in bacteria, Ann. Rev. Microbiol. **5:**35, 1951.

34. Talalay, P., Hurlock, B., and Williams-Ashman, H. G.: On a coenzymatic function of estradiol-17-beta, Proc. Nat. Acad. Sc. USA 44:862, 1958.

35. Tsugita, A., and Fraenkel-Conrat, H.: The amino-acid composition and c-terminal sequence of a chemically evoked mutant of TMV, Proc. Nat. Acad. Sc. USA **46:** 636, 1960.

36. Vogel, H. J.: Repressed and induced enzyme formation: a unified hypothesis, Proc. Nat. Acad. Sc. USA 43:491, 1957.

37. Yanofsky, C., and Crawford, I.: The effects of deletions, point mutations, reversions and suppressor mutations on the two components of the tryptophan synthetase of *E. coli,* Proc. Nat. Acad. Sc. USA **45:** 1016, 1959.

Future Possibilities in the Genetic Study of Congenital Malformations

L. S. PENROSE, M.A., M.D., M.R.C.S., L.R.C.P.

The complacent idea that man is a nearly perfect animal species is shattered rudely when the frequency of congenital malformations of all kinds is first appreciated. The large proportion of cases among them of gross morphologic anomalies, often almost incompatible with life, is particularly disturbing. When Malpas, in 1937,* showed that 1 per cent of births suffered from central nervous system defects, he encountered surprise and incredulity. The explanation of selective sampling was invoked to explain his high figure. Indeed, incidence frequencies do show large differences from population to population. Also, the spectrum of specific conditions shows considerable variations. However, the general impression is inescapable of a medical problem of great magnitude.

Contrasting with the success attained in the control of many diseases which formerly seemed to be equally challenging, the intractable nature of the problems concerned in the origins and the prevention of malformations stands out in sharp relief. In the last year, this contrast apparently has been made stronger because of the advances in knowledge of the human chromosomes. A genetic predisposition to malformation could not be identified easily and might be dismissed as imaginary, but a perfect correlation of a morphologic somatic defect with a visible change in the morphology of the karyotype cannot be dismissed lightly. We are bound to accept the visible manifestation of hereditary causes.

Naturally, in the newly aroused interest in the subject, the predominating hope is that some advances can be made—at least in the field of prevention. Since so many malformations can be caused experimentally by nutritional insults, it is reasonable to expect that some of those that occur naturally might be prevented by attention to diet and to correction of deficiencies. This line of reasoning has obvious limitations, since nutritional levels so rarely are inadequate to an extent comparable with those in animal experiments. The same limitation applies to the prevention of defects like those caused in animal experiments by toxic agents or by radiation. The opposite viewpoint—that the recognition of chromosomal aberrations as important causes makes alleviation or prevention impossible—also is unrealistic. Superficially, it might seem that the nondisjunctions, the fractures and the translocations which occur are evidence of an unalterable built-in mechanism which, like point mutation, must be tolerated as part of the normal evolutionary process. Indeed, there is a path between the extreme environmentalist and the fatalistic philosophies which leads, through arduous researches, to advances in knowledge whose possible uses can be seen only dimly at present.

In the first place, the genetics of resistance or of susceptibility to teratogenic influences has been studied very little, and it may be that the risks of dietetic defects are peculiarly high for some mothers and some fetuses. If these risks were known, they could be guarded against. Then, again, the risks involved in germ cell maturation are

* Malpas, P.: The incidence of human malformations, J. Obstet. Gynec. Brit. Emp. 44:434, 1937.

289

not the same for all people. There are well-known genes which tend to produce chromosome aberrations in lower animals and in plants. In man, these also can occur and might, like the "claret" gene in *Drosophila,* visibly mark the susceptible mother. Apart from this, the significance of paying attention to maternal age already is known and could be of special value in the prevention of mongolism. Indeed, there may be hormonal or other chemical influences which can affect the germ cells in ways which as yet are not seriously considered. These questions could form the focus of much experimental inquiry. Much work has been done on the formal genetics of genes with clear-cut effects in the individual who carries them, but relatively little on genes whose effects are shown mainly in the offspring.

Finally, there is the question of cellular pathology. Here, an entirely new field has been opened up by the recognition of aneuploidy as a fundamental cause of human malformations. Formerly, this was observed almost exclusively as a common cause of anomalous structure in plants. The chemistry of aneuploid cells needs to be attacked. At present, we can only guess, by analogy with plants, that the water balance is disturbed; but the problem is of fundamental interest genetically. In a trisomic individual, how does the extra dose of DNA affect the formation of enzymes and of proteins, for example? It seems that the formerly neglected malformed trisomics may hold a key to the problem of gene action.

Antibodies, Viruses and Embryos

JAMES D. EBERT, Ph.D.

It has been said—I think only half in jest —that the addresses of scientists are concocted of two principal ingredients, "Pointing with pride" and "viewing with alarm," the proportions being varied according to the occasion and the outlook of the speaker. By its very nature an invitation to speak on "Perspectives" limits one's approach, for who can "point with pride" at unsolved problems? A further limitation is imposed if one uses the term *congenital malformation* to denote only gross anatomic abnormalities present at birth, thus attempting to dissociate structural from cellular and molecular abnormalities. The latter limitation is the more serious, for it impinges not only on the discussion of "Perspectives" but may seriously impede advances in understanding. For are we not agreed that anatomic abnormalities are but an expression of abnormalities of structure, or association, or interaction of molecules? An understanding of malformations will depend in large measure on complete structural analyses of the nucleic acids and proteins, including the lipoproteins, no matter whether we are considering sickle cell disease, in which molecular abnormality is translated directly into structural abnormality, or the syndrome of defects following maternal infection with rubella in which the number of steps between molecular and anatomic expression is unknown. Admittedly, molecular defects provide attractive, immediate experimental targets, but we should not be persuaded to center our attack on them to the exclusion of other problems which demand attention. I do not wish to imply that attempts to understand abnormal development should await solution of the problems of normal development, for it seems altogether likely that studies of teratogenesis may contribute importantly to our understanding of normal development. Biochemical and genetic approaches to teratogenesis should provide specific tools for implementing the classic approaches of experimental embryology— defect, isolation and recombination experiments—at cellular and molecular levels. The goal of students of teratogenesis should be not merely to fathom the mechanism of action of a given teratogen but rather to use it as a tool in understanding normal embryogenesis.

Progress has been made in elucidating that the primary genetic material in cellular organisms and many viruses is deoxyribonucleic acid (DNA) and in tobacco mosaic and other viruses, ribonucleic acid (RNA); yet we lack answers to a number of fundamental questions: By what mechanisms are nucleic acids replicated? What, in molecular terms, are mutations? How do they relate to the coding system by which nucleic acids carry genetic information? The evidence for the genetic role of the nucleic acids is clear: the infectivity of tobacco mosaic and other viruses resides in RNA; genetic transformation of bacteria is effected by DNA; in isotopically labeled bacteriophage, DNA, and only DNA, is carried over from one generation to the next. Once the structure of RNA is known in the same detail as that of DNA, we may expect for RNA, experiments comparable in clarity with those of Meselson and Stahl[25] and Lehman, Zimmerman, Adler, Bessman, Simms and Kornberg,[20] which demonstrate that the replication of DNA may be accomplished by separation of paired nucleotide chains, with each chain remaining intact and serving as a template against which new complementary partners are built, without obligatory intervention of RNA or protein.

Yet these questions serve only as a prelude to questions of the functions of the nucleic acids in development. As Wilt and I emphasized on another occasion,[14] to understand the mechanisms of differentiation will require that increasing attention be paid to the interactions of genetic and epigenetic systems.[26] We wrote, in part:

It is no longer meaningful to speak of resolving the apparent contradiction between genetic constancy and the orderly establishment of populations of specialized stable cells. Is there any doubt that a more effective working hypothesis states that there are differential heterocatalytic activities of genetic materials depending on the type of cell in which they are located? There can be no doubt that the same set of chromosomes may have a different appearance in different kinds of cells; nor can we question the statement that all of the genetic material may not be functioning simultaneously. Taken as a whole, the evidence suggests that we should search for the chemical basis of such differential heterocatalysis, and perhaps even for differences in the genetic material itself. In turn, the differential physiological activity of the genetic material must reflect its interaction with epigenetic components and with their products—the epigenetic elements themselves being an expression of the heterocatalytic activity of the genetic material.

Viruses, almost literally packets of information, present novel and searching ways of determining how the epigenetic material is influenced by genetic and environmental elements, and how, in turn, it influences the genetic material. Animal viruses, including the tumorigenic viruses, have been treated as genetic units, with emphasis on their infectivity and integration into the genetic apparatus of the host, leading to a consideration of the effectiveness of viruses as tools in effecting incorporation of inductive nucleic acids or nucleoproteins. Attention

has been focused on the possibilities of recombination between vertebrate somatic cells. I have discussed experiments from several disciplines which suggest that epigenetic recombination by RNA or RNA-protein may be meaningful.[12,14] It was held likely that proper conditions for demonstrating the exchange of protein-forming machinery between cells will be found. The specificity of such phenomena must be examined with care, a goal which has not always been achieved.

Embryonic induction embraces not only epigenetic recombination but also interactions mediated by specific small molecular stimuli. The difficulty of analysis is compounded by the fact that, experimentally, not only specific molecules are capable of modifying the course of development, but also changes in pH, urea and other treatments can shift the fate of embryonic cells. Niu[27] and Yamada[35] have summarized the literature of embryonic induction, emphasizing the evidence implicating RNA and RNA-protein. I say RNA and RNA-protein, for the roles played by the nucleic acid and protein moieties have not been clarified. In fact the questions of passage and localization of RNA, RNA-protein, or other inductive agents are not resolved fully.

In view of the inconclusiveness of the evidence that might enable one to determine whether or not specific protein is essential for the action of RNA, and in view of the positive evidence for the involvement of microsomes in protein synthesis (reviewed[14]), experiments have been conducted to determine whether microsomes of adult tissues can act as specific inductors when incorporated into embryonic cells. Inconsistencies in earlier findings might stem from failure to prepare physiologically active RNA or RNA-protein, or failure of RNA or RNA-protein to enter the cell or to compete effectively with its counterpart in the recipient cell. The experiments of Kramer and Straub[18] who found that the transfer of "enzyme-inducing capacity" by RNA was promoted by treating the recipient cells with RNA-ase, and of Clayton and Okada[4] who employed the combined action of specific antiorgan sera and RNA, suggest that attention should be paid to measures that facilitate the passage and the competition of the inductive agent. The incorporation of tissue microsomes has been promoted by combining them with an RNA virus. I have described the results of experiments in which the inoculation of the labile chorio-allantoic membrane with a mixture of cardiac microsomes and the Rous sarcoma virus, a virus having an affinity for muscle, has produced tumor masses which contain to a varying degree, intermingled among typical sarcoma cells, muscle or musclelike elements.[12] The incidence of clearly recognizable cross-striated muscle is low, but there are found among the tumor cells large numbers of cells and fibers which are musclelike. It was emphasized that the reaction is not "all-or-none"; both the quality and the quantity of muscle produced varied widely. No growths have resulted from the inoculation of heart microsomes alone, and inoculation with virus alone evokes the characteristic Rous sarcoma.

Until such time as the specificity of the requirement for the Rous sarcoma virus (or, indeed, for any virus) in the reaction is demonstrated, an explanation based on the concept of epigenetic recombination cannot be convincing. Insofar as the specificity of the requirement for the Rous sarcoma virus is concerned, only one additional line of evidence may be mentioned. In experiments like those described for cardiac muscle, attempts to induce kidney structures in the chorio-allantoic membrane employing kidney microsome-Rous sarcoma virus combinations have failed. Are these negative findings meaningful? The experiment does not follow one of the tenets established at the outset of the work, namely, that the virus and the normal tissue have some affinity. It may be necessary to combine kidney microsomes with an appropriate virus from a renal tumor. Conversely, the failure may reflect only the limited range of potentialities of the cells of the chorio-allantois.

In thinking of viruses, we commonly think first of infectivity and of the possibility of recombination. However, we must keep before us other aspects of the behavior of viruses. The virus may be doing no more than, to put it perhaps naïvely, opening the door, permitting incorporation of materials that otherwise might be ineffective. Or, by modifying the pattern of nucleic acid metabolism of the recipient cells, the virus may make it possible for the microsomes to compete effectively. Might other methods of altering the recipient cells be equally effective?

Emphasis on the interaction of virus and recipient cell naturally leads to the question whether viruses may prove to be useful tools in exploring the development of cell specificity. Often, viruses are sufficiently sensitive to distinguish differences between closely related cell lines. Moreover, it seems evident that the host cell-virus relation is reciprocal: changes in the host may influence the ability of a virus to multiply, and may lead to a modification in cytopathologic effects. In addition to variations in host cells, we may expect virus variations as a consequence of host-virus interactions, although perhaps not always as striking as those reported by Rose and Rose[29] who found that amphibian renal and fat body tumor agents grown in tissues other than those for which they have a natural predilection may acquire from the new environment a new specific affinity; for example, the renal tumor agent acquired an affinity for cartilage of a specific location—digit, or elbow, etc.

There can be no doubt that Gregg's demonstration[16] of the incidence of congenital malformations in children whose mothers had contracted rubella during the early months of pregnancy played an important role in focusing attention on infections as causes of congenital defects. Yet, we are able to state with assurance only that maternal infections early in the gestation period result in a characteristic spectrum of developmental abnormalities and that the manifestations in the early embryo are different from those in the adult, a conclusion that emerges also from sporadic examinations of the effects of viruses inoculated directly into the embryos or the embryonic membranes. There is a compelling need for systematic studies and comparisons of the effects of inoculation of specific viruses into the embryo at successive intervals during ontogeny, under uniform conditions of dosage and other controllable conditions. Pending such studies, any conclusions that are drawn from the fragmentary evidence available must be tentative.

Blattner and his associates[2] have described the abnormalities occurring in chick embryos 22 to 24 hours after inoculation of Newcastle disease virus at 36 hours and at 12-hourly intervals thereafter. Characteristic defects in the neural tube, the lens, the auditory and the olfactory primordia, the visceral arches and the limb buds were observed. For each age group there is a different but typical complex of defects. Susceptibility to the virus is greater in the younger than in the older embryos, as evidenced by the highest incidence of lethality in the youngest embryos and the decreasing extent of the defect in most organs in each succeeding age group. The findings were interpreted on the basis of the concept of the critical or susceptible period in teratogenesis.[33] Since the route of inoculation is over the blastoderm, it might be expected that surface ectodermal structures would be involved first. It may be pointed out, parenthetically, that McKenzie and Ebert[23] observed that the effects of the metabolic inhibitor, antimycin A, on the early chick embryo in vitro depend also on the surface to which it is applied. The Newcastle disease virus appears to be restricted in its propagation to cells lining a surface in contact with their environment, a conclusion in line with the finding that the neural tube, the lens vesicle and the auditory vesicle, all of which are affected by the virus, are involved

when they are exposed to the exterior at the time of inoculation.

Robertson, Williamson and Blattner[28] stress that an important critical factor in determining susceptibility to the virus at this embryonic stage is the amount of proliferaton and differentiation occurring within the organ at the time of exposure, and argue that the virus finds a highly suitable environment for proliferation in areas of high metabolic activity. They state that it is generally agreed that over-all metabolism is at its highest level in the early embryo and gradually declines with age, but they do not document their statement. Their findings are clear-cut, but the interpretation, based on an uncertain higher metabolic rate providing better grounds for virus proliferation, does not appear to be justified. In fact, it must be emphasized that proliferation of the Newcastle disease virus in the early embryo has not been demonstrated. Robertson *et al.*[28] are aware of this deficiency and suggest an alternative explanation, based also on the concept of susceptible periods, but requiring not the proliferation of virus but the "toxicity" of the virus.

From this discussion several critical questions emerge: (1) At what stage in their development can embryonic cells be infected by a given virus? When will embryonic cells support proliferation of the virus? (2) Are the well-documented examples of malformation produced by viruses actually the consequence of viral infection and proliferation or of "toxic" effects otherwise not defined? (3) Is it possible that cells of the early embryo may be infected, but that the virus remains in a latent stage until the maturation of conditions favoring proliferation? (4) To what extent must we consider latent viruses, including viruses without distinctive pathogenic action in the adult animal, as causative agents in teratogenesis?

We can scarcely begin to answer these questions. Matumoto, Saburi, and Nishi[24] state that they have been able to cultivate the Rift Valley fever virus in the 1-day-old chick embryo. However, the virus was inoculated into the yolk, some 5 to 10 mm. from the blastoderm, and in harvesting the virus, the entire contents of the egg were homogenized. Thus, although it is said that the pantropic strain begins to increase within 24 hours after inoculation, reaching a maximum at 48 hours, and that the neurotropic strain reaches a maximum at 2 to 3 days, it cannot be said whether the virus has proliferated in the embryo or in the extra-embryonic regions. Matumoto et al.[24] refer to the successful cultivation of several other viruses by the same technic, including dengue, distemper, herpes simplex, Japanese encephalitis, vaccinia and variola.

One of the more intriguing teratogenic viruses is influenza A. Hamburger and Habel[17] inoculated the 48-hour chick embryo with both influenza A and mumps viruses. No specific abnormalities resulted from the inoculation of mumps virus, but influenza A evoked a characteristic syndrome—microcephaly, microencephaly, retardation of the amnion and twisting of the axis. But when the inoculations were made at 96 hours, no specific anomalies were produced by either virus. In fact, Kung[19] demonstrated that all of the tissues of the 4-day chick embryo are susceptible to influenza A virus. (Several other studies indicate that viruses produce a generalized infection in embryos rather than the specific tropism characteristic of the postembryonic host; reviewed.[14]) The inoculation of older embryos (12 to 15 days) with influenza A results in a pattern of specific tissue susceptibility—in the respiratory epithelium. With influenza A, then, we observe apparent "specificity" as a teratogen, generalized infection and specific infection. Again we may ask several questions: (1) To what extent is this pattern characteristic of other viruses? (2) What is the meaning of the tissue specificity at 12 to 15 days? To put it another way, if the several tissues of the embryo were cultured separately in the presence of the virus, would they be susceptible? Is there a loss of ability to accept and support the virus in all tissues but the "specific" ones?

In attacking these problems, the initial approach need not be highly sophisticated. In fact, what are needed most are detailed descriptive studies of the ability of viruses to infect embryos—of several species—at progressive stages in development. Carefully controlled experiments are required in which a given virus is examined critically during ontogenesis. When does it infect the embryo proper? When does it infect the membranes? Is there a period during which congenital malformations are produced? If so, is infectivity required? What aspects of the recipient cell-virus relationship are involved in the sequence pantropism to tissue specificity? Although information on any of the viruses would be useful, certain of them may present better experimental possibilities than others. It is believed that viruses that show unusual degrees of specificity in newborn and in adult animals will be favorable targets. As examples of this we may cite the Coxsackie viruses: Coxsackie A being myotropic[30] and Coxsackie B neurotropic.[21]

It will be especially useful to know for each virus the extent to which specificity requires the intact organism. Do viruses tend toward pantropism when studied in vitro? It is interesting to note that Et. Wolff and Goube de Laforest[34] have shown that avian variola virus produces a cytopathology in organ cultures of skin comparable with that found in vivo, but cytopathology in tissue culture is much different from this normal picture. This question is directed toward an elucidation of virus-host relations at two levels: the development of host defense mechanisms and the nature of the virus receptors. For many animal viruses, it is characteristic that their host cells are endowed with phagocytic powers, e.g., the epithelial cells of the respiratory and the alimentary mucous membranes, the alveolar cells of the lung, the vascular endothelial cells and the endothelial Kupffer cells.

Viruses like vaccinia with a wide range of host cells rely on random collisions with host phagocytes. For such viruses, one would expect the pattern of their effects on embryos to follow the formation of phagocytic cells. Animal viruses with a restricted range of host cells have developed a specific mechanism of attachment preliminary to the intake of virus. Such cellular receptors have been described for influenza, Newcastle disease, mumps and fowl plague viruses, and their chemistry has been elucidated in part. For example, it appears that the influenza virus cellular receptors are built up like the soluble influenza virus hemagglutinin inhibitors, that is, they are conjugated proteins with oligosaccharide prosthetic groups. The size of the oligosaccharide may vary with the type of mucoprotein. The oligosaccharides have as terminal units acetylated neuraminic acid residues, joined to an adjacent sugar residue through a neuraminidase-susceptible glycosidic linkage. Perhaps it is not too early to inquire whether these receptors are present in undifferentiated cells—and to examine the relationships of their formation to the acquisition of other specific properties of cell surfaces. For example, we would like to know the ability of embryonic cell surfaces to provide attachment sites for viruses. Does an increasing degree of cell-virus specificity with age reflect a loss in some cells in the appropriate virus-attachment sites? Or, rather, does it reflect a loss in ability to support viral growth on the part of all but one population of cells? Or, conversely, does it reflect increasing capacity in either or both of these attributes coupled with greater "affinity" for the virus?

An unusually interesting attempt to ascertain the effect of age on susceptibility to viruses is Chaproniere's[3] study of the cultivation of myxoma virus in rat tissues in vitro. Embryonic and newborn rat tissues are more susceptible than older tissues. Chaproniere could not link the changing susceptibility to known changes in cell population or permeability to virus, to production of inhibitors, or to the lack of factors that could be supplied by embryo extracts. It is especially curious that the loss of suscepti-

bility with age does not apply to two tissues of the reproductive system—the gonad and the uterus.

It is hardly necessary to point out that Duran-Reynals[8] emphasized the importance of age in relation to resistance of the host. It is clear that the resistance of the host does influence the rate of growth and the spread of tumors induced by viruses in adult animals; Duran-Reynals' conclusion that the age of the host may be of prime importance in the adaptation of viruses to other species is borne out by the finding that we may despeciate animals by making them immunologically tolerant, in order to transplant tumors successfully. Yet, although we know that embryos have the capacity to recognize an antigenic stimulus (reviewed[13]), we have no evidence of the operation of full-fledged immune mechanisms, either cell-mediated or humoral, during early embryonic development. One must seek other sources of variation in the host to account for this progressive change in the pattern of effects of viruses. However, by this statement I do not wish to imply that immune mechanisms may play no role in the production of congenital malformations related to viruses or other infectious agents, for the possible influence of maternal resistance to infection on the physiology of the embryo must be considered.

If we allow our thoughts to traverse only the conventional path, we might conclude that maternal resistance is to be considered a positive force, opposing the production of malformations. Yet our increasing awareness of immunobiologic phenomena like auto-immunization, the graft-versus-host reaction, and the incomplete immunologic reactivity of the embryo to antigenic stimuli force us to focus our attention not on the conventional but on the exceptional; in this light, immune mechanisms take on new importance in the formulation of new approaches to the problems of congenital malformations. The ideas to be advanced are attractive; yet some would argue that they have received more serious attention than is warranted by real evidence. However, I elect to emphasize them in the expectation that they will provoke more critical experimentation and thought. No attempt will be made to be exhaustive in coverage, the subject having been treated *in extenso* recently.[9,10,13,15]

The resolution and the specificity of antibodies make them effective tools for describing the patterns of synthesis and of localization of macromolecules. We may predict that in the combination of labeling and quantitative precipitating technics and the quantification of labeling methods, when used in conjunction with isotopic and microchemical methods for analyzing net synthesis of protein by microsomes, descriptive chemical embryology will reach a new level of sophistication and technical ingenuity. But it is with effects of immune mechanisms, both antibodies and cellular immune reactions, on cells that we are concerned. In the past few months, we have witnessed what is perhaps the most dramatic effect of an antibody on cells yet described; the daily injection for a period of 8 days in a variety of newborn mammals of an antiserum to a protein with specific nerve-growth stimulating properties results in the disappearance of up to 99 per cent of the sympathetic nerve cells.[5,22] Yet the mechanism of action—whether the antibody combines with and inactivates a growth-stimulating factor normally present in the circulation, or whether it exerts a cytotoxic effect by combining with the antigen in or on the surface of nerve cells—is unknown. *Nor is the mechanism of action of any "cytotoxic" antiserum understood.* Equally obscure are the mechanisms of what we call, for want of more precise information, cellular immune reactions, reactions mediated by cells, e.g., the homograft reaction.[10,13]

Although we do not understand these reactions fully, we should not lose sight of the fact that they are reactions to be reckoned with in studies of congenital malformations. Antibodies and cell-mediated reactions are more than experimental tools of the embryologist; they may be teratogenic agents in man. I emphasize only two of the principal arguments which may prove to be of heuristic value; they spring from convergence of several disciplines. One of these arguments has been put so effectively by Bardawil and Toy that I need only quote from their treatise on choriocarcinoma:[1]

> The placenta and fetus occupy a unique position in the genetic cosmos of the mother, since they arise in part from her own tissues, and, in part, from those of the father. Thus, every pregnant woman carries within her uterus a genotypically distinct biological entity and, hence, a potential if not actual foreign body. It is reasonable to wonder whether fetal or placental constituents, whether normal or pathological, might not function as a sustained antigenic stimulus, leading sooner or later to the production of one or more antibodies in the maternal reticuloendothelial system. Reflex localization of such antibodies . . . might be expressed in a variety of disease syndromes attributable to autosensitization.

The second argument stems also from a consideration of auto-immunization. It is not uncommon to find that an auto-immune disorder may stem, or at least receive added impetus, from an infection, likened by some to a "natural adjuvant," analogous to the adjuvant employed in producing auto-immune reactions like induced aspermatogenesis. Perhaps we should inquire whether the occurrence of congenital malformations may be associated with infections only indirectly, the infectious agent serving only as an "adjuvant" in eliciting an auto-immune reaction. Serious auto-immune disorders in the adult are the exception, rather than the rule, but at present we have no way of estimating—in fact, we have not considered—the effect on the embryo of what in the adult is a subthreshold cytotoxic reaction. The teratogenic effects of infectious agents may be a consequence not of infection of the embryo but rather of their role in augmenting maternal immune reactions against either embryonic or maternal antigens. We may speculate further that to be most effective as teratogens (or at least to explain the syndromes of malformations commonly described) the antibodies should be directed not against highly specific antigens but against common antigens. If we are to conclude, as Wilson[33] has, that the ultimate action of all teratogens seems to be to produce either cell death or an alteration in the rate of cell growth (mitosis), then we might center our attention on antigens of the nucleus or the mitotic apparatus. It is not clear whether nucleic acids (either DNA or RNA) and nucleoproteins are antigenic.[9,11] Evidence for the production of circulating, precipitating antibodies under conventional experimental conditions remains unconvincing. On the other hand—and possibly more pertinent to this discussion—there is well-documented evidence that the sera of patients with systemic lupus erythematosus contain an antibodylike substance capable of reacting with highly purified DNA. The evidence favors the view that the precipitating factor represents an antibody to DNA, and that it is one of several auto-antibodies elicited in the disease.[7] The mitotic apparatus of the sea urchin is antigenic,[31] but whether effective antigens are present in the mitotic apparatus of other organisms is unknown.

However, it is not clear why Wilson has excluded from his consideration the "ultimate action" of teratogenic effects on cell surfaces which might result in fundamental alterations in patterns of morphogenesis.[6] If we are to consider the cell surface as a likely target for at least some teratogens, then it would not be remiss to include in our sights the antigens of cell surfaces, possibly stressing the lipoproteins.

The problems I have discussed are not new, many of them having been formulated years ago, but in different terms. We have known from the time of Franklin P. Mall, whose classic *Study of the Causes Underlying the Origin of Human Monsters* (1908) I read again only a few weeks ago, that the character of abnormalities produced in an embryo depends on its genotype and conditioning and its stage of development at the time of exposure. There is a compelling

need to attack the problems of development with the full range of ideas and technics of microbiology and molecular biology. We may expect confidently that students of embryology, genetics and teratology will contribute to and share in the rewards of such a concerted attack. In his *Advancement of Learning,* Bacon wrote:

I take it those things are to be held possible which may be done by some person, though not by every one; and which may be done by many, though not by any one; and which may be done in a succession of ages, though not within the hourglass of one man's life; and which may be done by public designation, though not by private endeavor.

REFERENCES

1. Bardawil, W. A., and Toy, B. L.: The natural history of choriocarcinoma: problems of immunity and spontaneous regression, Ann. New York Acad. Sc. 80:197, 1959.
2. Blattner, R. J., and Williamson, A. P.: Developmental abnormalities in the chick embryo following infection with Newcastle disease virus, Proc. Soc. Exp. Biol. Med. 77:619, 1951.
3. Chaproniere, D. M.: The effect of age on the susceptibility of rat tissues to myxoma virus in culture, Virology 4:393, 1957.
4. Clayton, R. M., and Okada, T. S.: Combined influence of antisera and ribonucleic acid preparations on tissue differentiation. Delivered at the Colloque Internationale d'Embryologie, College de France, Paris, 1959.
5. Cohen, S.: Purification of a nerve-growth promoting protein from the mouse salivary gland and its neurocytotoxic antiserum, Proc. Nat. Acad. Sc. USA 46:302, 1960.
6. DeHaan, R. L.: Cell migration and morphogenetic movements *in* McElroy, W D., and Glass, B. (eds.): A Symposium on the Chemical Basis of Development, pp. 339-374, Baltimore, Johns Hopkins Press, 1958.
7. Deicher, H. R. G., Holman, H. R., and Kunkel, H. G.: The precipiting reaction between DNA and a serum factor in systemic lupus erythematosus, J. Exp. Med. 109:97, 1959.
8. Duran-Reynals, F.: A hemorrhagic disease occurring in chicks inoculated with

the Rous and Fujinami viruses, Yale J. Biol. Med. **13**:77, 1940.

9. Ebert, J. D.: Immunochemical analysis of development *in* McElroy, W. D., and Glass, B. (eds.): A Symposium on the Chemical Basis of Development, pp. 526-545, Baltimore, Johns Hopkins Press, 1958.

10. ———: The acquisition of biological specificity *in* Brachet, J., and Mirsky, A. (eds.): The Cell, vol. 1, pp. 619-693, New York, Acad. Press, 1959.

11. ———: Annual Report of the Director of the Department of Embryology for 1958-1959, Carnegie Institution of Washington Year Book **58**:363, 1959.

12. ———: The formation of muscle and muscle-like elements in the chorioallantoic membrane following inoculation of a mixture of cardiac microsomes and Rous sarcoma virus, J. Exp. Zool. **142**:587-622, 1959.

13. Ebert, J. D., and DeLanney, L. E.: Ontogenesis of the immune response, pp. 73-111, Nat. Cancer Inst. Monograph No. 2, 1960.

14. Ebert, J. D., and Wilt, F. H.: Animal viruses and embryos, Quart. Rev. Biol. **35**:261-312, 1960.

15. Edds, M. V., Jr. (ed.): Immunology and Development, pp. 1-59, Chicago, Univ. Chicago Press, 1958.

16. Gregg, N. M.: Congenital cataract following German measles in the mother, Tr. Ophth. Soc. Australia **3**:35, 1941.

17. Hamburger, V., and Habel, K.: Teratogenic and lethal effects of influenza A and mumps viruses on early chick embryos, Proc. Soc. Exp. Biol. Med. **66**:608, 1947.

18. Kramer, M., and Straub, F. B.: Role of specific nucleic acid in induced enzyme synthesis, Biochim. Biophys. Acta **21**:401, 1956.

19. Kung, L. H.: Histological studies of early chick embryos infected with influenza A virus, Thesis (M.A.), St. Louis, Washington University, 1948.

20. Lehman, I. R., Zimmerman, S. B., Adler, J., Bessman, M. J., Simms, E. S., and Kornberg, A.: Enzymatic synthesis of deoxyribonucleic acid. V. Chemical composition of the enzymatically synthesized deoxyribonucleic acid, Proc. Nat. Acad. Sc. USA **44**:1191, 1958.

21. Levaditi, C., and Henry-Eveno, J.: Affinités neurotropes de la souche Coxsackie B et myotropes de la souche A type I du meme virus chez les souriceaux nouveau-nés, Ann. Inst. Pasteur **82**:751, 1952.

22. Levi-Montalcini, R., and Booker, B.: Destruction of the sympathetic ganglia in mammals by an antiserum to a nerve-growth protein, Proc. Nat. Acad. Sc. USA **46**:384, 1960.

23. McKenzie, J., and Ebert, J. D.: The inhibitory action of antimycin A on the chick embryo, J. Embryol. Exp. Morphol. **8**:314-320, 1960.

24. Matumoto, M., Saburi, Y., and Nishi, I.: Rift Valley fever virus in the one-day-old chick embryo, J. Immunol. **82**:219, 1959.

25. Meselson, M., and Stahl, F. W.: The replication of DNA in *Escherichia coli,* Proc. Nat. Acad. Sc. USA **44**:671, 1958.

26. Nanney, D. L.: Epigenetic control systems, Proc. Nat. Acad. Sc. USA **44**:712, 1958.

27. Niu, M. C.: Current evidence concerning chemical inducers *in* Evolution of Nervous Control, pp. 7-30, Washington, D.C., Amer. A. Adv. Sc., 1959.

28. Robertson, G. G., Williamson, A. P., and Blattner, R. J.: A study of abnormalities in early chick embryos inoculated with Newcastle disease virus, J. Exp. Zool. **129**:5, 1955.

29. Rose, S. M., and Rose, F. C.: Tumor agent transformations in amphibia, Cancer Res. **12**:1, 1952.

30. Sacerdote de Lustig, E., and Parodi, A.: Action du virus de Coxsackie sur le muscle d'embryon de poulet cultive in vitro, Compt. rend. Soc. biol. **148**:1648, 1954.

31. Went, H. A.: Some immunochemical studies on the mitotic apparatus of the sea urchin, J. Biophys. Biochem. Cytol. **5**:353, 1959.

32. Williamson, A. P., Blattner, R. J., and Robertson, G. G.: Factors influencing the production of developmental defects in the chick embryo following infection with Newcastle disease virus, J. Immunol. **71**:207, 1953.

33. Wilson, J. G.: Experimental studies on congenital malformations, J. Chron. Dis. **10**:111, 1959.

34. Wolff, E., and Goube de Laforest, P.: L'application des cultures d'organes embryonnaires a la culture de virus pathogenes, Compt. rend. Acad. Sc. **248**:490, 1959.

35. Yamada, T.: Embryonic induction *in* McElroy, W. D., and Glass, B. (eds.): A Symposium on the Chemical Basis of Development, pp. 217-238, Baltimore, Johns Hopkins Press, 1958.

Medical Problems, Psychological and Social

ROBERT DEBRÉ, M.D.

Congenital malformations are morphologic anomalies as the result of disturbances in the embryonal development, no matter what the causes. In reality, their definition and diagnosis are facing a certain number of difficulties which, in part, offer an explanation for the uncertainty regarding their frequency. However, it is certain that congenital malformations occupy an important place in child pathology. They constitute one of the principal causes of stillbirths and infant mortality.

The causes of congenital malformations are manyfold, whether acquired or hereditary.

I

In man, only few agents have given proof of their teratogenic influence. These are the ionizing radiations, the antifollicular substances and certain synthetic hormones. In the domain of infectious diseases, only the embryopathy of rubella has been definitely established. However, the percentage of malformations observed in children whose mothers had measles during pregnancy is quite variable in accordance with the statistics.

Toxoplasmosis results in severe cerebral and ocular lesions. But, these do not constitute malformations in the very sense of the word.

The study of these agents points to two general origins of teratogenesis: that of the sensible period and that of specificity of action.

Other factors have been suspected but have not been definitely proved. The part played by deficiencies, so definitely demonstrated in experimentation with animals, remains doubtful in man. Certain infectious agents have been suspected as the result of special observations, but none can be demonstrated. However, the problem of teratogenic influences on the part of recently isolated viruses remains an open question.

Mechanical factors and uterine malpositions may be responsible for certain malformations, such as clubfoot or a congenital luxation of the hip, which simulate a true malformation. Anoxemia is certainly a determining factor in the origin of numerous accidents contemporary with birth. The part it plays is not demonstrated during pregnancy.

In the like manner, the influence of environment usually is deduced from indirect factors, seasonal variations, influence of the mother's age, etc. The significance of such arguments remains uncertain.

Such a situation may be explained: (1) if there are multiple teratogenic agents, each of them being responsible for only a slight number of malformations; (2) if they do not cause any easily detectable disturbance in the mother; and (3) if their effect depends on other additional maternal or fetal factors.

II

Only a limited number of malformations may be traced to a definite genetic cause. It may be a predominant gene with regular manifestations or a chromosomic aberration.

Even so, interpretation is very delicate. One and the same malformation may indicate various hereditary or acquired causes, as the case may be. An isolated malformation may be the result of a recent mutation of a predominant gene or may indicate the presence of a gene receding to the homozygous stage.

Most frequently, the intervention of genetic factors is suspected solely on the basis of statistical arguments deduced from the study of family traits. Thus, the incidence of familial malformations usually is superior to that of the population in general. The concordant numbers are higher in monozygotic twins than in dizygotic twins. At times, consanguinity promotes their apparition.

Such findings may be explained either as an influence of predominant genes with feeble and irregular manifestations, or as the influence of multiple genes.

These facts point out the very intimate interaction between ambient and genetic factors. Also, they invite a discussion on the significance itself of such genes and the conditions of their distribution within the population.

Also to be mentioned are: the influence of the maternal genotype, the relations between the maternal and the fetal genotypes and, finally, the possibility of enzymatic lesions of the placenta which it is known has the same hereditary constitution as the embryo.

III

Remarkable progress has been achieved in the treatment of congenital malformations. However, in certain cases, it is only a question of extending the survival of individuals incapable of any useful physical or intellectual activity.

The presence of such children is a menace to the harmony of the parents and threatens the future of the normal brothers and sisters, without any advantage to the former. Therefore, they must be placed in specialized institutions. The lack of appropriate facilities in this domain is flagrant.

However, the true objective remains the prevention of malformation on both the population and the family levels. A better knowledge of the etiologic factors is necessary in order to approach this problem efficiently.

Closing Remarks

SIR GEOFFREY MARSHALL, K.C.V.O., C.B.E., M.D., F.R.C.P.

Chairman, ladies and gentlemen: We now come to the end of the last session of this First International Conference, and I promise to be very brief. I live and work in London, and we are very grateful to The National Foundation and to the International Medical Congress, Ltd. for citing this great conference in our city. It is a fine thing that so many of you have come so far to take part in what I think will go down as part of the historic feature in the progress of a great specialty. Twenty-nine countries are represented here.

We are grateful to Mr. Basil O'Connor, mainly, because through him this Conference has been organized. At this time, when scientific investigation is flourishing and growing at a speed never before known to man, it is producing results, some of which are not altogether beneficial to man. It is a fine thing that we have some leaders who seem to pass ahead and devote their energies, their abilities and their fortunes to channeling science to the directions from which it can be most beneficial to future generations.

Now, there are various people that we must consider and thank. From the other side of the Atlantic, Tom Rivers, who has done an immense amount of work. From ours, those that characteristically sit in the background, including Professor Boyd, who has done a vast amount of work. And I don't think that in the Hall there is a secretary like Miss Kerr, who really has been indefatigable and always good-humored. For giving their services, the members of the Women's Voluntary Service. They really have been perfect dears, and they have made life much easier for many of us by mothering us. And then, we mustn't leave out the translators and the interpreters. One feels very tempted to drag in the old aphorism about translations that they're like a beautiful woman: if they are beautiful, they are not always faithful; and if they're faithful, they're seldom beautiful. But I think it would not be quite true of our interpreters, and what we do thank them for is that they followed so marvelously almost every speaker; in fact, I think we can say every speaker who kept this side of the sound barrier. If they got into supersonic speeds, then naturally, they disappeared behind that barrier. And so, gentlemen, we've come to the end, now, of what I believe has been a great Conference, and I believe there has been a great deal of talk, but it represents a vast amount of work, and I believe that this Conference will stimulate a vast amount of more work and much more rapid progress in the future. Thank you all for having come here.

INDEX

Abortions from rubella, 108
Abramowitz, L. J., 110
Achondroplasia, incidence, 40-42
Acromelanism, 78
Adams, C. E., 218
Adler, J., 10, 291
Age, maternal, as source of variation in incidence of congenital malformations, 45-47
Albinism, gene action as cause of, 77-78
  resistance to irradiation, 81
  "synthetic," creation of, 78
Allison, A. C., 65
Alzamora, V., 220
Aminopterin, use as abortive, congenital malformations from, 102
Amnion, pathology, role in explanation of embryonic maldevelopment, 99
Amprino, R., 135
Amputation (congenital), arms, early records of, 7
  constriction rings about limbs, fingers or toes, 15
  gene action, 12
  legs, early records of, 7
Analogues, amino-acid and purine, abnormalities produced by, 276-277
Ancel, P., 188
Anderson, D. H., 189
Anencephalus, incidence, influence of maternal age and birth order, 46
  stillbirths, in Birmingham, 50, 51
  in Scotland, 47, 49, 51
Anencephaly, in Dundee (1950-59), 257-263
  comparisons of maternal age- and parity-distributions of affected births, 258
  etiologic influences, duration of gestation, 260
    influenza, 259
    mumps, 260
    social and physical environment of mother, 260
  frequency of hydroamnios, 260-261
  incidence, at birth, 257
    of central nervous system defects in subsequent siblings, 261-262
    in first-born, 258
  prognosis for future reproduction in affected families, 262
  seasonal distribution of conceptions leading to anencephalic infants, 259
incidence, 40

Anencephaly *(Continued)*
  in rats, from maternal treatment with vitamin A, 180
Angeletti, P., 152, 153
Anophthalmia-microphthalmia, incidence, 40-42
Anselmino, K. J., 247
Antibody, transfer from mother to young, 223
Antigenic properties of growth factor, 153-154
Antimetabolites, teratogenic effects, 102
  use in study of metabolic requirements of developmental processes, 184
Arey, L. B., 29
Arms, congenital amputation, early records of, 7
Atresia, anal, incidence, 40-42
Auto-immunization, possible effect on embryo, 297
Autosomes, aberrations of number of chromosomes, congenital anomalies due to, 70-72
Avčin, Marij, 269, 271
Averill, R. L. W., 218

Babel, 55
Bacon, Francis, 298
Bacteria and other micro-organisms as pathogenic factors in congenital malformations, 100
Bailer, J. C., III, 28
Baird, Dugald, 97, 123, 128, 129
Barcroft, Joseph, 247, 248
Bardawil, W. A., 297
Barr, M. L., 84
Barron, D. H., 244, 245, 247, 269, 271
Bartelmez, G. W., 253
Bass, M. H., 30
Beatty, R. A., 170, 218
Beck, 129
Beerman, W., 170
Bell, E., 175
Bellows, M. T., 110
Benoit, J., 170
Bérézin, A., 43
Berkson, Joseph, 31
Bertam, E. G., 84
Bessman, M. J., 291
Beswick, 58
Billet, F. S., 170
Billingham, R. E., 232
Biology, developmental, relation to congenital malformations, 16

303